CONFEDERATE COURIER

CONFEDERATE COURIER

BY Helen Jones Campbell

ST MARTIN'S PRESS NEW YORK

PUBLISHED IN CANADA BY
THE MACMILLAN COMPANY OF CANADA LIMITED
70 BOND STREET, TORONTO 2

Acknowledgments

In the preparation of this narrative I received the invaluable assistance of the late Right Reverend Monsignor Edward P. McAdams, rector of St. Joseph's Church, Washington, D.C. Father McAdams was born in Maryland and had lifelong acquaintance with many families mentioned in these pages. He was a pupil of Anna Surratt's husband, Dr. William P. Tonry, at Loyola College, Baltimore, a close friend of her son, the late Dr. Reginald Tonry, and an acquaintance of John Harrison Surratt, Jr., in the latter's old age.

I received from him countless details of fact, and photostatic copies of the Weichman-Bishop McGill-Father Doubrille correspondence, which prevented Weichman's further study as a seminarian.

The late Right Reverend Henry St. George Tucker, Presiding Bishop of the Episcopal Church in the United States, made possible the use of *Memoirs*, the small book published by his grandmother, Jane Ellis Tucker, wife of Nathaniel Beverly Tucker, Confederate agent to Montreal, Canada.

The Right Reverend Monsignor Thomas M. Conroy of Ft. Wayne, Indiana, gave me an affidavit covering his knowledge of the later years of Louis J. Weichman and of the circumstances of his death.

The Reverend A. DuTilly, Georgetown University, provided me with information on John Surratt's life in Canada. Father DuTilly's great-uncle, Joseph, aided Joseph's wife's brother, Father Charles Boucher, in protecting the fugitive John Surratt in Canada.

The Reverend Herman I. Storcke, S.J., introduced me to

v

present-day members of Charles County, Maryland families with knowledge of the Maryland Peninsula's history and tradition.

Mrs. William Harrison Surratt, daughter-in-law to John Harrison Surratt, Jr., her son and daughter, Wilton D. Surratt and Mrs. Thelma Surratt Skinner, gave me the friendliest cooperation in my work. Dean C. M. Surratt (Sarratt) of Vanderbilt University gave information on the origin of the Surratt family in America.

Personnel of the United States Archives, the Manuscript Division of the Library of Congress, the Mariners' Museum, Newport News, Virginia, have been unfailingly helpful. Special thanks are due to Miss India Thomas and Miss Eleanor Brockenbrough of the Confederate Museum, Richmond, Virginia, for calling my attention to the manuscript book believed to have been kept by Stephen F. Cameron, and for countless courtesies.

As ever, I must acknowledge the interest and help of Dr. G. Glenwood Clark, College of William and Mary.

HELEN JONES CAMPBELL

Yorktown
Virginia

Characters

JOHN HARRISON SURRATT, JR., *Confederate courier, charged with*
murder of
ABRAHAM LINCOLN, *President of the United States*
JOHN WILKES BOOTH, *The murderer*
ANDREW JOHNSON, *Who then became President*

Also accused of the murder were:
MICHAEL O'LAUGHLIN and
SAMUEL B. ARNOLD, *School friends of Booth*
DR. SAMUEL A. MUDD, *A country doctor*
NED SPANGLER, *a stage hand at Ford's Theatre, all four of whom*
were sentenced to life imprisonment, and
LEWIS THORNTON POWELL, alias LEWIS PAYNE, PAINE,
MR. WOOD, *Former Confederate soldier*
GEORGE T. ATZERODT, *Boat and carriage builder*
DAVID HERROLD, *A poor-witted youth, and*
MRS. MARY EUGENIA SURRATT, *Mother of John Harrison, Jr.*

The last four persons were hanged by a Military Commission
whose members were:
JOSEPH HOLT, *Judge Advocate of the U.S. Army*
COLONEL H. L. BURNETT, *Assistant Judge Advocate*
JOHN A. BINGHAM, *Special assistant Judge Advocate*
The Commission was dominated by:
EDWIN M. STANTON, *U.S. Secretary of War*

Officials in the trial of John Harrison Surratt, Jr., were:
GEORGE P. FISHER, *Judge of Washington D.C. Criminal Court*
EDWIN C. CARRINGTON, *Prosecuting Attorney*

JUDGE EDWARDS PIERREPONT, *Special assistant to Carrington*
NATHANIEL WILSON, *Assistant prosecuting attorney*
ALBERT GALLATIN RIDDLE, *Secretly employed by E. M. Stanton "to manage the case"*
DAVID S. GOODING, *U.S. Marshall*
ROBERT SUTTON, *Chief of official reports to the U.S. Senate*

Members of the prisoner's family:
JOHN HARRISON SURRATT, SR., *Father, deceased*
MARY EUGENIA JENKINS SURRATT, *Mother, deceased*
ISAAC DOUGLAS SURRATT, *Brother*
ANNA EUGENIA SURRATT, *Sister*

District Jail officials:
BROWN, (?), *Warden*
COLEMAN, BELL V., *Captain of the guard*
W. I. C. DUHAMEL, *Jail physician*
ROBERT WATERS, *Oldest member of the guard*

Jail visitors seeking evidence:
JAMES H. ASHLEY, *Ohio Congressman, working for the impeachment of President Andrew Johnson*
GENERAL BENJAMIN F. BUTLER, *also working for the impeachment*
W. B. MATCHETT, *D.C. clergyman, clerk to the Judiciary Committee of the House of Representatives, and professional informer*
RICHARD MONTGOMERY, *Professional spy who sold information to both factions of politics*
WILLIAM RABE, *Prisoner who reported on other inmates and their visitors*

Prosecution witnesses:
JOSEPH K. BARNES, *Surgeon General*
R. P. BIGLEY, *U.S. detective*
CHARLES BLINN, *Train station watchman in Vermont*
W. E. CLEAVER, *Convicted murderer who provided perjured testimony*
SGT. ROBERT H. COOPER,
SGT. JOSEPH M. DYE,
JOHN W. GARRETT, *Caroline County, Virginia, farmer*

Miss Clara Harris, *Murder witness*
Susan Ann Jackson, *Surratt servant*
Andrew Kallinback, *Surratt neighbor*
John Lee, *U.S. detective*
John M. Lloyd, *Tavernkeeper*
Eddy Martin, *Who speculated in southern cotton with
    U.S. government assistance*
L. J. A. McMillan, *Ship's doctor for Canadian steamship line*
John B. Pettit, *Surratt neighbor*
Charles Ramsdell, *U.S. soldier*
Major Henry Rathbone, *Murder witness*
R. G. Reece, *U.S. detective*
David S. Reed, *Washington D.C. tailor*
Theodore B. Rhodes, *Washington resident*
E. L. Smoot and Thomas Smoot, *Surratt acquaintances*
Joseph B. Stewart, *Murder witness*
Henri B. Ste. Marie, *Papal soldier*
George W. Strayer, *New York railroad worker*
Z. B. Glines and Gunboat Drohan, *Ferry operators*
John T. Tibbit, *Union mail carrier*
Louis J. Weichman, *Friend of John Surratt*
Charles H. M. Wood, *Washington barber*
Benjamin W. Vanderpool, *New York lawyer*

Confederate officials and employees:
Jefferson Davis, *President Confederate States of America*
W. H. Bramwell, *Disbursing clerk*
James Seddon, *Secretary of War*
Judah P. Benjamin, *Secretary of State*
Stephen F. Cameron, *Confederate dispatch carrier*
Lt. John Yates Beall, *Confederate raider duty*
Harry Hall Brogden, *Confederate Signal Corps; later
    secretary to Jefferson Davis*
Lt. Bennett G. Burley, *Confederate raider duty*
Lt. C. A. Cawood, *Confederate Signal Corps*
Clement C. Clay, Jr., *Commissioner to Confederate Consulate,
    Montreal*
Thomas Nelson Conrad, *Scout, and Signal Corps agent*
Dr. Stowton S. Dent, *Member of the "Doctors' Line"*
J. P. Holcombe, *Commercial Agent to Halifax*
Augustus S. Howell, *River-runner*
William Carroll Jewett, *Confederate dispatch carrier*

SQUIRE THOMAS A. JONES, *Agent in charge of Confederate underground mail route.*

BRIG. GENERAL EDWIN G. LEE, *Commissioner to Confederate Consulate*

JOHN PORTERFIELD, *Confederate financial agent in Montreal*

MRS. ANTOINETTE SLATER (NETTIE), *Dispatch carrier*

COLONEL JACOB A. THOMPSON, C.S.A., *Commissioner to Montreal Consulate*

NATHANIEL BEVERLY TUCKER, *Agent for food and cotton exchanges*

MAJOR RODERICK G. WATSON, *Underground mail station operator*

MISS MARY WATSON, *His daughter and assistant mail station operator*

Defense lawyers:

JOSEPH HABERSHAM BRADLEY, *Chief Counsel*

JOSEPH HABERSHAM BRADLEY, JR., *Counsel*

RICHARD T. MERRICK, *Counsel*

Defense Witnesses:

FRANK H. ATKINSON, *Elmira, N.Y. businessman*

ANGUS and ANNIE BACHUS, *Washington saloon keepers*

DAVID BARRY, *Surratt neighbor in Prince George's*

DR. AUGUSTUS BISSELL, *Inventor*

THE REV. CHARLES BOUCHER, *Canadian priest*

LIEUTENANT COL. EVERTON J. CONGER, *U.S. Army*

JOSEPH CARROLL, *Elmira businessman.*

JOHN CASS, *Elmira City Assessor*

JOHN P. BROPHY, *To whom Weichman admitted his perjury*

MISS DEAN, *Visitor to the Surratt home*

FRANK CHAMBERLAIN, *Hotel owner, Canadaigua, N.Y.*

LOUIS J. CARLAND, *To whom Weichman admitted his perjury*

JOHN A. W. CLARVOE, *U.S. detective*

WILLIAM DIXON, *Washington fire chief*

JOSEPH DUTILLEY, *Assisted John Surratt in Canada*

J. N. EASTMAN, *Naval Observatory assistant*

LT. BERNARD EARLY, U.S.A., *Patron of Wood's barber shop*

EDWARD A. MURPHY, *Patron of Wood's barber shop*

WILLIAM FAILING, *Hotel Clerk in Canadaigua, N.Y.*

HONORA FITZGERALD, *Boarded in Surratt household*

Ford, Henry Clay, James R. and John T., *Theatre owners*
Captain Bennett Gwynn, *Surratt neighbor in Prince George's*
James J. Gifford, *Stage carpenter at Ford's Theatre*
The Rev. Abraham D. Gillette, *Attended Powell to the scaffold*
James Grymes, *Operated underground station on the Potomac*
Eliza Hawkins, *Alias Rachel Semus*
C. B. Hess, *Ford's Theatre actor*
John Holohan, *Boarder in Surratt household*
Eliza Holohan, *Wife of John*
Olivia Jenkins, *Niece of Mrs. Surratt*
J. Zaddock Jenkins, *Brother of Mrs. Surratt*
A. Kiesecker, *Washington neighbor of Surratts.*
Mrs. Fredericka G. Lambert and son, Talmadge A. Lambert, *Washington neighbors of Surratts.*
The Rev. Peter Lanahan, *Long time friend of the Surratts*
James L. Maddox, *Old Capitol prisoner with Weichman*
John Matthews, *Actor and friend of Booth*
James A. McDevitt, *U.S. detective*
Major James R. O'Bierne, *Provost Marshal for the District of Columbia*
Captain Richard Morgan, *Led search party to Surratt home*
James W. Pumphrey, *Livery stable owner*
John V. Pyles, *Prince George's County magistrate*
Major Almiron C. Richards, *Washington police head.*
D. C. Robinson, *Clerk, Brainard Hotel, Elmira*
The Rev. Louis Rocoffort, *Confessor to Weichman*
James Sanger, *Bookkeeper in Montreal hotel*
Rachel Semus, *Servant to Mrs. Surratt; alias Eliza Hawkins*
Charles M. Skippom, *U.S. detective*
Captain Harry Smith, U.S.A., *Searched Surratt house*
J. B. Tinsley, Jr., *Clerk in Richmond hotel*
The Rev. Jacob A. Walter, *Confessor to Mrs. Surratt*
William J. Watson, *Washington resident*

Prince George's County neighbors, and others:
Charles B. Calvert, *Congressman*
George G. Calvert, *Holder of Surratt mortgage*
William Campbell, *N.Y. resident who gave perjured testimony*
Salmon P. Chase, *U.S. Secretary of Treasury*

ASIA BOOTH CLARKE, *sister of John Wilkes Booth*
HALL COLGATE, *Messenger boy of Richard T. Merrick*
E. T. CONNER, *Clerk in Rome bookstore*
SANFORD CONOVER, *Professional perjuror. Alias for Charles Dunham*
SAMUEL COX, *Hid Booth and Herrold*
COLONEL ULRIC DAHLGREN, U.S.A., *Killed in assault on Richmond*
THE REV. PAUL DOUBRILLE, *Superintendent St. Charles Seminary*
CHARLES DUNHAM, *Who used alias of Sanford Conover as a professional perjuror.*
JOHN N. FLOYD, *U.S. Secretary of War under Buchanan*
SQUIRE GEORGE H. GARDINER, *Surratt neighbor. Sold Booth a horse.*
ADMIRAL LOUIS M. GOLDSBOROUGH, USN, *His flagship, Swatara, brought John Surratt home for trial*
CAPTAIN D. H. L. GLEASON, U.S.A., *To whom Weichman reported abduction plan.*
THOMAS H. HICKS, *Governor of Maryland*
COLONEL ROBERT JOHNSON, U.S.A., *Secretary to President Andrew Johnson*
GENERAL U. S. GRANT, U.S.A.,
JOHN HILL, *Negro slave of James Grymes*
LUCINDA HOLLOWAY, *Witness to Booth's death*
JAMES ARCHIBALD JENKINS, *Brother of Mrs. Surratt*
MRS. MARY DONOVAN JENKINS, *Sister-in-law of Mrs. Surratt*
J. ZADDOCK JENKINS, *Brother of Mrs. Surratt*
FATHER LAPIERRE, *Canon to Bourget, Bishop of Montreal*
MR. LAPIERRE, *Brother of Father LaPierre*
THE REV. JOHN MCGILL, *Bishop of Richmond; patron of Weichman*
EDWARD V. MURPHY, *Reporter and Philadelphia friend of Weichman*
JOHN NOTHEY, *Prince George's neighbor of Surratts*
JOSEPH T. NOTTE, *Prince George's neighbor of Surratts*
THE REV. FREDERICK NEVE, *Superintendent of English College in Rome.*
MRS. EMMA OFFUTT, *Sister-in-law of John M. Lloyd*
HENRY QUEEN, *Surratt neighbor*
ANDREW V. ROBEY, *Surratt neighbor*

DORLEY J. ROBEY, *Prince George's Co. neighbor*
DR. RICHARD STEWART, *Refused Booth shelter*
JOHN M. THAYER, *Ohio Senator friend to Stanton*
MISS ANNA WARD, *Friend of Mrs. Surratt*
THE VERY REV. BERNADINO FLORENCE WIGET, *Pastor and friend of Surratts.*
GIDEON WELLES, *U.S. Secretary of Navy*
WILLIAM P. WOOD, *Superintendent of Old Capitol Prison.*
FARNUM N. WRIGHT, *Perjuror in Conspirators' Trials*
JOHN F. POTTER, *American Consul General to Canada*
A. WILDING, *Vice-consul at Liverpool, England*
MR. HALE, *Consul at Alexandria, Egypt*
FRANK SWAN, *Consul at Naples.*

Vatican officials and Papal Army:
GENERAL RUFUS KING, *American Envoy*
CARDINAL ANTONELLI, *Papal Secretary of State*
LT. COL. ALLET,
KANTZLER, *The General pro-minister*
CAPTAIN LAMBILLY, *Company 3*
SGT. HALYERIL
CORP. WARRIN

Contents

List of Illustrations

I

It was August 9, 1867, and Washington City never had seen such a day.

The trial of John Harrison Surratt, Jr., charged with the murder of Abraham Lincoln, had been in session for more than two months and every day public clamor grew louder. The question of his guilt or innocence tore the city apart just as two years earlier the trial and execution of his mother for the same crime had lashed it into hysteria.

Now the son's jury had been out two days and nights; it was almost sure to bring in a verdict today. If it found him innocent, said flippant bystanders, no doubt he'd get a fine government job tomorrow. If it found him guilty, his friends and supporters replied darkly, it would be on the same perjured testimony that had hanged his mother. If the jury did not agree, the talkers were sure, old Judge Fisher would discharge it and the performance would go on all over again.

The crowds had begun to assemble around the Criminal Courts building at daybreak. Space inside its courtroom and halls had been occupied all night by newshawks, curiosity seekers, and persons whose interests could not be immediately identified. They had napped in chairs, on tables and floors. Now the daylight arrivers sought standing room by open windows or in shady spots close to the path along which the prisoner must walk to court to learn his doom.

Would he hang? This day would surely tell. Still the crowds came on singly and in groups, stern-faced men, goggling boys, blue soldiers and other young men, some with arm or leg missing, whose lined faces spoke of Confederate gray not long past.

With the bright day came men in high hats and frock coats, carrying with them the pomposity of government departments.

With all of them came new rumors of camp and town, of White House back door and War Department, of bawdy houses and Negro huts. But no matter where they came from, their talk centered in one question: Would he hang?

His mother had been hanged. Would he hang, too?

Answer to the question depended on the political views of those talking, for native Washingtonians, slashed into two camps, held tenaciously to their prewar opinions. On this morning they had sallied forth to support those opinions with furious words encouraged by calls at bars conveniently located along the way to the Criminal Courts. That is, the menfolks had. Ladies for the most part stayed at home where they would express equally firm convictions in parlor, small formal garden, or across a backyard fence.

The war had been over for two years, and the Union preserved after a fashion, but nothing had gone back to being as it had been, said the Washington ladies, and mourned as they said it.

Six years before, they had waked from their sleep to cannon shots across the Potomac and had seen hordes of blue soldiers stream from Virginia's greening hills into their own quiet little city. They had watched in dismay as regiments of those soldiers had set up shop in tents, in public buildings, along dusty streets, and even in the Capitol's rotunda. The war might be over but the soldiers remained, and certainly none of the queer strangers who had clogged the streets during the war had gone home where they belonged.

The only people who had gone were the servants and in their place were untrustworthy dark strangers who asked for daily handouts, forty acres and a mule, and no more work ever. Old Washington days were gone forever, and even Virginia, Mother of Presidents, was no longer Virginia. She was Military District Number One. Washingtonians, most of them of Maryland or Virginia origin, who had resented the intrusion of war on their placid existence, now resented even more the continued presence of interlopers who had come in force and had stayed to prey on the nation.

These people, the carpetbaggers, Freedmen's Bureau officials, Radical Republicans, had destroyed everything that Washington stood for, the city's people whispered to one another. Even those citizens who had fought and prayed and paid for the preservation of the Union now resented these outlanders who had brought their goodly land to violence, discord, and confusion, and into every evil way.

These were the people who had taken over the government when the president's murder had turned the crowds, wildly exulting over the defeat of the South, into maddened rioters. Leading them in verbal and emotional excesses had been the Secretary of War, Edwin M. Stanton, who the very moment breath had left the body of Abraham Lincoln had made himself dictator. He still was dictator. He had hanged the mother. Would he now hang the son?

Only a few hours after the crime he had announced that he knew who the criminals were. They would be hanged and buried before the president's body would be consigned to the ground, he promised loudly.

One of them had been Mrs. Mary Jenkins Surratt of Surrattsville, Prince George's County, Maryland.

John Wilkes Booth, member of the great theatrical family, who had fired the shot, was captured and killed. Yet eight persons, some of them Washingtonians, were arrested and thrown into prison, held incommunicado, charged with the murder.

In spite of protests by many government officials, legal authorities, and newspapers over the world, these civilians were ordered to face a military commission. "Unconstitutional," said the public; civilians could not be tried by the military when established courts were open and available. But they had been.

When, on the opening day of the trial, the prisoners had shambled into court weighted down with anklets, handcuffs, ball and chain, hooded so they might neither hear nor see, and by the rules of the court denied the right to speak a word in their own defense, such an outburst had shaken the city and nation that Stanton had wavered. He had permitted the hoods and heaviest chains to be removed while the prisoners were in the courtroom.

This was only the beginning of weeks of shock. Witnesses had told horrifying tales of Jefferson Davis as instigator of the crime, of a plan to assassinate all the cabinet members, too, to burn New York City, poison its wells, pack explosives in coal cars, infect the North with smallpox. The spy, John Surratt, had been in it up to his neck, swore prosecution witnesses.

Each day's testimony had rocked the town anew as eager hands grabbed copies of *The National Intelligencer* and *Evening Star* hot off their presses. No story was too lurid to repeat, no embellishment too wild. Respectable gentlemen punched each other in the nose for disagreeing over guilt or innocence. Less respectable citizens booted each other into ditches. Negroes, with knives carried handily in boot tops, stabbed indiscriminately and occasionally slashed a throat. Many political personages carried arms.

When four defendants had been sentenced to life imprisonment and four had been hanged, arguments did not stop. Rather they increased as new stories went around and reports of wholesale perjury came out. Witnesses had been terrified into perjury, said responsible Washingtonians. One of the perjurers had been John Surratt's close friend and college roommate, Lou Weichman. Stanton had questioned him, frightened him silly, and then committed him to the Old Capitol Prison to think his story over.

His testimony had hanged Mrs. Surratt, but after her death he suffered such great remorse that he had confessed to various friends.

"I didn't want to hang," he had said. "If they'd let me say what I wanted to, she wouldn't have hanged."

The town roiled with the story. The secretary called Lou to account. Lou denied it and hurried out of town to a job the secretary found for him in Philadelphia.

But the story had not died. Too many respectable persons had heard him: Professor John S. Brophy of Gonzaga College, Father Rocoffort, John T. Holohan (a connection by marriage and resident of Mrs. Surratt's house, who burned the ears of every one who would listen to him), and dozens of others. Edward V. Murphy, a reporter, who had known Lou in his Philadelphia home, told how he had seen him in manacles as he was transported to Old Capitol to "think it over."

No sooner had this quieted down when the news broke that a

school for perjury had been conducted in the New National Hotel. A New York newsman, paid by Stanton, had written testimony and coached witnesses in its delivery. Eight such witnesses had testified and not one of them, including their tutor, had testified under his own name. This was the testimony that had linked the Confederate officials and John Surratt to the murder. Without this testimony there could have been no charge against them.

Arrests followed, and after a long trial the newsman, Samuel Conover, had been sentenced to federal prison.

Then in February, 1867, came the Supreme Court's decision that military trial of civilians was unconstitutional. Now talkers could say openly that the military court had been no court at all; it had been a sham court with predetermined verdicts. Its illegal executions had been murder.

A mounting rumor had it that five of Mrs. Surratt's judges had found her not guilty, that Secretary Stanton had rejected this decision and had sent word to the Military Commission[1] now acting as a jury that it should return a unanimous verdict of guilty. This was for the sake of political unity in the country, but the five unconvinced officers had appended a recommendation of mercy which would go to President Andrew Johnson who, Stanton reminded them, had power to pardon her or commute her sentence. The president had not done so.

No one could be found who would admit he had seen the recommendation. No one could ask about it for the Secretary had forbidden all persons connected with the trial and execution to discuss it, or even mention it. He had tried to influence Archbishop Spaulding of Washington to instruct his clergy to avoid the subject. The Archbishop could not be cowed so the story continued to float, unconfirmed.

All this and more had been on every tongue for two years and it awoke again in renewed fury with the trial of Little Johnny Surratt who would learn today, probably, whether or not he would hang.

It seemed impossible in a civilized city in a civilized nation, even from a court using much of the perjured testimony that had

[1] A Military Commission prosecutes, judges, and then sentences an accused person.

influenced the illegal court of 1865. Then there had been no time for measured, reasoned thought; there had been only bedlam, hysteria, and wild emotion skillfully aroused and sustained by the Secretary's spokesmen. Today was different, the citizens argued, and two years of peace, spurious but still peace, had followed those earlier, terrible days. Surely it couldn't happen again, but last week had made anything seem possible.

On Friday defense lawyers had taunted the prosecution into bringing into court the official record of that 1865 trial and there, attached to it, lay the recommendation for mercy with the signatures of five of Mrs. Surratt's judges. Reporters had raced with the news and over the week end the story had appeared in their papers.

Judge Advocate General Holt, who had headed the prosecution in the military court, swore he had given the recommendation to President Johnson who had refused to consider it. The president denied he had seen or heard of it, and called for the secretary to appear with the case record for him to examine. Stanton refused and on the fifth of August the President requested his resignation. Stanton refused. The president appointed General Grant to replace him and the secretary barricaded himself in his office, fearing he might be removed bodily. Then, supported by his Radical colleagues, he filed Articles of Impeachment against the president.

But there was more, much more to the story, the talkers agreed. Stanton had promised freedom to John Surratt, exoneration of his mother, if only he would involve Andrew Johnson in the murder of Abraham Lincoln. He had promised almost everything to everybody in his struggle to stay in power. So the stories went, gathering momentum with every telling, but always coming back to the question, would another Surratt hang?

The thought held not only the excited crowds but also President Andrew Johnson who tossed sleepless on his White House bed, and also the sullen Negroes who thronged the courtyard, their sharpened knives handy in their boot tops. In his cool, shaded house Joseph Holt, Judge Advocate General of the Army, moaned lightly in his sleep. On the avenue in the old State, War and Navy Building, barricaded behind War Department doors, the war secretary, no longer fiercely indomitable, lay in misery on a couch. He had removed his small, steel-rimmed spectacles, and his tears ran unhindered down his chin into his long gray beard, still immaculately trimmed and scented.

Down the Avenue came the sound of marching men, clatter of metal, squeak of leather, splat of feet in rolling dust.

"It's the soldiers," wailed the secretary, "they're coming to move me out—"

Senator John M. Thayer, who had followed the secretary in his disgrace, rose from the chair where he had vainly tried to rest, or if not to rest to assay the harm his support of the secretary might do to his own career. He looked out the window.

"I don't think so," he said. "I think it's only soldiers drilling around the White House."

The secretary turned wearily on his couch.

"Those damned Surratts," he moaned.

In his grimy cell in the old jail, the prisoner lay as he had lain all night, wide-eyed and sleepless.

In the Criminal Courts building, the jury debated.

2

The boat made a soft splash as it eased into the shallow water. Its passage down to the shore from concealment in a live oak tangle had been difficult, for fall rains had softened the ground to a sandy mush. Water oozed over their shoes as the young men, puffing under its awkward weight, slithered along the rank weeds now slimy from the ebbing tide, and with a final grunt of accomplishment slid the flatbottom into the river.

"Wait, Johnny." The sergeant pulled out his field glasses. "Let's take another look. Mebbe it's not late enough."

He balanced gingerly on the shoreline where the water, lapping gently against the heavy clumps of sword-bladed sand grass, rocked the boat on its swell and retreat. Beside him a thin, nar-row-bodied youth, whose hair shone like a bright cap in the after-noon sun, watched silently as the lean soldier turned deliberately from north to south, pulling into the sweep of his glasses the panorama of the Potomac making out toward Chesapeake Bay.

"Tide's turning, all right," pronounced the sergeant, "but the sun's still right bright out in the stream. Looks quiet enough." He peered again at a dark spot on the water. "That's just driftwood, but wait a little, anyways."

Johnny nodded, and the heavy-shouldered man panting beside the boat nodded, too. "Vaiting I like better as rowing by daylight where is damyanks vit guns." He laid down the padded oars and grinned. The boy laughed softly with him.

The sergeant pulled out his pipe, tamped its tobacco with a long thumb before he lifted a rifle from the boat and eased it into his elbow crook. The move exposed on its stock the U.S.A. im-print it had worn years before, when Secretary of War John N. Floyd had hurried it and thousands of others like it into the South only a short time before Fort Sumter's guns had shocked the world. The glass through which Sergeant Harry Hall Brogden in-vestigated his immediate universe bore the same imprint but the butternut clothing on his spare form, the coarse yellow bro-gans on his feet shouted C.S.A. issue to all comers.

"Look here." He spoke as gravely as if he had not searched the same land and seascape with his glasses for at least an hour before he had given word for the boat to be uncovered and carried down to the water. Even now he spoke as carefully as if he expected a federal patrol to rise like an exhalation before him. The oarsman and youth waited impatiently.

"Well, mebbe you might go on now." He was impatient, too, but cautious. "Reach the Maryland side, watch yourselves. If you're caught, you're hung."

Johnny shrugged.

"Higher than John Brown. Get caught, and we don't even know you."

"Sure enough. Come on, Atzerodt, don't keep the Yanks wait-ing."

The man, whose heavy shoulders were topped by a thick neck

and a thatch of gray hair that curled up against his hat, grinned mirthlessly. "Ve go."

Johnny flashed his long legs over the boat's sides and settled his thin shanks on its narrow board seat. Brogden gave a mighty push and the flatbottom moved with unexpected lightness into the stream. From Mathias Point on the Virginia shore the sergeant watched the boat, pulled by Atzerodt's powerful strokes and steered by Johnny with an oar from the stern, make its way into the channel of the river. It headed slightly upstream toward the entrance to Pope's Creek on the Maryland side. As its weathered blue-gray sides blended with the gray-blue water, the soldier turned back and moved slowly toward the long, low house half hidden by overhanging trees.

By the time he had reached the Grymes dwelling and turned once more to look anxiously at the river, the sun had slanted below the Virginia hills. Long fingers of deepening shadow advanced from high bluffs until autumn dusk blurred the boat's slow progress into the deep ravine that led to the old Dent Plantation landing.

The flatbottom scraped lightly along the Maryland shore and swung against the landing's lashed posts, as its passengers relaxed from the tension of once more easing the Confederate mail boat past the very noses of Federal gunboats patrolling the Potomac. Cautiously the oarsman beached it at the foot of the bluff, atop which blue-coated sentries walked their posts with an eye on the river and ears alert for the sound of muffled oars.

While the sentries paced their unsuspecting rounds, below them the angular youth crawled noiselessly up the bluff's steep side and disappeared into the wooded dusk. On the shore the oarsman slid his boat quietly out into the water and was once more lost under cover of deepening shadow.

As the boat floated silently away, Johnny Surratt turned toward the land. His way led through the peninsula of southern Maryland to his former home, Surratt's Villa, in Prince George's County, and thence by the best means he could find into Washington where his mother and sister now lived; then after resting the night, north by railroad car. After eluding Federal Secret Service operatives at the Canadian border, he would finally breathe

the safe air of Montreal. At the St. Lawrence Hall hotel he would present his dispatches whereupon the heartfelt thanks of Jacob Thompson, harried Commissioner for the Confederate Government, would be extended to John Harrison Surratt, Jr., personal courier in the service of Jefferson Davis, President, Confederate States of America.

3

This was October 1864. As Little Johnny Surratt slipped along country lanes to the farm where he had left his horse a few days before, he passed through an area whose citizens accepted his river-running as a creditable and patriotic occupation. He had learned his politics at his father's knee and now, mounted on his father's big bay horse, he jogged the roads of the neighborhood that for good or ill had shaped those political opinions.

His name, Little Johnny, had been given him by his mother who saw in him a miniature Squire Harrison of Surratt's Villa, Prince George's County, Maryland. By the time he had reached his teens the baby pudginess that had induced the pet name had given way, but even as he shot up to his father's six-foot-three the name held. This pleased the boy, whose entire life would be influenced by the memory of that father in the home he had provided. There had been substantial comfort in the villa with its eleven rooms, its porches and yards, its stables with the black carriage horses and blooded mounts for father and sons, pastures with farm animals, fields, and well stocked poultry houses. There was, too, the father's general merchandise store, small but busy, his bar at the crossroads which also contributed to the family prosperity.

The squire's business prospered more through his native shrewdness than from his personal effort, for his interest, aside from his ledgers, lay in field, fox run, and politics. He was no student of political science, but given a local problem or a governmental policy to consider, he was indefatigable in its pursuit. Long before Little Johnny's understanding of national portents was molded, his father, his voice rumbling loudly from behind a bright red beard, dominated not only his family but the people in his area.

Squire John Surratt was powerfully built but by the time Johnny could throw a long leg across a saddle, he had thickened through neck and shoulders. Later, when the boy could take the creeks and fences of a cross-country run, his father, from close application to the joys of table and bar, had acquired a paunch that kept him immobile in his chair for the greater part of each day. By the time states' rights and abolition found their acrimonious way into Prince Georgians' daily conversation, the old squire's physical activity had been succeeded by activity of tongue. As planter, tavern owner, storekeeper, magistrate, and postmaster he received the respectful attention of his neighbors.

Prince George's County had not been the original Surratt home. Virginia had welcomed four Huguenot brothers early in the eighteenth century. Later the brothers had gone their separate ways with only John's ancestor lingering on the Potomac shore to become a substantial planter. Born shortly after the beginning of the nineteenth century in Fairfax County, Virginia, John had been given the good Virginia name of John Harrison.

In his mother's Alexandria home he had met Mary Eugenia Jenkins whose Maryland parents had sent her cross-river to attend Miss Winifred Martin's School for Young Ladies. There she had embraced the Catholic faith of her teachers, and in her fifteenth year had married Protestant John Harrison Surratt. Their three children, Isaac Douglas, Little Johnny, and Anna Eugenia, had been reared in their mother's faith.

The Jenkins family had preceded the Surratts in the colonies by nearly a hundred years, and within two generations their name dotted the deed and will books of the four counties that make up the narrow peninsula of Maryland, southeast of the District of Columbia. Various Jenkins scions served in the Revolutionary War and two years after its end Francis Jenkins, planter of Prince George's County, died leaving his lands to Thomas Jenkins. In

1790 when the District of Columbia had been cut from lands ceded by Maryland to the new federal government, the main street of the capital city had been laid from the door of the President's House to Jenkins' Hill, once the property of Thomas Jenkins. There the seat of government had been established and the site became Capitol Hill.

Staid old Alexandria across the Potomac had developed along with Washington and young John Surratt had entered into construction works in his home county with labor provided by slaves he leased from his neighbors. Following his marriage he moved across the river into the outskirts of Washington City, but soon after the birth of his oldest son, Isaac Douglas, his Washington home had burned to the ground and in 1840 he had bought 1200 acres in Prince George's County from George H. Calvert of Riverside Plantation.

In 1850 he had opened his store where the Washington road crosses the highway leading from Piscataway to His Lordship's Kindness Plantation and on to Upper Marlboro. Soon after, for the convenience of stagecoach passengers, the villa had become a tavern. This had called for a bar, which was set up in the building that housed the store. Later, John Surratt, now respectfully addressed as Squire, sold plots adjoining his store. A blacksmith shop moved in and a new little town known as Surratt's began to thrive.

By the middle of the nineteenth century changing economic conditions had reduced most of the huge colonial holdings in southern Maryland. Tobacco had depleted much of its soil, and such great investment in manpower had become necessary to till its fields that gradually the old plantations had been divided into smaller plots which were sold to landless farmers or rented for a percentage of their yield. Small stores began to appear at crossroads, mail and stagecoach runs reached into remote communities, small places such as Beantown, T. B., and Bryantown began to expand.

Squire Surratt found it agreeable to sit in his comfortable ladderbacked rocker on his store porch and pass the time of day with his neighbors, or dispense the gossip of the countryside along with his personal opinion of the national scene. Johnny, all ears, listened to the oracle that was his father.

Business prospered, but rumblings of national discontent increased as did the number of planters who clustered around the squire to discuss prices and politics. Among these was the squire's brother-in-law, J. Zaddock Jenkins, of Burches Venture Plantation, who often brought friends laden down with gossip fresh out of Washington.

Zad, an Old Line Whig, was often called on by earnest gentlemen in search of votes. Usually they came with the blessing of Captain William P. Wood, superintendent of Old Capitol Prison. The squire had grown up with Billy Wood, over in Alexandria, but the latter had won his disdain by his association with a Washington politician named Edwin M. Stanton. However, Zad dutifully presented the seekers at the squire's bar, although he and the squire were loudly at outs over politics.

"Queer," the squire would opine, "how Billy Wood lets that shyster lawyer, Stanton, lead him around by the nose. Mighty queer," he would say, with lips pursed, eyes narrowed as if he were staring into a future that thoroughly displeased him.

Zad, furious at these performances, always replied in kind and so acquired the dubious honor of being the most outspoken Union man in Prince George's.

The squire's conferences on state and national affairs grew in length until they extended through most of the day, and he sat hours at a time, relaxed and ponderous, in his hand a glass that the Negro boy, Dan, kept well filled. Food, drink, politics. These were the county's life.

The aging squire began to sell off his land and offered as an excuse the unreasonable price of field hands, to say nothing of the outrageous taxes imposed by Washington. As he mouthed his opinions, Johnny came to learn that a gentleman's inconveniences all stemmed from Washington and its unpardonable meddling into things that were the business only of the state and its citizenry. About all a gentleman could do, reasoned the squire, was to sell off his property, own as little as possible, and so avoid the triple evils of federal control, unjust authority, and scandalous taxation.

Johnny, listening, hoped his father would not sell the store. He loved its smell of saddles, harness, peppermint candy, and salt fish, tobacco in casks and hams suspended from the ceiling.

He loved too the scent of the bar just through the door, the liquor fragrance on the warm summer air. But most of all, and all his life, even when it was no longer his, he loved Surratt's Villa.

The villa was not sold but its lands were sheered off in small tracts and part of their proceeds applied to the mortgage held by Mr. Calvert. Johnny was ten when on October 6, 1854 a post office was opened and his father received the Washington appointment as postmaster. Officially the little town became known as Surratt's but Prince Georgians, accustomed to calling it Surratt's Villa, soon turned it into Surrattsville. The old squire's little town now bears another name, but to Prince Georgians it remains Surrattsville.

Soon after the post office opened, Johnny entered Father Wiget's school, St. Ignatius, on Tenth Street in Washington, where Isaac Douglas formerly had been a pupil. From there he went to St. Mary's Preparatory School outside Baltimore, and in the fall of 1859 he was admitted to St. Charles Seminary, near Elliott Mills. Here he majored in French and was listed as an exemplary student.

Hardly had he entered St. Charles when vociferous haranguing in Prince George's County arose over the South's first moves toward secession. At home on vacation in the spring of 1860, he heard his father hold forth loud and strong on the April Secession Convention in Charleston, South Carolina. The squire followed the convention verbally through the May session in Richmond, and with invigorated comment throughout the June and final session in Baltimore. Every step was loudly decried by Zad Jenkins, who railed against the indisputable facts that Maryland's sympathies were with the Secessionists and her electoral delegates had, to a man, supported the Southern candidates.

Zad derived some comfort from the local election that November, for Charles Benedict Calvert of Riverside Plantation, a Union Whig, was sent by his district to the Maryland House. He would take his seat March 4, 1861, the day that Abraham Lincoln would be inaugurated President of the United States.

It accomplished nothing for Squire Surratt to bellow that Mr. Calvert had been elected not by his own community but only by the vote of Union-minded people in populous Calvert County.

Johnny noted, however, that his father (perhaps because the Villa's mortgage was held by the new Representative's father) contented himself with pounding his cane impatiently on the floor when the Calvert name was mentioned instead of delivering his usual verbal onslaught against administration supporters.

The county was sadly torn, for enmities that rankled in Washington were wide open in Prince George's. Old Line Whigs, abandoning their broken party, had stampeded in numbers to the Know-Nothings and now, with others who never in their lives had voted the Democratic ticket, whirled violently in its favor.

Civil rights, states' rights. The words were heard on every side. They floated over dinner tables, boomed across bars where hands shook in anger and friend disputed with friend administration, abolition, territory slave or free. They crossed plowed fields as neighbors mounted their horses, left their crops behind, and sought store porches and other country gathering places to battle in miniature the troubles that had descended on them in magnitude. The strife went on over pipes and bottles, in houses and stores, outside church doors and in courtrooms. But no matter how much the planters argued, contended, blamed, or contradicted their leaders, no matter how much they iffed and should haved, matters became no better.

Governor Thomas H. Hicks, pressed to call a special session of the Legislature to consider the state's stand on secession, failed to do so. Instead, he reported to Washington that Baltimore plotters planned to prevent Lincoln's inauguration, and to seize the capitol. The river men, angry at the governor's refusal, grew furious at his report. Their rage was whipped higher yet by the congressional investigating committee's report that it found no evidence of such a plot.

Yet no one realized with what fateful speed events were moving or that the crisis of secession lay only a few months ahead.

4

River-running across the Potomac was the immediate result of the Act of Secession passed by the Virginia Assembly. Perhaps nothing had so rudely aroused the people of the river states to the consequences of a broken government as the bafflement of interrupted mail service. Incredulous fury followed the announcement of the blockade ordered by Abraham Lincoln, and the discovery that it was no longer possible to post the most innocent of letters to the opposite side of the river or receive the most urgently needed reply. Within hours of that discovery river people, no matter what their enthusiasm for the new Confederacy, began to seek communication with their families across the stream.

For two centuries Maryland and Virginia planters had shared the same social, economic, and political interests. The river that now floated gunboats to divide them had long united families on its banks. Serving as a colonial highway, its length supported the planter's stout wharves which faced the river's deep water or snugged up some meandering creek for protection from the furious gales that stormed in from the Chesapeake.

Out of the Maryland creeks, Trinity, St. Mary's River, Pope's Creek, Port Tobacco River, Nanjemoy, Mattawoman, and Piscataway, barques and brigs heading for England and the planter's markets stopped also in Virginia's Nomini Bay, Mattox, Upper Machadoc, or Gunston Cove. For neighborly visits, planters skipped cross river by sailboat or slave-manned rowboat to the plantations on the Virginia side.

Early roads had grown out of horseback trails from back gate to back gate of the Potomac plantations, and from paths down which tobacco casks were rolled to wharves where the British merchant ships put in. These paths had given way to the high wheels of ox-carts, to calashes and carriages of the eighteenth century. By the middle nineteenth century Maryland

JOHN HARRISON SURRATT, JR., at twenty-one.

Mrs. Mary Eugenia Jenkins Surratt

Hanged by a Military Commission in Washington, July 7, 1865.

At no time did Mrs. Surratt appear at her trial without her widow's bonnet and veil. If General Wallace saw her like this (above) he must have visited her cell, although records say she was forbidden communication even with her family, her priest and her lawyer.

peninsula roads, traversed by the barouches and rockaways of its lesser gentry, still led inevitably to the water.

With the outbreak of war in 1861 the Potomac, a focus of this network of roadways and creeks, took on new importance. Its waters provided the only easy access to Washington. The nightmare possibility that Maryland might vote secession and so leave the capital of the Union high and dry in the center of Confederate territory panicked federal authorities. By one means or another, Maryland must be kept in the Union.

In April Governor Hicks yielded to increased pressure and called a special legislature to consider secession. Delegates were named at an election held in July but long before that date Union pressure on Confederate sympathizers began. Several legislators were arrested, charged with high treason, and sent off to Fort McHenry to await trial. Military law was imposed on Baltimore. July's ballots were cast under the guns of soldiers. United States marshals patrolled Baltimore and the peninsula counties' polling places. Even with wholesale arrests it proved impossible to defeat all the secession-minded men, and Squire Surratt growled happily from his porch that he had said so all the time.

Four days before the special session was to open, arrests of pro-Southern delegates began. Brigadier General N. P. Banks, commanding the military district, ordered his officers to prevent the session, to "arrest the presiding officers of both houses, clerks, secretaries, all subordinates. Any resistance will be suppressed no matter what the consequences."

Maryland hummed, buzzed, and then roared in a rising tide of fury but, guarded by soldiers, her elected representatives were shipped up to Fort McHenry and imprisoned.

As the general elections of November drew near, Marylanders waited further evidence of what they termed Northern might against Southern right. They were not surprised when General Banks ordered that "sufficient men be sent to points where elections are to be held."

Placards over the countryside announced a free and open election yet other placards instructed all Unionists to point out to U.S. marshals anyone who had lately returned from Virginia. Men from the First, Second, and Third Maryland Union regiments were granted furlough to go home to vote. Later, Massachusetts soldiers boasted gleefully that they had voted in Baltimore that day as openly and as often as they pleased.

This assistance, coupled with the vote of the northern and eastern sections of the state, assured that Maryland would stay in the Union.

Washington breathed easier but revolt grew in the river counties. Prince Georgians found themselves legally retained in the Union while they supported the Confederacy with money, deeds, and passionate speech. Wholesale arrests soon showed the futility of the latter.

Under an outward passivity a solid body of secession sentiment was growing, and a sullen resentment of the federal government that was to outlast the war by many years. County factions consolidated into two groups: a small handful of Unionists, and those who worked in a far-reaching and effective underground for the Confederacy. Day by day the underground mail routes grew; more and more Prince George's young men slipped across the Potomac at night to find their way into Southern camps.

Home on vacation from St. Charles, Little Johnny was swept up by the excitement of these swiftly moving events. Stirred by the tension around him, he listened to and accepted his father's pronouncements on all these matters. By now, Johnny's silver-gilt head topped his father's ruddy thatch. The older man was round and flabby, but the boy had the narrow hips, flat thighs, and sturdy shoulders of the outdoor man.

The squire had relegated himself to his rocking chair, but Johnny, like any other country lad, could ride anything on four legs, and with pistol or musket hit anything he could see. He could paddle a canoe, row a boat, and trim a sail with the best of the river gentry. He could dance all night, swig his brandy, and still be fresh at the next day's dawn. He chafed at his father's stern admonition that he was still a boy and had best get back to his studies; the war was not for him, not yet. Reluctantly he returned to school.

In 1862, hurriedly summoned from school, he arrived home to find his father dead. In the front parlor of his villa, Squire Surratt lay in a long black coffin before the fireplace, across from

Anna's piano which, decorously closed, deepened the room's funeral darkness. The window blinds were tightly drawn behind stiffly starched lace curtains fastened into straight folds with tacks furtively thrust into polished sills. White cheescloth covered the battered gold-framed mirror over the mantel so that no irreverent reflection might lighten the mourning parlor, whose master lay with white roses resting on his breast.

In life he would have shouted ribaldry at those roses. His mocking tones would have reached clean down to the cabins, where the children would have trembled but their parents would only have grinned and said "Marse Jawn bellerin' agin," and have gone undisturbed along their leisurely way.

But ever since that evening, months before, when Dan had come running to the house, gasping, "Miz Mary, Miz Mary, come quick!" there had been ominous quiet in villa and cabins. That noon Dan had helped the squire from the outdoor heat into the coolness of the villa dining room and had eased him into the great chair at the table's head. The squire had eaten his usual noonday meal of fried fowl with cream gravy, candied yams and mashed potatoes, salad greens cooked with pork, slabs of cold ham bordered with transparent fat, fried corn seasoned with red pepper and cream, biscuits hot from the oven, shredded cabbage cold in vinegar and sugar. Added to this, cup after cup of hot coffee sugared and creamed within an inch of its life, and the old squire's, too. No, no dessert, he had replied in answer to his wife's inquiry.

"I feel all right," he had shouted at her surprised question. "Cain't a man say he's in no humor for watermelon without everybody lookin' at him like as if he's at death's door?"

Only an hour later he had toppled from his chair to the floor. He had not spoken again in all the months that remained to him. He had lingered helpless and disinterested, then he had died as suddenly as he had fallen and with less fanfare.

So now he lay dead in his own parlor, with his son kneeling by his side. Until time should come to carry him to Piscataway churchyard, his coffin rested on straight chairs and a low wooden trestle to support its heavy middle. At each end stood one of the little tables that as long as Johnny could remember had held tall crystal lamps on either side of the fireplace. Now, draped in white cloth that fell to the floor, they held white candles that softened in the heat of the day. All these, the wilting white roses and the smell of death, gave off unease. It seemed uncomfortably possible that at any moment the old squire might leap to his feet and bellow what in Gawdamighty's name was all this mess? Hell's horns! couldn't a man even die in peace?

Tears ran down the boy's cheeks. He dabbed them hastily away on the sleeve of his Sunday coat. He moved his thin legs, stretched his neck from the white stock bound too closely around it, and slowly slipped the rosary beads through his bony young hands. He could not remember the prayers. He could remember only his father's ruddy head thrown back to laugh, his white teeth flashing through his beard, his voice echoing.

"War," Pa had said often enough, shifting to a more comfortable spot in his chair. "We'll soon show 'em about war. They won't fight, not th' Yankees. They're just atalkin' with their mouths open and their tongues aflappin'. I give 'em to about Christmas, an' they'll git enough an' go on home." Christmas had come and gone.

Johnny's eyes turned from flickering candles to the quiet hands whose fingers curled slightly, as if from long practice around a goblet's stem. He rose from his knees as Uncle Zad stepped forward to take his place beside the bier. Across the hall in the dining room gathered the Jenkins relatives. Aunt Mary Donovan Jenkins offered a comforting pat on his shoulder. Through the window he could see other relatives and neighbors on the piazza, but for once the blue soldiers stayed away from the house.

He followed his aunt upstairs to his mother's room, where she sat in her best black silk dress, prayer book in hand. At her feet Anna rested on a footstool, her head in her mother's lap. Through the window came the sweetness of honeysuckle and the odor of ham frying in the kitchen. Across the backyard Rachel's daughter, Jinny, screeched shrilly, "Miz Mary 'Genia say they be 'roun twenty fo' supper."

Anna sniffed her mother's smelling salts, her swollen lids purple against her colorless skin. At the sight of her brother her eyes filled again, and she buried her face in the comforting lap.

Johnny stared at his mother, whose unlined face, usually so warm with color, today showed pale composure. Shadows circled her eyes and tiny wrinkles gathered in their corners. Above her high forehead smooth brown plaits rounded her head without a trace of gray. Yet to Johnny she was no longer young. She was forty-two.

A bustle in the yard announced Father Lanahan's arrival, and Johnny, in his new responsibility as head of the house, went down to greet the priest who would bury the squire.

Supper over, the house quieted down. Neighbors went home by twos and threes in light wagons and buggies whose wheels stirred up a world of dust behind them. Uncle Zad and David Barry prepared to sit the night with the squire's body, and tired Father Lanahan went to the room prepared for him on the second floor. Mrs. Surratt sent back her untouched supper tray, and Anna ceased crying to toss restlessly on her cot at the foot of her mother's half-empty bed.

Next morning a hearse came out from Washington, and the sweating hands of Uncle Zad and neighbors lifted the heavy coffin into it. Little Johnny mounted his father's horse. Years had passed since the squire's big bay had followed the hounds or carried his master even so far as Uncle Zad's home, but now, bearing Little Johnny as chief mourner, he followed his master to his burial.

Behind them unhappy Dan drove Father Wiget, Mrs. Surratt, and Anna. Uncle Zad's family, with Uncle James Archibald assisted by his body servant, old John, came next. Mama Jenkins, the Jenkins grandmother who had not left her son Zaddock's house for many years, and Isaac Douglas, the squire's oldest son, were missing.

Neighbors Joseph L. Notte, Captain Bennett W. Gwynn, John Nothey, Squire Gardiner and Thomas Jones, Captain Samuel Cox, and their families started a little later so they could trot their horses; their pace would have scandalized other followers in a funeral train.

Isaac Douglas had been one of a group of resentful young Marylanders who had celebrated the inauguration of Abraham

Lincoln by taking off for the deep South. As dashing a rider as ever topped a horse, he had signed up with the Pony Express and now, booted, spurred, and with a holstered pistol, he pounded the roads between Matamoros, Mexico, and Santa Fe, New Mexico, bringing word of the Mexican trouble for Mr. Arunah S. Abell's *Baltimore Penny Journal.*

While Johnny rode as chief mourner, his neighbors wondered what the boy could make of his father's involved affairs. Mrs. Surratt could manage the tavern and farm—she'd been doing it all along—but the post office was different. Sidelong looks passed between the men; since Maryland had been bludgeoned into staying in the Union, there damn sure would be a Union man to carry the Yankee mail.

The morning after the funeral, Uncle Zad rattled his old buggy into the villa yard with Justice John Pyles beside him. In the parlor the latter sat down cautiously on the horsehair sofa, after Mrs. Surratt sank into a chair by the window. Blue shadows still underlined her eyes, and her usually busy hands lay quiet in her lap. Zad, his gray beard subdued by his wife's shears in recognition of the squire's obsequies, eased his chin into his collar and perched stockily on the chair that yesterday had supported a coffin.

Since the squire didn't leave a will, Zad spoke up in his briskly confident voice, Mary Eugenia'd have to qualify as administratrix. There'd be some other things to straighten out and Justice Pyles had come along to see if he could help. Have t' talk about money, Zad continued.

Wasn't enough farm stock to worry about, of course—good idea the squire'd had to sell it off before the Yankees drove it off—but the villa and the land—what was left of it—and the store, the bar, and the lot next to it. There was that land the squire'd sold to John Nothey twelve years or so ago, and not a penny nor even interest paid on it. Might have to foreclose that.

Then there was the place outside Washington City that John Marshall hadn't paid a cent on for years. He didn't see why the squire'd always been s' soft with people that owed him money. Thing that made it so bad was, if Mary Eugenia couldn't collect what was owed her and pay old Mr. Calvert, he might think he'd have to foreclose on the villa mortgage. Then where'd the Surratts be? All their property gone. Except the Washington City House, of course. Good brick house, good location on Seventh Street. Hate t' sell it, no mortgage nor anything on it, but might have to.

Justice Pyles nodded. "Might," he said.

Johnny came into the room and bent to kiss his mother's pale cheek. She smiled a little sadly. Johnny's formal manners were the more endearing when she remembered how short a time had passed since she had chided him for breeches torn in climbing the stable ridgepole or sliding down a grapevine in the wood. His clumping schoolboy feet, sharp elbows that constantly sought the light through jacket sleeves, came back in a flash. To see him now, in tight white cotton breeches, round-tailed jacket, and white stock, no one could believe he'd ever lifted his own handkerchief to blow his own nose; just look at the elegant way he wears that kerchief in his jacket cuff.

"It's all right," she answered his inquiring look. "Mr. Marshall and Mr. Nothey still owe us for the land they bought from us. When they pay us, then we'll pay Mr. Calvert."

"If they pay," said Zad bluntly. "I don't see it happening right away. Better settle up everything quick as we can. Johnny knows, of course, he can't go back to school." Here Johnny looked up quickly but Zad continued. "Someone's got to stay here, and since we don't know where Isaac is, it's bound t' be you, my boy. Sorry but there's no money and I can't help but a little bit. Haven't got the means." He'd spent $3,000 t' help get the Lincoln people elected, he went on ruefully, and now it looked like th' same people was going t' up and free his field hands. If they did that, he couldn't even farm. Wasn't much he could ever do about money again, looked like.

"There's another thing I've been giving some thought to." He pulled an old pipe from his pocket and filled it thoughtfully. Mr. Pyles shifted his cud and listened. "Something'll have t' be done about the post office. Government aint one t' let it run along without a postmaster. They's a-plenty men that'd take it over, but as I see it, it's rightly Johnny's place. Old squire opened it, no one else's ever run the mail through here. Johnny's a bit young, but we could get him enough signers, I dare say."

"Signers?"

"Yeah. Has t' be a petition, but we think, Mr. Pyles and me, we think we could get enough if we started right away. Can't hang on too long. Washington's likely t' send someone else."

Pyles nodded. "Likely."

"Now, one thing more, Johnny. The squire he was pretty loud against President Lincoln. Folks around here don't mind that, but you can't get a thing out of Washington that-a-way. You got t' be a good administration man, loud and strong."

"I got t' go into Yankee politics to keep our own post office? Aw, no. Huh."

"No way comes to my mind, these days, 'less you do some tongue-clangin'."

"Well," said Justice Pyles, struggling manfully with his cud, "first thing a politician's about to ask you when you go up for a post office, or something, is, 'How many votes can you poll for me?' and if you lick-low and say, 'I'm just a poor taxpayer that wants justice,' tain't likely you'll get it. What you got t' do is tongue-clang right up to him. 'I kin promise you 200 votes, easy as not,' you say. Then if he believes you and you git in, you got to keep on supportin' him t' stay in."

"Politics," snorted lately disillusioned Zad. "Heh. The president, he's a good man, I do believe, but he's got a lotta people up there, 'round him in Washington City, that ain't so-much-of-a-much. Still, you want a post office, you got t' keep votin' 'em in. Course, Johnny, you ain't old 'nuff to vote yet, so we got to do most of this for you. Think maybe Cap'n Billy Wood might help me a little."

He turned to his sister, who had sat silent through the conversation.

"Now you too, Mary 'Genia. You let me know what you think. Pleased t' have you step t' supper any time you can. Your grandma'll be pleased t' see you, Johnny, any time at all."

On his way through the kitchen yard to his buggy, Zad stopped to sniff the preserves Rachel had been making, and where, now, a cluster of small helpers was cleaning up sticky pans and kettles. They eyed them hungrily while Rachel polished up a line of earthenware jars.

"Look's like you won't starve this winter." Zad spoke with grim good humor.

"No, sah, Mista Zad. Not 'less some them Yankee boys comes depredatin' 'round before I gets these jars up t' the ell-room. Got t' move right smart t' beat them hongry boys."

5

The year 1862 taught Prince Georgians about war at home. Union soldiers sent in to handle the elections remained and others joined them until more than 6,000 troops camped in the river counties. Assigned to picket the Potomac and the roads leading to it, they settled down at points near the river's main traffic lines.

The road sentries went on duty at eight in the morning, and in the belief that darkness was necessary for contraband transport, the river pickets took their posts at nightfall. By daylight the soldiers with time on their hands roamed field and farm, helping themselves to whatever caught their fancy.

Poultry, vegetables, every unprotected edible disappeared. Woodpiles dwindled, then fences. Stock roamed unhindered through gateless fences or out of fenceless fields. Horses ended in Union cavalry, the cattle as steaks in Yankee stomachs. The early months of that winter cleared the counties of livestock, for all that was not lost or stolen was hastily marketed. Unplowed, unplanted, and unprofitable fields remained.

Peninsulans learned to hide whatever they owned beyond their hourly needs. A few sticks of firewood pushed out of sight under a building, a few eggs gleaned from vanishing flocks, a tiny pat of butter, a small tin of sugar, whatever could be spared was tucked away against the time when none could be found for love or money.

At Surratt's where store and bar held a blue haze of Union soldiers, one hiding place was favored. The big frame Villa with its center hall from which two rooms opened on either side, upstairs and down, had been enlarged by a small ell at the end nearest the outside kitchen. In this ell's ground floor room the squire housed his business records, books, ledgers, and papers in utter confusion. The small room above, unfinished except for flooring, held the odds and ends of household discards. Here, during the first years of the war, were hidden the family valuables and staple foods that would not perish in summer heat.

Resentful anger burned fiercely that year in Prince George's as inconvenience and destruction were added to political frustration. County people badly wanted revenge and no vengeance was too fantastic for discussion.

Abduction talk had been in the air ever since Governor Hicks's announcement of a Baltimore plot against Abraham Lincoln. The idea thrived on wishful thinking. It spread into Confederate scouting service and inflamed Thomas Nelson Conrad and his teen-age friends. Conrad and his friends, who had returned hastily from Northern colleges to participate in the glorious rebellion, had met early capture in their scouting and running mail across the river. After their release from Old Capitol Prison in Washington, they resolved to remove the commanding general of the Union forces before the war could get a good start.

General Winfield Scott's headquarters on the Avenue west of the War Department offered an opportunity for easy capture, they said, and as good scouts they so informed their Richmond superiors. To their chagrin they were ordered to think no more of it. It would accomplish nothing, they were told. The North would simply replace the fat old general with a younger one who would do the South more harm. Reluctantly Conrad and his scouts abandoned the tempting prospect of a pot shot at old Fuss-and-Feathers as he rode down the Avenue, his flabby belly sagging against the saddle of his overloaded horse.

But the plan had its effect for, brought in by river-runner grapevine, it filled the peninsula store talkers with excitement. "Mighta been better t' let the boys go on with it," opined the talkers. "Yankees started this war, didn't they? Better let 'em find out quick what it's like. . . ."

Johnny's appointment as postmaster, effective September 2, 1862 held local interest for a short time only. Election gossip was the order of the day. The contest promised to be bitter with Zad Jenkins in the center of the fray.

The night before election day, Johnny leaned over the store counter to talk to Joseph Notte, clerk and barkeep.

"Know where I can find some stout-hearted defenders for the flag of the Union?"

Notte, picking his teeth with a sharpened goose quill, grinned agreeably. "Seems as if you ought t' find a-plenty. Seems like I read somewhere's lately there's around five hundred eighty Prince George's men, draft-age. So far's I kin find out there's been two of 'em turn up in blue. Seems there ought t' be enough left to d'fend the whole county—ef it needs it."

Johnny chuckled. "Looks like it. Cap'n Billy Wood's coming out t'night with a flag. John Murphy got it for him at the Navy Yard. Uncle Zad says it's got t' fly for the election, no matter who says not."

Notte replaced the quill between his teeth with a thumbnail and ground down on it ruminatively before replying. "You leave it to me," he advised. "Think I can work it out. Think I shorely can."

The voice of a parched county gentleman recalled him to the bar, but he stopped for a twist of tobacco from under the counter. Something in the half-heard chuckle under the ledge made Johnny ask again, "Are you sure? Uncle Zad says it's got to. Don't you get me into trouble over this."

"No—no. No trouble. Nothing I'd like better."

That night Lou Weichman, Johnny's roommate at St. Charles, came out for one of his occasional visits. He arrived only a short time before a Washington band drove in. Traveling in light wagons and carriages, the musicians played at every crossroads and were followed by speechmakers who filled the air with administration fervor. After a lengthy session in the bar and a hearty supper in the tavern, the players serenaded the ladies and county voters along with Union soldiers who gathered around for the fun.

Uncle Zad arrived early bringing with him his daughter, Olivia, to spend the night with Anna. Beruffled and rustling, pink with excitement, the girls watched, giggling, from the front piazza. Not far away Zad engaged in conversation with Captain Billy Wood, Old Capitol Prison superintendent in Washington, and administration vote-getter, whose sharp little eyes observed the laughing group of young people.

"Let's listen to the speeches." Anna's chirping voice carried easily to where the captain listened. "They're sure to talk about Old Abe, and maybe we can find out why he won't wear socks."

Captain Billy Wood turned away rubbing his bearded chin, his shoulders shaking. He appeared to be on the best of terms with everyone. From a short conversation with Johnny he learned that a guard for the flag had been easily obtained. Mr. Collinbeck, old Mr. Tibbetts, and John Nothey had wanted to watch, and Uncle Zad had shown up with the silver-mounted fowling piece with which Grandfather Jenkins had peppered the British at Yorktown. But they had been persuaded the ground was too hard and cold for their old bones; they'd agreed to let younger men do it. Zad had advised them to take along a little something to ward off the autumn chill. Got pretty cold long toward morning. The captain agreed; nothing like a little snifter when there was a disagreeable job to do.

Election day dawned bright and crisp. Early morning roads stirred into dust by daylight were lined with rattling buggies, light wagons, and a sprinkling of carriages. In the latter, the beribboned and feathered bonnets of ladies strove against the stern countenances of masculine relatives beside them. The latter would go straight to the polls and, well fortified by liquid refreshments, take care of the serious business at hand. The ladies would dine with friends and discuss with avidity the events in which they could not participate but which filled them with excited curiosity just the same.

At breakfast Lou and Johnny were elegant in their best clothes. They were to drive the light trap pulled by the bay saddle horse with a white face. The carriage blacks had been sold long before, and as Lou was too timid to learn to ride, Johnny obligingly hitched his mount to the trap.

"No," Johnny said firmly. Anna and Olivia might not go. There would be trouble around the county town of Marlboro on this day. Besides, this was no time for Anna to tell anyone that Abraham Lincoln looked like a gorilla.

Lou widened his round, childish eyes. "Does he?"

"Anna's never seen him," explained Johnny, "but she loves to tell that Secretary Stanton said so."

The boys did not return until late that night, and it was again breakfast time before they related the events of the day. Uncle Zad was in trouble again, and maybe serious trouble. But even as he spoke, Johnny doubled over with laughter. "I didn't have a thing to do with it," he strangled over his words, "but I do wish you could have seen how mad he was, Robey, I mean." He hiccuped and started again.

The men watching the flag at Marlboro had had no trouble at all. They had watched, shivered, and sampled the bottle that would ward off chill. No one knew more than that; but at daylight when the clerks came to open up the polling place, they found young Andrew Robey. On his wrist—here the boys were overcome again—a handcuff chained him to a small staff from which floated the bright Confederate battle flag.

It had taken some time to arouse the sleeper, and his consternation when he awoke was pitiful—or would have been if the onlookers had not been too busy guffawing and pounding each other on the back.

Johnny dried his eyes again but remembering Uncle Zad's fury sobered instantly.

Before the day was over things had turned out to be very bad indeed. Andrew Robey, appointed U.S. marshal for election day, had been stationed at the polls to assure administration voters of no trouble and to provide plenty for anyone suspected of favoring secession. A little jittery after his night at the flagpole, Andrew had tottered about on unsteady feet, and his father, Dorley V. Robey, incensed at his neighbors' chuckles, entered into argument with everyone on every subject that came up. Uncle Zad, by this time a couple of drinks to the good, had fallen afoul of the government's right to confiscate a man's property without due process of law.

The gov'mint had a right to take anything it needed for the war, shouted Dorley in wrath at Zad's stupidity. It could take anything in the world a man had—all the gov'mint had to do was say so and it was just and right for it t' take over anything. Anything at all.

Wan't a dem word o' truth to it, Zad had declared. Any such doin's as that wan't constitutional. A man had t' be paid just recompense—through due process o' law. He'd show anybody, any time, right where they could find it in the Constitution itself. An' on that subject, no reasonable man could say that no little $300 was just recompense for a field hand that cost a thousand. No man in his senses would settle for that. Everybody knew he s'pported the Union, but Lincoln had sure enough slipped on this prop'ty business. It was all right, mebbe, for a man that hadn't a thing in the world t' lose by it t' talk like that, but to his mind—and here Zad's last drink had betrayed him and he yelled to the world what he really thought—"Any gov'mint, by Gawd, that takes a man's prop'ty without due process o' law an' proper recompense is run by a lot o' thievin', lyin' politicians that's got no business into it, an' it's a traitor to its own respons'ble voters that's always s'pported it."

Outraged Dorley V. called on the U.S. marshal to arrest the damned Secessionist and carry him away to the jail house before he could set pen to ballot. Spectators had looked on in amazement as the leading Administration man in the county was hauled away by an Administration marshal.

Captain Billy Wood had come along about that time, Johnny related, and got Uncle Zad out of jail as soon as the polls had closed. In words to curl his listener's hair Uncle Zad had promised Robey that he'd fix him one of these days. Robey had only smiled, but it hadn't been a pleasant smile, either.

Years afterward, in looking back, Johnny would see that this election battle had been the beginning of all his troubles. Uncle Zad brought suit for false imprisonment against Andrew Robey, and Dorley V. retaliated by again reporting Zad as a suspicious character, this time to General Lew Wallace, military commandant of the area. Zad smoldered, sputtered, exploded, but succeeded only in rousing the neighborhood to take sides in the free-for-all.

The dispute rebounded on Johnny. His father's friends advised him against trying to keep on good terms with them and still maintain an alliance with the North. When the South won the war, they said, he would find he had lost more than he had gained by such tactics.

His conferences with his father's friends seldom passed unnoticed by the Unionists, who then sent messengers for equally sage and friendly sessions. The only member of the latter group who did not offer advice was Andrew Robey, and in time Johnny sensed that this lack was more ominous than any spoken warning.

Anxiously he discussed his situation with Lou Weichman, his closest friend and frequent visitor. Lou, a native of Philadelphia, had been sent South to school through the efforts of Bishop John McGill of Richmond, who in early manhood had been a successful young lawyer in that city and a patron of Lou's father's tailor shop. John McGill had found the boy intelligent and appealing. He had assisted with Lou's school bills, and later, after he had entered the priesthood, Father McGill had continued to provide the funds for Lou to study and eventually be admitted to St. Charles as a prospective member of the Catholic clergy.

Lou, two years older than Johnny and a year ahead of him in school, was a very personable young man. A trifle under Johnny's six-feet-three, straight and broad shouldered, he impressed Anna Surratt as more elegant and scholarly looking than her brother. Lou had never ridden a horse or fired a pistol, while Johnny's outdoor life showed up in bleached brows and lashes that shone almost white against his flaming sunburn. Johnny's thin, fair skin burned when he rode in wind and sun, and he was forever riding in wind and sun. Through the center of his broad, high forehead, white where it had been shaded by his hat's broad brim, ran a deep blue vein that thickened under the stress of excitement. The old squire's forehead had had such a vein, and in him its thickening had warned of a storm to follow; but unlike his father, Johnny seldom gave way to temper. His eyes, gray as slate, their brows slashed by a thin, high nose, were hooded under long lashes. As the responsibility of his chosen work bore down on him, only those who knew Johnny well could read those baffling eyes.

Lou exerted himself to appear the sophisticate. Thick chestnut hair curled gently above his collar's edge, shone in scallops above his neat ears, and lay in deep curves above his smoothly rounded forehead. The small upturned mustache he had triumphantly produced strove to impart a trace of masculinity to his boyish expression. Large, prominent brown eyes set in rounded sockets emphasized the curve of full cheeks, arc of smooth brows, and suggested dimple in his chin. In well-tailored pants and smart, round-tailed jacket, he displayed manners as elegant as his appearance.

At Surratts' he basked in the warm friendliness of Johnny's family. In his desire for approval, he entered into political discussions with sufficient zeal to win favor with Prince George's conversationalists. He listened to them in the store, hung over the bar, sipped their potables, and responded with gentility to verbose patriotism generated by liquid inspiration. He agreed with their grievances, sympathized with their plaints, and encouraged the complainers. But inwardly, self-interest tore him. His father supported the Union, but his patron who could determine his future was now Bishop of Richmond. Lou could understand how Johnny, holding down his father's armchair and postoffice, became confused and angered by conflicting loyalties demanded of him.

The county's few Union followers implied that he held his office only by their tolerant consent. Like many another officeholder, Johnny needed the tiny income. Times had become hard. Yet it was difficult to put aside the memory of his father's political views. Ruefully Johnny found himself all but estranged from Gus Howell, his friend since childhood, and from Captain Bennett W. Gwynn, his father's oldest neighbor.

But—it was a Surratt post office, wasn't it? Yet to keep it he had been forced to tie up with the Republicans, whom his father had hated worse than sniveling sin. He could scarcely tolerate his position, but what else could he do?

Lou shook his head with genuine sympathy. His own problems were very much the same.

"What's that you're doing?" Johnny asked his mother on an afternoon toward the end of September as he paused beside the chair where she sat on the piazza, sewing in hand. "What're you making now? Clothes for the Free-Issues? If they're going to issue forth free, you want them to have new breeches for the occasion?"

His sarcasm was directed at Lincoln's notice of September 22 that any slave whose master was still in rebellion against the government on the following January 1 might on that day issue forth as a free man. The proclamation had flashed out of Washington and in a twitch of time the word "Free-Issue" had been born. Planters squalled the term scornfully, but financial panic backed their screams.

"I leave the fine work for Anna," Mrs. Surratt replied placidly. "I just found a little linen I had laid away some time back. Maybe she'll run some hemstitching on handkerchiefs for you. No—these aren't servants' clothes—they're some of your old breeches I'm cutting down for the Collinbeck boys. Thread this needle, will you, Johnny? I declare, I can hardly see at all, any more."

"Cotton's down to six cents, I just heard," offered Johnny as he jabbed the thread at the needle.

"The bar's well patronized." His mother looked critically across to where the store porch edge held a row of relaxed customers.

"All our business goes on at the bar. Hurray!" he handed the needle triumphantly to her. "Mail's coming in. Better I go."

He drifted across the lawn, his long legs in their light cotton pantaloons casting distorted shadows over the dusty road.

"How're you, Mr. Tibbit," he greeted the carrier who hauled the mail out from Washington.

The man answered with a surly nod and looked around the porch where conversation died out at his approach, where carefully bland looks met his gaze, carefully polite tones said, "G' afternoon," and lapsed into silence.

Inside the door Johnny emptied the bags on a small table behind the mail shelves before returning them to the carrier. Tibbett nodded again, crossed over to the bar for a lifesaving drink before moving on to the next step.

No one followed him into the bar, no one clustered around the shelves where Johnny sorted the few letters and papers, but as the carrier's wheels rattled away conversation broke out on all sides.

"Hear he don't care s' much for his Yankee mail job."

"Gits paid, don't he?"

"Thass what he wanted, wa'nt it?" The small neighborhood gossip squabbled amiably on.

"Here comes Doc—" The talkers hushed to peer intently

down the road at an approaching cloud of dust punctuated with hoof beats. Dr. Stowton S. Dent jogged up, dismounted, and threw his reins to Dan who caught them, grinning.

"Evenin', gentlemen." A chorus welcomed him as he headed toward the bar.

David Barry looked up expectantly. "How's things?"

The doctor patted his pocket lightly. "Fine, seh, just fine." Barry moved to his side and with magnificent unconcern accepted the small, rumpled envelope the doctor slipped into his hand.

"Thanks, eh, thanks." Barry gulped his drink hastily and made for his horse.

"Heard Miz Barry'd been worryin' right much—" John Nothey's smile circled the porch as Barry took off down the road. One by one the neighbors stepped up for a private conference with the doctor.

Johnny watched. As usual the doctor's missives, marked "Kindness of Bearer," outnumbered the properly stamped envelopes he sorted behind the mail rack. The doctor moved toward him; a small packet of letters fell on the table. As he dabbed at them with his hand stamp, Johnny noted unfamiliar names, unknown addresses in northern cities. He dropped them in the outgo bag.

Well, why not? Johnny asked himself. If a doctor posted a half dozen properly stamped letters, why should a postmaster inquire if he was doing a favor for some patient or if he had stumbled over the letters in a hollow tree? All over the Maryland peninsula, postmasters were asking themselves the same uneasy question.

Johnny began to notice that every time Gus Howell leaned over the Surratt bar, a group of planters sauntered in. Whenever Dr. Dent or some other doctors appeared, questioning parents of absent sons promptly stopped by. The Mills boys, the Claggetts, Stones, and a dozen others drew followers who materialized from thin air at the sound of their voices.

All these men dropped strange letters for Johnny's outgo bag. Not only were these mail runners, the whispers ran, but there also were couriers who carried messages straight from the Richmond government; they were aided along their way by Signal Corps operators responsible for contact lines between North and South. Along these lines, the whispers said, went papers, letters, messages, and small packages. Sometimes the private mail runners were helped by the couriers who received important information gathered by the mail runners in their travels.

No matter what their status, southern Maryland recognized these men as part of the great Confederate underground and protected them in every way. Inquiry from a stranger brought only a blank stare.

6

Johnny, always an enthusiastic letter writer, wrote Lou asking him for a visit. He arrived promptly. Indignantly Johnny related his troubles and learned that Lou, too, had growing difficulties brought on by the war. The St. Charles Seminary had notified him that unless he paid his overdue tuition he could not return for the fall term. He had written an impassioned letter to Father Doubrille, head of the school, threatening him with Bishop McGill's displeasure, but his sharpness had brought him only a definite refusal of admittance. They heard of a teaching vacancy in a nearby village, Pikesville, and decided that Lou should apply.

This struggling little school, also called St. Charles, boasted one building, a shaky frame structure that once had been a farmhouse. Father Walton, favorably impressed by Lou, at once agreed to employ him, and as the three men were talking, another aspirant for the job appeared. His suave manners, foreign appearance, and elegant French impressed the boys immensely. Johnny and the stranger held a lively conversation that afternoon as they strolled up and down the pleasantly shaded lawn. Happily for Johnny he could not foresee the circumstances under which he would again meet Henri Benjamin Ste. Marie of Canada West.

As for Johnny's post-office job, he had made one effort to right himself with the federal authorities. On December 16, 1863 he called on postal authorities in Washington and asked for his father's appointment. He was assured, or so he thought, that it would be issued not later than January 1, 1864.

The promise did not materialize. To his great indignation, the appointment went to Andrew V. Robey. Robey, not only Uncle Zad's enemy, was also an outsider, a man so lately moved into Prince George's that he was not a landowner, slaveholder nor, as late as the last election, a qualified voter.

Johnny quietly cast about for work to help the family's precarious situation. And then came an offer that was to alter his whole life. He was asked to carry the Confederate mail.

The first mail runners had been chiefly boys who, purely as a personal project, gathered up their neighbors' letters, crossed the river where they could, and headed for Richmond and points south. As time went on they became welcome guests in homes along the way because of news both personal and military that they picked up in their travels.

In its first two years, while national unity still faintly survived, war had not completely severed the affections of North and South. Stories of friends arrested and held incommunicado in Washington prisons had not yet aroused the passions that later flamed through Virginia and southern Maryland.

Northern recruits picketing the Potomac had not learned the danger potential in spies and Confederate sympathizers crossing the river at will. Federal soldiers winked and let Rebels pass on the flimsiest of pretexts or for a small sum. Pretty girls flicked long lashes at sentries who declined to search petticoats that often concealed letters and sometimes official dispatches.

The demand for private messenger service grew, until scarcely a night passed that the Potomac was not crisscrossed by runners laden down with private mails or by couriers lightly encumbered by cipher messages. As the traffic increased so did its hazards. By 1864 a private letter posted in a concealed basement station of a Richmond Ninth Street Faro Bank required a dollar and a half in silver deposited with it to insure its delivery by mail runner into Washington.

The lower peninsula country favored these underground operations. Veined by branches and creeks, all its narrow rutted roads still led to the river.

Along these roads traveled not only private mail but military information from Washington. A steady flow of contraband left Philadelphia factories and via Baltimore reached Pope's Creek or Port Tobacco, to be ferried across to Virginia and carried down to Richmond. Remote farm buildings, tobacco barns, and cellars of river houses sheltered this merchandise while en route to the South.

While the river people and Northern business firms worked out their individual delivery problems, so did Confederate officials. Southern ports bustled with seagoing tugs, side-wheelers, and schooners turned privateersmen. At first Southern mail was carried to the Bahamas, where it was unwittingly, perhaps, picked up by federal ships and transported to Northern ports. The federal post-office system then delivered it to its destination with little more delay than in prewar days.

Nor had the Confederacy, at first, encountered difficulty with its diplomatic approaches to foreign countries. Nearly four thousand miles of seacoast with innumerable inlets, harbors, and bays made open contact with Europe simple. But as the federal blockade intensified, more and more ships were stopped and too often diplomatic mail pouches had to be thrown overboard.

Later, Confederate commissioners in London, Paris, and Brussels, and those stationed for a time at the Vatican, in Madrid, and in St. Petersburg maintained communication with their government but only by tedious and roundabout means.

As water routes grew difficult, a western land itinerary was attempted. Messengers rode horseback into Kentucky and, aided by Southern sympathizers, skulked northward to one or another of the Great Lakes cities, where they crossed by ship to Canada. From Montreal an unbroken stream of messages flowed to France, to England, and through them to other parts of the Continent.

But with time the western land routes through enemy territory grew more dangerous. By 1864 only the swift but hazardous route of the Potomac remained practical. This was the route that Little Johnny knew well and had traveled often.

Carriage or horseback travelers from Washington could reach Pope's Creek in six or seven hours, cross the river in another, and follow an ancient roadway to Port Royal on the Rappahannock River. Here the 300 feet of the Rappahannock could be traversed by ferry and only eighteen miles from its southern landing lay the open road to Richmond.

Daily the official couriers went this way. New York papers, picked up in Washington, reached the Potomac by dusk and the next morning before their news was twenty-four hours old they were in the hands of Jefferson Davis and his cabinet.

Before the Federal Secret Service awoke to the dangers of the river country, several routes to the South were well established. One of the best known routes out of Washington went by way of Bennings Bridge and Anacostia. Another favorite crossing was by harmless-looking oyster boat straight over to Alexandria, on the river's southern bank.

Mail runners preferred Prince George's and St. Mary's counties. Occasionally they could cross the Potomac in Thomas Nelson Conrad's sailing boat, *Rebel Queen*, or by an India rubber skiff that bobbed like a bubble on the gray water. Often they went with George Atzerodt, who ran regular trips in a three-man row-boat out of Port Tobacco or, when the hunt came too close, from the mouth of the Nanjemoy and other hidden landings along the shore.

More venturesome runners used rowboats with plugged bottoms. After landing they pulled the plugs, submerged the boats to await their return crossing.

Such exploits, hilariously related, won widespread admiration and the runners became famous throughout the county.

Johnny's new job came through a neighbor, Squire Thomas A. Jones.

Picked up as a river runner early in the war, Squire Jones had been released from the Old Capitol Prison in March 1862 and had accepted appointment as Confederate mail agent largely because he believed that he had been put upon by Yankee soldiers and that their actions had contributed to the death of his wife.

Before the war Jones had lived with his family and a few slaves where Pope's Creek empties into the Potomac. His comfortable house with huge end chimneys and a covered colonnade running to its kitchen edged the bluff nearly a hundred feet above the water. From front windows set in its rain-washed clapboard walls, Jones could see up the Potomac, across to Mathias Point seven miles away, and downstream for nearly nine miles.

In peacetime he had admired this view while he farmed his 540 acres of good land but when the shad ran in spring he often observed it from a rowboat propelled by his stout-armed slave, Henry Woodland. After the shad came soft-shell crabs, hard shells, oysters, and fin-fish to contribute to the small store of cash accumulating in his ironbound locker chest, and to the tables of dreary little river hotels now thronged with strangers.

This crowding into previously untenanted hostelries had begun at the opening of hostilities when the area suddenly became flooded with persons in haste to cross the river. They had relatives they must find at once, the strangers explained, or they had business hazards that must be reduced. They had dying friends who must be visited down South, or they lived there and must get home. Almost before he knew it, Squire Jones was crossing the river daily with cargoes of strangers rather than fish.

As the traffic increased he fished by day from a lead-colored skiff until the federal soldiers and the gunboat crews grew accustomed to his presence. He dipped his gill nets into the river, or angled by the hour, motionless and half asleep. The Federals paid him no mind when he went out at low tide where the big-mouthed bass fed.

At first he made no money from his river crossings, for he recognized the necessities of his passengers and his sympathies with the South were so enlisted that he assured himself he offered only his Christian duty. However, as his farming and fishing declined he set a rate of a dollar per person per trip.

On the night of September 14, 1861 Union soldiers picked up a Negro boy, John Hill, who said he belonged to James Grymes of Mathias Point but that he had crossed the river with Squire Jones, who had landed a boatload of passengers on the Virginia shore. Under sharp questioning he admitted that both Squire Jones and Squire Dent ran nightly ferry lines and that his own master, Grymes, carried the passengers away from his house as quickly as they landed. Squire Jones kept his three-man rowboat up a gut on his land and when he had passengers he signaled with a white flag by day or lamp at night, so Grymes could be ready with carriages when the boat landed.

Two nights later Union soldiers reached the Jones home, surrounded the house, and beat on its doors demanding the squire. Mrs. Jones and her several small children watched in terror as the bluecoats shattered the windows, battered down the doors, and surged into every nook and corner of the comfortable old rooms. Pawing through every chest, desk drawer, and cupboard, the intruders tossed clothing, curtains, blankets, furniture in heaps on the floor or out the windows. They tore beds to pieces, ripped straw ticks and featherbeds with their knives, but uncovered no master.

Their pockets crammed with Jones's account books, business records, and private correspondence, the soldiers took off leaving Mrs. Jones unconscious from shock. Frustrated in their effort to capture the owner, the soldiers eased their disappointment by smashing Henry Woodland's boat to pieces.

Crossing Pope's Creek to the Dent home, they entered by force, searched the house, and confiscated all papers they could put their hands on. Servants whom they forcibly held for questioning admitted that Dent and Jones had left earlier that night to carry twenty-five people across the river.

Next night the soldiers searched Port Tobacco, but once more arrived only after the splash of oars had died out of hearing. They caught Jones the night of October 4, 1861 as he beached his boat at Pope's Creek, carted him off to Washington, and clapped him into a temporary jail at Thirteenth Street and the Avenue. The next several months Jones spent writing wordy letters in which he demanded a hearing, but received no replies and no action. He fumed helplessly in the jail basement, for letters from home told him his sick wife failed rapidly.

In vain he begged Secretary Seward through such Marylanders

as Josiah Dent, H. Winter Davis, Peter W. Crain, and Thomas E. Hambledon, but it was not until Congressman Calvert asked for the release of "one of my constituents" that action came. Then, after Jones agreed to take the oath of allegiance, he was freed but his release came too late. His wife was dead.

Shortly after his return home he was approached by Major William Norris, C.S.A., who offered an appointment as dispatch agent between Richmond and Canada. Penniless and bitter, Jones refused, not so much because of his oath (he held this had been given under duress) but because his children would be endangered. Motherless as they now were, he said, he could not leave them fatherless also.

However, he was willing to handle communications across the Potomac and maintain a ferry service for Confederate agents provided he would never be called upon to divulge to the Richmond government the names of any of his river runners. So, with no written contract nor further communication with Confederate officials, he established an efficient, permanent ferry and mail service across the river.

Jones gave orders that no mail should be landed on his property and that carrier boats must remain on the Virginia shore until signaled to cross. Once landed, the mail must be hidden up the bluff until it could be picked up by persons who for reasons of safety rotated their services.

Dr. Stowton S. Dent, whose interest in the Southern mail was animated by his two sons in the Confederate Army, often carried it. Everybody knew him, everybody liked him. Federal officers, soldiers, slaves, planters, all welcomed the bluff, hearty doctor who gave professional advice unstintingly whether paid for it or not, and who handed out pills and noxious liquids as freely to one man as to another. He could go anywhere without exciting suspicion, so almost every day he stuffed contraband letters and messages into his enormous pockets and the tremendous boots that reached to his huge knees and rode his shaggy mare along the country roads to smuggle the Rebel mail through Union picket lines. Dent was one unfailing link in the famous "Doctors' Line."

Squire Tom Jones's station soon became the most important ferrying point along the river. Near it stood the homes of other persons who assisted in the running arrangements. About five miles upstream lay Cox's station, and a little to the east of it stood Rich Hill, the Cox home. Next door to Jones, only a few hundred feet down the shore, lived pretty Mary Watson. Her father, Major Roderick G. Watson, had been part of the mail route and at his death Mary had taken up where he left off. The high attic roof of the large Watson house was pierced by dormer windows from which Mary watched for the mail boat as it set out from the Virginia shore. If enemy troops at hand made the landing seem perilous, she flew a black warning flag easily seen through field glasses trained on her window.

Detachments of Union soldiers paced the bluff top from dusk to dawn. The courier boats invariably put out early in the evening so Mary Watson frequently draped her black shawl over the third floor window ledge right above the heads of pickets who lounged in her yard waiting nightfall and duty time.

Across the river on the Virginia side lay the plantation of Dr. Richard Stewart, richest man in King George's County, who as a hot Secessionist was under constant watch from the gunboats on the river. Not far from him at Mathias Point stood the Grymes house, half hidden by overhanging trees. In the dense foliage of a nearby ravine, behind piles driven across its mouth, the runner boats lay hidden by day. Between these points Jones and his unnamed agents operated the ferry and mail service.

Jones's unprepossessing appearance aided him in his work, for he was slightly under middle height and a thatch of faded hair grew stiff and straight above his mournful face. He talked in a low, complaining voice, moaned about his sparse catch of fish, about his absconding Negro farmhands, about his poor crops. He chewed meditatively on scrawny mustaches that dribbled down each side of his tobacco-stained mouth and deliberately gave out the impression of a dim-witted countryman.

Nevertheless, every afternoon when the sun had fallen behind the hills his runners put out from the Virginia shore and, unless warned by Mary Watson's black shawl, slipped easily across to Maryland. Their activities were so widespread that no sooner was one runner picked up than a replacement popped out of some hitherto unused nook in one of the creeks along the river's edge. Even with their inexhaustible supplies of men and means, the Federals could not quite destroy the system; on the day the Confederacy fell, the river ferry was operating as efficiently as when first set up by Tom Jones of Pope's Creek.

Johnny had been making trips for Squire Jones for several months before an opportunity came to join the regular secret service couriers. By that fall of 1864, couriers were in critically short supply. Many had been captured, and others had taken up more profitable lines, such as carrying drafts for Southerners prudent enough to place their funds in Northern banks but who could now get their money only by a draft presented at the teller's window. Slipping back through the lines with a belt full of gold paid an attractive premium, and Richmond was full of businessmen who preferred their Northern connections to remain unknown to their Southern friends. As the death of the Confederacy neared, passports and escape routes were urgently needed by the Main Street speculators who could not afford to be stranded when the dying nation breathed its last.

These men paid well to get their letters through. And if, as sometimes happened, payment in the North was larger, then so much the better. And if, as also sometimes happened, the urgent scrawls were perused in the office of Confederate Secretary of State Judah P. Benjamin before making the trip North, many others were read in the office of Union Secretary of War Edwin M. Stanton as they passed through Washington.

However, none of these side lines would Johnny accept. When, thanks to the approval of Squire Jones, he reported to Lieutenant C. H. Cawood, Confederate Signal Corps Officer for the Potomac area, he made this very clear.

He gave his mother a slightly different story. "If Abe Lincoln won't have me, Jeff Davis will." He smiled teasingly at her as he explained his new job, sketching its nature perhaps too broadly. "It'll help us with the move into Washington," he urged. They couldn't farm without labor; they couldn't pay the mortgage without farming. If they moved into town and took in a few roomers, and then rented the Surrattsville property, tavern, store, and bar, the rent money would pacify Mr. Calvert until something could be done about collecting from John Nothey and paying off the mortgage.

Johnny and his mother had recognized all along that the move was inevitable and a job a necessity, but the things he did not tell her about his new work were more important than the things he detailed. He said simply that he was only delivering letters; he would be in no danger at all. Not from the Yankees, and not from their draft. He would be perfectly safe.

Possibly he did not say that as a courier he would be part of the Confederate Secret Service, and that like other operatives, he would receive no set salary, only his expenses. Change of costume, a legitimate expense, would be approved by the State Department in whose service he would be. Many such couriers equipped themselves with at least three outfits to transform their appearance at will, but Johnny's work would require little divergence from his ordinary dress. In the city he would represent himself as a typical Southern gentleman in light trousers, long frock coat of gray. For Northern travel he would wear a Scotch plaid shawl of the kind made popular by the president. The latter's shawl was a small affair that barely draped his stooping shoulders but Johnny, with an eye to elegance, wrapped his narrow frame in a long fringed fabric that fell to the middle of his body.

To his mother he made light of these arrangements and the suggestion of danger. Even if he were stopped, he explained gaily, he knew what to do. Search all they wanted, the Yankees could find nothing but the clothes on his back and a trifle of money in his pocket. There could be nothing illegal in either.

But Mrs. Surratt continued to worry. Shouldn't he buy a draft substitute through an Exemption Club? He refused sharply. The Yanks never could catch him. When she persisted, his mouth tightened and the squire's vein in his forehead thickened.

Before his unusual irritation she gave way, but worry lived with her.

7

As Johnny began his courier service, the most urgent official Confederate need was for rapid, sure communication with Canada and much of that need revolved around the explosive prisoner-of-war negotiations.

From the first days of the war, Northern newspapers had dwelt on the inhumane treatment meted out to Northern men in Southern prisons. Southern newspapers retaliated with accounts of the sufferings of Southern men in Northern prisons, which they explained were wilfully imposed by Union officials. The North had at its command all the food and medicine needed for adequate care whereas, these papers unfailingly pointed out, the blockade of Southern ports was a Northern move which now penalized Union soldiers.

In April 1864 General Grant's order that not another Southern prisoner would be exchanged on any terms brought anger to the boiling point. More than 23,000 Confederates were wasting away in Northern prisons, while Union men were starving in the South where their jailers were unable to feed them or themselves. In vain the Confederate government made offer after offer; Grant refused to be moved.

Release of Confederate prisoners took on the urgency of a crusade. Confederate personnel in Canada was increased, and couriers to whom vital dispatches could be entrusted for delivery above the border became the need of the moment.

Among the Confederates to whom dispatches must be carried was J. P. Holcombe, commercial agent, whose office handled purchase orders for armaments bought in Europe, munitions and a miscellany of war goods from New York. These were shipped to Halifax and there transshipped to Bermuda or other ports frequented by blockade runners. Information on politics, prisoner release activities, public opinion, subversive moves in New England and the western states also found their way across his desk.

Nathaniel Beverly Tucker of Richmond planned the exchange of Southern cotton for Northern bacon, pound for pound. From his Canadian residence he corresponded with Abraham Lincoln and Secretary of State Seward, and for a time, prisoner exchange or no, business went on as usual.

Commissioners Jacob Thompson and Clement C. Clay were ordered to Canada in April 1864. Clay's work was to assist prisoner release while Thompson, working through pacifist societies, was to endeavor to alienate the western vote in the November elections when Lincoln would be up for his second term.

General Edwin G. Lee, cousin of Robert E. Lee, recovered slowly from wounds received the year before. In Canada on detached service, he would succeed Clay who had been ordered home. Prisoner release entailed helping escapees across the border into Canada and then providing them maintenance and transportation back to their military units. A weekly sailing packet out of Halifax carried them to Bermuda, where blockade runners returned them to Southern ports.

Proceeds from the sale of several hundred bales of cotton were allotted to this purpose and $25,000 in credits was deposited in a Liverpool, England bank. Other funds were kept in the Montreal branch of the Bank of Ontario where John Porterfield, a banker from Nashville, Tennessee, kept an eye on them for the Confederate government.

During that summer of 1864, North and South vacillated between hope and despair, waiting the outcome of the November elections. The defeat of Lincoln, said the western Peace-Democrats, would end the war and in all parts of the country people prayed for their success. Jacob Thompson kept in touch with these and other pacifists.

Confederate funds arranged an uprising at the National Democratic Convention with the release of Confederate prisoners held in Johnson's Island, Rock Island, and other Illinois and Great Lakes prison camps. Messengers kept the trails hot between Canada, Richmond, and the western states. Hysterical excitement accompanied the messages that bound Confederate centers and Washington in the same network of political unrest and espionage.

Failure ended the first prisoner release attempt. Captains Charles H. Coles and Bennet G. Burley, who had led the attack on Johnson's Island, were captured along with Lieutenant John Yates Beall. Documents that would establish their status as military men acting in line of duty were urgently needed to prevent their execution as brigands. Couriers hastened north from Richmond with these credentials.

Other prisoner release schemes were attempted and failed. Finally, the South offered to yield every point in dispute if the North would only take back its own dying men. Pressure on Washington increased. Feeling, North and South, ran high over Grant's refusal.

Every Northern man released came home an invalid to be cared for, he said, while ". . . every man we release becomes a soldier against us. If we liberate prisoners we will have to fight until the whole South is exterminated . . . to release Rebel soldiers would insure Sherman's defeat and compromise our safety . . ."

Prisoner plans flared again. If release of Southern soldiers would do this, then the prisoners would be released one way or another, said the planners. Couriers sped between Richmond, Canada, and the West. Lieut. Colonel John Martin and Lieutenant John W. Headley, sent out by General E. G. Lee, investigated prison camps around the Great Lakes and reported that only with outside help could wholesale releases be accomplished.

Military power in the South waned. The Confederacy's death rattle could be heard, but the courier lines held. Runners crossed the Potomac in their rubber skiffs or rowboats; scouts skulked through back roads and bypaths. Out of Washington went the Doctor's Line, carrying missives in medicine cases or pockets, cuddled deep beside precious personal letters. Couriers went north by cars, blockade runners and British packet; west by foot or horseback, yet the network of message routes shrank. Carriers were stopped, searched, disappeared. "Several times I have attempted to send messages to you," complained Jacob Thompson in Canada in a letter to Secretary Benjamin in Richmond, "but I have no assurance that they ever reached you."

Fall brought rioting in New York. In Richmond a halfhearted

attempt to assassinate Jefferson Davis failed. Thomas Nelson Conrad offered to try again to capture Abraham Lincoln. Secretary of War Seddon gave Conrad a travel order, which included assistance from the Southern army should he ask for it.

In Washington, Conrad's scouts waited in Lafayette Park for the president's carriage, but warned of betrayal escaped before they could be apprehended. Later in September a group of butternut-clad men leaned over a Washington bar and, gulled by their thirst, talked aloud of an abduction plan. Only by minutes they escaped the War Department's clutching hands. A group of Northern clergymen offered to end the war by abducting Jefferson Davis and, following their offer, Stanton sent Captain Billy Wood down to Richmond to see if it could be done. Wood had no trouble running the river and sneaking through the lines but he thought abduction impractical. Nothing came of it except more inflammatory talk, more whispers of abduction, capture, prisoner release, North and South. Nothing else, said the whispers, could end the war.

In Baltimore a young actor, handsome and famous, met a school friend at Barnum's Hotel. Would he help release the South's dying soldiers? All that was needed was a hostage, an important hostage for whose return the North would release every Southern soldier in its prisons.

In Prince George's County Little Johnny carried his letters and between times discussed with his mother how to save their mortgaged home.

October 19 came and on that day a band of twenty-one escaped Rebel prisoners swooped down on St. Albans, Vermont, in retaliation for Dahlgren's raid on Richmond and Sherman's march to the sea. They looted banks, killed one citizen, wounded others, and escaped over the border to Canada. Once more couriers scurried with documents to establish the military status of the raiders. That month, in Montreal the popular young actor John Wilkes Booth played a short engagement, opened a bank account, and arranged for the shipment of his personal property and stage costumes to Canada and then south by blockade runner.

In New York, Union troops surrounded the polling places to control the voters and also to quiet the draft riots.

The Wallace Pictures

The trial of the so-called "Lincoln Conspirators" is probably the only American trial from which have been preserved pencil sketches of the accused made by a judge while listening to evidence that would determine life or death for his models.

A catalogue issued by the General Lew Wallace Study in Crawfordsville, Indiana, describes this unfinished oil painting by the General, who sat on the Military Commission which tried the conspirators. The scene is the Capitol grounds in Washington on the occasion of Lincoln's second inauguration. The marble slabs symbolize the broken nation, and war clouds darken the sky above. To the men tried by the Military Commission General Wallace has here added Booth and John Harrison Surratt, Jr., and he has omitted Mrs. Surratt.

Anna Eugenia Surratt

In Prince George's County, the old squire's widow and daughter packed their household effects and moved into Washington.

Johnny's courier work was his only happiness that bitter autumn of 1864. For months now the Surratt family's only income had been the small uncertain sums paid by Union troops for entertainment at tavern and bar. As food became scarcer and the influx of soldiers increased, their very numbers encouraged them to take more and more without payment or by-your-leave.

After notice from Mr. Charles Calvert that settlement of his father's estate, of which he was executor, could be delayed no longer, Mrs. Surratt again insisted to John Nothey that he pay something on his debt. The demand brought no return; nor did the request to John Marshall. There was no way in which a Maryland peninsula man could pay his debts.

When she had decided to move into Washington, Uncle Zad found a tenant of sorts for her farm. John M. Lloyd, who had been discharged from the Washington police force under circumstances not made public, now yearned to try his hand at taverntending and the pleasant occupation of standing behind a bottle-laden bar. The fifty dollars a month he would pay Mrs. Surratt for this privilege would be turned over to Mr. Calvert. It appeared the only solution and in October 1864 the move to Washington had begun.

The Washington house stood at 504 H. Street. Between it and the corner of Seventh Street lay a small green handkerchief of a yard and a front porch edged with iron grillwork fronted its sedate gray brick walls. From the front door a hall ran the length of the house, opening on parlor, back parlor, and parlor bedroom. Open stairs led to the second floor, on which there were three large bedrooms, one behind the other. A narrower stair to a third floor opened into a small room that provided passage to a larger chamber.

The lower floor, called the basement, held the kitchen, a small outkitchen, and pantry. In front of them a dining room's wide windows faced the street at ground level. Hundreds of residences built on this plan still stand in the old sections of Washington and house now, as then, the thousands of government workers who seek lodging with townspeople. Mrs. Surratt's house stands too but today it bears little resemblance to the comfortable home of 1864.

Strangers crowded Washington, and renting rooms to them produced the Surratts' only income. Rachel remained in the tavern kitchen, but her young daughter, Jinny, came to Washington with the family. Dan came with them too, and later on, if she could afford a cook, Mrs. Surratt would employ one of the Free-Issues who filled the city streets.

Every day for almost a month a loaded wagon traveled from the villa to the town house, and no matter what appeared on its surface, somewhere underneath lay small stores from the ell room: a bag of potatoes, a jar of lard, a glass of berry jam, the pitiful remains of the farm's once packed supply pantries.

These practical measures interested Anna not at all. She was convinced that life in the city would be little short of heavenly. Only a few blocks of houses, some of them belonging to very important people, separated her from the glamorous shopping and theatrical district down the Avenue.

At Sixth and the Avenue in the New National Hotel lived Mr. John Wilkes Booth, a handsome young Maryland actor the whole town was mad about. On F Street next to Ninth stood Father Wiget's new Gonzaga College; at Tenth and G there was beautiful St. Patrick's Church where zealous young Father Walter was pastor. Washington would be exhilarating. There would be excitement, places to go, things to see, and best of all, Lou Weichman had come to live with them.

Lou had finished his term at Pikesville while he waited for the war to end. But it dragged on, and danger from the Union draft increased. He paid a hundred dollars for a substitute in the Army, and for added safety as well as its excellent salary he obtained a clerkship in the federal War Department.

This job, in the Commissary of Prisons' office, paid him eighty dollars a month but unfortunately it required him to join the Home Guards for defense of the city. However, remembering Mrs. Surratt's good country table, Lou jumped at the chance to move to the Surratts' and share the big front bedroom on the second floor with his college roommate.

Other rooms on that floor were quickly taken by Mrs. Surratt's cousins, John and Eliza Holohan, and their two children. When John T. Holohan had found his Baltimore marble and granite business suffering from wartime ills he had closed it out in favor of a government post in Washington. He soon found the business of bounty broker more lucrative.

Vivacious Eliza chafed a little at the crowded quarters of the H Street house. Her Baltimore life had been gayer than that in the shabby, genteel Surratt parlor. To entertain herself she employed all her airs and graces to overwhelm plain Honora Fitzpatrick who had come to live with the Surratt family while her father served as a sergeant in the Union Army. Honora was severely plain, with a face that flushed too easily. In the presence of her elders her tongue lagged over the simplest words, but alone with Anna it clattered at both ends.

Johnny liked the house lively. When things were quiet he worried. He had picked up a lot of information on his trips and was troubled over what he saw in Washington: the captured Confederate artillery on display in front of the War Department, the Confederate prisoners of war led along the streets under guard, and the deserters. Bands of the latter, buttons slashed from their gray uniforms, trudged into town almost every day from the south. The denuded gray jackets were almost as plentiful on the Avenue as the resplendent blues.

Following the November elections that year, angry impatience set in across the nation. The North fretted over disloyalties in the western states and the harassments of the escaped Confederate prisoners along the Canadian border. In Washington, radicals in the Republican ranks, growling their complaints daily, made the president a whipping boy for their own animosities.

In the South as the strangling blockade and the futile peace moves brought defeat into view, the people sank into bitter despondency and pleaded for the exchange of men held in Northern prisons.

Abuse of Abraham Lincoln mounted in both North and South. Starving women and children by a barbarous blockade was not enough, scratched Southern editorial pens; Northern politicians would condemn their own soldiers to death from starvation and lack of medical care if because of their deaths more Southerners died too. Sectional hatred spumed forth in a bloody froth of words.

Fantastic words revived fantastic plans. Capture. Abduction. Whoever could capture the leaders, abduct civilian leaders too, could hold them hostage for favorable peace terms. Whoever destroyed the political heads of nations would bring about peace. The North would give up at once without its despot president, said the South. The South would give up at once without its despot, Jefferson Davis, said the North.

On November 25 John Wilkes Booth and his famous brothers, Edwin and Junius, played *Julius Caesar* at the Winter Garden, in New York, while next door the LaFarge Hotel was fired by Rebel escapees under Lieutenant John W. Headley, down from Canada for the purpose. Eighteen other hotels flamed briefly that night. The Rebels were captured and once more getting military identification was urgent.

By this time many couriers had become too well known to carry dispatches. New faces were necessary. The western route was called again into use. Stephen F. Cameron, chaplain with Morgan's Raiders, volunteered and was ordered to courier duty. Hidden in his clothing were dispatches to Confederate Commissioners Clay and Thompson, and to General E. G. Lee.

Thomas Nelson Conrad headed North. John Surratt made his trips South.

From every side events converged on Washington to determine the fate of Johnny Surratt.

In March, 1864, Dahlgren's raid on Richmond had brought hatred to a flaming peak. Colonel Ulric Dahlgren, Second U.S. Cavalry, led what was planned to be the final blow of the war, when he stormed the Confederate capital with a column of picked cavalrymen. Dahlgren was killed and the raid failed, but its consequences were fantastic.

On Dahlgren's body Confederates found the official orders for his raid. They found also the outline of a speech to his men in which he ordered Richmond burned, Northern prisoners released and armed, and turned loose to sack the city. They were to capture Jefferson Davis and his cabinet. If capture was impossible, their assassination was approved.

These papers, forwarded through military channels to General Robert E. Lee and then to President Jefferson Davis, were photographed and published over the world. English, French, and Canadian newspapers made much of them.

The Confederate government filed a formal protest with Washington. In reply, the federal government did not deny that the raid had been approved by both Stanton and President Lincoln. It did, however, deny approval of the destruction of Richmond or the assassination of the Confederate president and his cabinet.

The denials met with general incredulity, and the words abduction and assassination took on a realism that had lingered.

8

On the evening of December 23, Johnny and Lou stopped downtown to finish some last-minute Christmas shopping. As they passed the New National Hotel at Sixth and the Avenue, Dr. Samuel A. Mudd of Bryantown hailed them with outstretched hand. With him, instantly recognized by both boys, was John Wilkes Booth.

"We were just speaking of you, Mr. Surratt," said Dr. Mudd. "Mr. Booth wishes to meet you. Mr. Booth, Mr. Surratt."

Johnny turned in such amazement that he scarcely remembered to murmur Lou's name in introduction. He looked down at the compactly built man, who barely topped his shoulder. Mr. Booth tossed back the furred cape of his handsome greatcoat and with studied grace removed his tall silk hat, revealing eyes that glowed slumberously black under heavy lids. He offered a big, beautiful hand.

"I have been eager to meet you, Mr. Surratt. I have been told you are familiar with every part of the Maryland peninsula," said Booth.

He awaited Johnny's shrugged acknowledgment before he continued. He was looking for land—a plantation; Dr. Mudd had mentioned Surratt's Villa and that its owner was settled in Washington.

Johnny had heard that golden voice floating over footlights. Here, on the bleak winter street, its warmth glowed with cultivated beauty.

He knew, said the actor, Squire Gardiner of Prince George's—had visited him only last Sunday—they had attended church and he had met Dr. Mudd. As neither Johnny nor Lou was yet able to frame an adequate reply, he invited them to a drink at his hotel.

In the book-lined room the boys sipped milk punches and completely forgot their shopping expedition. Almost at once Dr. Mudd excused himself to keep an engagement. Making his farewells, he asked Johnny to accompany him to the door, and for a moment they conversed in the hall.

When Mr. Booth had been in Prince George's, he had been looking for horses, or so he said, commented the doctor. Squire Gardiner had carried him around for a day or two, but he had bought only one, Gardiner's blind mare. Good runner but blind in one eye. This time he wanted to buy land.

"I told him about a good many parcels," offered the doctor, "but it seemed as if all he wanted to know was about roads—land on good roads, he said." He paused, and Johnny waited for him to continue. "I don't know much about him, but I hear he's courting Senator Hale's daughter. Radical man, Hale is, I hear. Northern family, the Booths. I'm sure I don't know exactly what he wants in our community, hardly seems likely he'll leave the stage to go to farming. Well—I just thought I'd mention it." He pulled his scraggly beard uncertainly.

Johnny nodded. "Thank you, sir. Nice of you. I'll keep it in mind."

The doctor donned his battered old beaver hat and moved away.

Back by the fire Lou found Wilkes engrossing. Wilkes had a

way of drawing people out. In his presence it was impossible to feel anything but at one's best and under his approval that best was likely to seem to its possessor little short of prodigious. In Wilkes, lavish conversation did not seem extravagant. Rather, he gave his listeners the feeling of spontaneous rightness and sincerity.

Wilkes could also be the best of listeners, the sympathetic, admiring friend by whom the speaker was evaluated properly, perhaps for the first time. It was thus that Lou was seeing himself as Johnny returned to the room.

Land came into discussion once more; its relation to highways and crossroads. At the actor's request Johnny sketched on the back of an envelope a rough draft of the vicinity of the Villa and its highways.

It had been pleasant to meet them, the actor assured his guests as they rose to go. He hoped to see them again. Perhaps they would take supper with him before too long.

"I'll ask him to supper some night if I get the chance," said Johnny as they reached the street. "I'll wager the girls'll be hysterical when we tell them about this."

"They will," agreed Lou moodily. "They'll be wild."

Holiday plans engrossed Anna and Honora, who met them at the door, for the season would be gayer than any of the Surratts had enjoyed in years. Although Isaac would be missed, the household would be full. Fathers Lanahan and Wiget had been invited to dinner. Milk punch was mellowing in a stone jar in the basement kitchen. Johnny must keep out of it, and Lou too, scolded Anna. Lou had tickets for Ford's for one night during the week. A gala season was at hand, to which Johnny now added the sensation of naming his new friend. The girls swooned in ecstasy but privately Johnny puzzled over the encounter that had brought the introduction to Wilkes Booth.

The holiday season came and went with laughter in the little home on Seventh Street, but for Johnny its gaiety was dampened by news of Sherman's wire to the President, begging to present him as a Christmas gift the city of Savannah. Guns boomed in Washington and flags waved in a bone-chilling rain. Some people rejoiced that Southern resistance must be so nearly broken by Sherman's march to the sea, but others shivered at tales of the desolation left in his wake.

Johnny was soon called to make a hurried trip to Montreal with dispatches concerning the financial affairs that kept Jacob Thompson on edge.

After Johnny's hasty trip north, Anna and Honora, dying of curiosity, could scarcely wait until he was out of his tight new boots and into old slippers before the parlor fire to hear his adventures. New York, he said, was wonderful. Fifth Avenue windows put anything on Pennsylvania Avenue to shame. Nowhere in Washington could be seen such expensive fur capes, such tiny bonnets dripping silly little veils. The bonnets, he chuckled, were absolutely beyond belief and the crepe masks the ladies wore, just ridiculous. Anna and Honora giggled happily, and even Eliza listened with respect to his descriptions of the pushing theater crowds, of the ladies furred and exotically scented, extravagantly shod and fastened into eighteen-button gloves.

"You didn't," ventured Anna timidly, "hear anything about Mr. Booth, did you?"

"Wilkes?" With elaborate casualness Johnny replied, "I dined with Wilkes at Edwin Booth's house—you know, the oldest brother."

"Mr. Edwin Booth's house?" Anna's awed words fell away into silence. John Holohan looked up from the *National Intelligencer.* "You wouldn't string us along, would you, Johnny?"

"Never in this world." The boy's deep-set eyes twinkled under their light lashes. "Wilkes had asked me to carry a message to his brother, and when I went to the house the first person I saw was Wilkes himself. Edwin came in a little later and asked me to dinner."

His mother looked at him sharply, but he continued. "His brother is just as charming as he is, only in a different way. He's older and quieter, but he's just as polished as Wilkes. His house is elegant."

A strained little smile pulled at Lou's mouth as Johnny described Edwin Booth's parlor, its rich deep carpets, its heavy crimson velvet draperies fringed in gold that fell, fold after fold, over lace-encrusted inner curtains. Gilt and marble tables upheld statues and small bronze figures. Huge mirrors hung in unexpected places. Enormous paintings lined every wall. Crystal chandeliers and candelabra on the side tables and mantels glittered with prisms that reflected the light of gas lamps and logs crackling in fireplaces.

A fat, cream-colored old poodle snoozed on a cushion in a wicker basket beside the fire. No member of Congress had more books than Edwin, Wilkes Booth's older brother.

"I don't see how you could talk to anyone like that, Johnny." Honora breathlessly broke the spell. "Didn't you feel out of place?"

"Johnny is a country-bred young gentleman," said his mother gently. "He is capable of forming acquaintances in the best society."

"It doesn't sound as if New York knew there's a war going on," Lou observed unhappily.

Johnny did not mention the jewelers' windows where he had seen diamond-studded watches pushing rings and brooches into the background, flower holders with delicate chains and jeweled clasps to fasten at a slender waist or fall from a pretty wrist.

In the South, men who could fashion such vanities were working eighteen dreary hours a day in the old and dimly lighted Tredegar shops in Richmond. Southern men made guns that might never be fired because the soldiers who could fire them were hiding behind muddy breastworks or plowing through watery ditches, grasping other guns for which there was neither powder nor shot.

As he sat surrounded by his admiring family, Johnny did not explain that the panorama of shipping in the East River had been impressive, jammed with the traffic of all nations save the one to which he had sworn allegiance. Neither did he add that, in the light of that knowledge, it seemed for the first time that perhaps cotton was not king.

Dan entered the room. "Gen'man sent this fo' you."

"It's nothing." Johnny smiled at the girls. "It's just that Wilkes is back in town. He's invited me to the theater next week."

In Richmond, Jefferson Davis and Judah P. Benjamin worried

over the dispatches they had received. Their concern deepened after news of the arrest of Captain John Y. Beall. Beall, with other Confederates, had attempted to capture two Union Great Lakes steamers in a plan to liberate prisoners held in Johnson's Island and Rock Island prisons, but had failed. Later he had been captured and accused of derailing a train on which Confederate prisoners were being transported to Fort Warren.

While Richmond officials worried, Washington senators and members of the House of Representatives petitioned Lincoln for Beall's release. It had been established, they wrote, that Beall was a regularly commissioned officer in the Confederate service, and that Jefferson Davis, as President, had accepted responsibility for his acts.

Lincoln refused, and John Yates Beall was hanged. This time the couriers' trips had been of no avail.

9

In Richmond on January 1, 1865 W. H. Bramwell, Chief Disbursing Clerk, Confederate State Department, opened a new account in his ledger, "Foreign Intercourse and Secret Service." His beautifully shaded writing flowed across the top of each debit page, and "W. H. Bramwell, clerk" headed each credit side. From that date dispatches to the Consulate in Canada would be carried only by couriers who could qualify for the Secret Service.

On that same day Johnny called on his new acquaintance, Mr. Booth.

"It really will be quite simple," Wilkes said briskly, "once we get a few more details in order."

Johnny, sitting beside the smoldering fire, moved uneasily. He shook his cigar ashes on the charring log, stretched his long legs before him, and returned to speechless contemplation. Wilkes had made a little money in the oil business, but the matter he had invited Johnny to talk about had not been oil. Neither had it been cotton, although, when the invitation had arrived, both Lou and Johnny had been sure it would be one of these.

It had appeared a little silly to Johnny when Wilkes peered into the closet, peeped under the bed and out into the hall before he spoke of it. "Even the walls have ears," he had smiled, and Johnny had smiled, too, but a little self-consciously. Booth's plan had been so startling that, although he sat safe and comfortable in the New National's best room, Johnny's scalp crawled.

"I hear he'll be going to Ford's on Wednesday, the eighteenth," said Wilkes, and Johnny stared, speechless.

"Ford's might be the best time and place."

Still Johnny had nothing to say.

"When you think it over, you will see this is the only way to turn advantage to the South. Our armies are helpless against this new draft. We need men; arms, too, but there is no way to get them. We are blockaded, starved."

Bitterness tinged his tone. In the firelight his face looked drawn, his usually winsome expression tightened into unfamiliar lines. Deep in his lustrous eyes a red glow reflected from the fire gave him a strange, unearthly look.

In war success went only to the adroit, his mellow voice went on. Physical power and equipment could be useful only with leaders who were sufficiently able to outwit their opponents. Only when the South became adroit could it dictate terms to the conscienceless Washington politicians.

Johnny rose slowly to his feet.

"If it were as easy as it sounds when you tell it, someone else would have done it the other times it's been tried. We need a miracle, all right, but if we failed, what then? Remember Beall? That was only a train robbery."

"Failure is impossible. I have it too well planned."

Johnny took up his hat, lifted his shawl to his shoulders, and leaving his brandy untouched in its glass, his cigar still glowing in its tray on the table, stepped out of the room into the winter night.

He had a problem of his own; the farm and the tavern were almost lost. No business. No money from Lloyd. None from

John Nothey and instead of a money-making venture, Wilkes offered only another version of the perennial scheme to abduct Abraham Lincoln.

On the street corner he stopped. He would not go home to H Street where Sonny Holohan blew on a shrill whistle and banged a wooden gun, where Anna and Honora chattered about their fascinating new acquaintance, and where his mother worried him about the draft. He walked to Naylor's where he hired from Davie Herrold a big black horse, and rode toward Surrattsville.

Booth's plan, The Enterprise, he called it, would not be put away. As he jogged along, turning his worries over in his mind, it came back. People thought Booth only an actor with handsome face and beautiful gestures, but he was more than that. He was a man of conviction and courage. Because of this conviction he had openly supported the South and because of his courage he backed that conviction with acts.

He had joined up with the Confederacy. He had posed as a doctor and bought drugs, chloroform, and quinine. He had shipped them through the western states, and run them into the Southern lines. He had boldly traveled on a pass authorized by General Grant himself, and had corresponded with the Southern authorities while he did so.

He had shipped away his personal effects, the heirlooms he would not leave with his Union-minded family, after his brother Edwin and his sister Asia had upbraided him for defending the Confederacy. He had placed a small amount in a Canadian bank for emergencies. His future and the South's now were one. Wilkes had thought it through, calculated the risks. By the time Johnny reached the farm he regretted that The Enterprise could not succeed.

He spent the night at the tavern, talking with Lloyd, Joseph Notte, and Captain Bennett Gwynn about his own financial problems, but by morning he was no nearer to saving the villa.

He wandered over its war-scarred ground. He leaned on the tavern bar, listening to familiar conversations. Preposterous, this thing that clung in the back of his mind. Wilkes had said that its very audacity guaranteed success. As Booth explained it, the attempt appeared almost justified. As Booth told it, it was not impossible. Wilkes talked so eloquently that no one who heard him could ever forget it. His thrilling voice and his gestures held his listeners spellbound. When he talked of his travels, his stage experiences, and of his family's exploits, he was almost hypnotic.

But The Enterprise would require more than fascinating talk. It would be, if accomplished, a great *coup d'état*. Lou would think it wonderful. If, Lou would say, taking the president of this pore-ole-busted-up-union out from under their noses wouldn't show the Radicals up, what would? And if it succeeded, to whom should they Grant the Meade of praise? Trust Lou to have a good pun somewhere handy.

Johnny leaned against the old bar and called to Joseph Notte for a drink.

It would be fun. The inauguration held up while the cabinet members screeched and tore their beards because they couldn't find the President—who had been hidden by some Southern river runners smarter than Yankee politicians. When the whole story came out, what a bellow would go up! How Pa would have loved it.

Notte put the drink before him.

After all, what else could help the South now? Not the armies. Peace negotiations had failed and would continue to fail, Wilkes said, until the South won some conspicuous military advantage. There could be no military advantage now; it was doubtful if it could be political for the people were falling away from their leaders.

The leaders, Wilkes explained, had failed: some through ineptitude and some through self-service. Even in Richmond, officers and politicians fought each other and President Davis. It was probably true, as Wilkes had said, that thousands who once had waved flags and shouted, "Long live Jeff Davis!" now muttered about bringing out ropes.

He swirled his brandy in its glass.

Wilkes was right. something had to be done, done right now.

Hastily Johnny left the room. Later he jogged on down to the river. Carelessly he asked Atzerodt how many persons his new boat would carry.

"Twelve," smiled the little man. "I have built him myself. He is very fast with three oars, and safe. Why?"

Johnny drifted back to town, wondering. He stayed away from

home. Too much confusion there. The girls' giggling, Sonny's everlasting whistle.

He must think; he must not be distracted.

January 2 seemed endless. A few days before Christmas he had taken a clerkship with the Adams Express Company for the sake of the dollars it would bring in. His assignments as courier were too few and far between to provide him with living expenses, but Washington costs went on in the little house on H Street. Until such time as he was actually needed for travel, after the holidays, he planned to stay in the office. All day at his desk his thoughts strayed past the monotonous forms and figures, away to three-oared boats across the river, to relay horses, to a famous hostage captured and thousands of prisoners released. He asked a day's leave; the manager refused.

On the evening of January 3 he met Wilkes again and admitted his willingness to assist in this thing that would end the war. On January 18, said Booth, the war would be over.

Johnny's hands were full now. The Enterprise needed boats on the river, relays of horses, ropes across roads to trip galloping pursuers. Food for men and mounts. Arms. But most of all, information. Every few miles a man who could be trusted. Wilkes, who knew nothing of the roads south except what had been sketched for him on the back of an envelope less than two weeks before, was helpless for practical arrangements.

Impatiently Johnny waited the week end. Again he hired a horse and rode to the country. The first person he met was Gus Howell. Leaning over the bar he listened with narrowed eyes to Johnny's recital.

"Yeah. Booth was out here, couple of times. I saw him."

"You saw Wilkes?"

"Everybody saw him. He went to church. Nobody sold him anything, though," and Gus laughed heartily. "Tell you what he wanted?"

"Land, he said. Dr. Mudd said he bought a horse."

Gus was quiet a moment. "Well, if he had anything else in mind I guess he'd say so."

Their talk turned to the mail routes. Only a pretty smooth man could get through the Yankee lines now. Even last year it hadn't been so hard; the year before that it had been easy. That far back most of the damyanks hadn't ever seen a horse, but now that the damned Pennsylvania apple-butter-makers had learned to ride it was a hell of a lot different. Heigh-ho. Better take a nap. Might have to be up most of the night. Gus sauntered off.

Instead of napping, Johnny rode over to Justice Pyles's house. Part of his uneasiness these days came from the knowledge that if he were caught with dispatches, his mother and sister might suffer. Most of the runners and all the couriers had made wills disposing of their property. A courier couldn't tell when he might be captured and receive, in lieu of trial, a speedy bullet in his heart.

Then, too, the talk went around that if the North won, the Northern Secretary of War Stanton would confiscate everything every Southerner owned.

Uncle Zad said it wasn't so; it wasn't constitutional, but whenever he opened his mouth he was quickly hushed down by someone who called his attention to Sherman. Anyone'd say, argued Prince Georgians, that what'd happened in Georgia just couldn't happen any place. Well, look at it.

Justice Pyles, in nankeen breeches and muddy boots, was plowing the Upper Farm as Johnny cantered in and stopped. Johnny watched for a moment as the thin old man struggled with the plow and the uncooperative mule that represented all that was left of his farm equipment. Throwing the reins to dangle over the big bay's head and white face, the boy followed the rail fence to a gaping hole, leaped through it, and stomped up the furrow to where the justice stood, watching his approach.

"Hard work?"

"Too hard fo' an old man like me," agreed the justice, "but you got to plant if you're goin' to eat."

Johnny nodded. "That's right. Here's something I'd like to get notarized. Might help my family to eat, later." He offered the paper which Lou and he flattered themselves they had worded in the best legal fashion. "I'm going away awhile. Thought I ought to get this taken care of before I go."

The old man dropped his lines; the mule waggled an ear and slumped down to make the most of the brief respite. The justice, leaning back comfortably into the fence corner, looked at the paper.

It was dated January 5, 1865. His lips moved as he followed its lines. ". . . transfer to the said Mary E. Surratt, in return for her maternal love and care and a thousand dollars, receipt of which is hereby acknowledged . . ." He raised a disbelieving eyebrow.

Johnny smiled with him at the polite fiction that anyone in Prince George's had a thousand dollars these days, and the old man resumed.

". . . and all his interest in the estate of his father, the late John Harrison Surratt of Surratt's, Prince George's County . . . h'm . . . h'm . . . What's this for?"

"I'll be away where the draft can't blow on me," smiled Johnny. "This'll give Ma a chance to do what she needs to so far's the farm's concerned. I'd hate for it to be confiscated on account of me."

"I don't know as this'd do any good . . . in the event of trouble," the old man mumbled gently. "Things get any worse, don't know whether this'd help her any, or not. Can't do any harm though." He thought a moment. "You've got to record this in the County-town to make it legal, but I don't know as I'd let it get notorietied around the county too much. Goin' far?"

He smiled a moist, brown-edged smile, nodded sagely, and lifted an arc of tobacco juice over the mule's ears, took a reef in his suspenders, motioned to Johnny to follow, and ambled toward the house in search of pen and ink.

To Johnny the week hung on forever. Tied down to his desk in the Express office, he could only think and fret. On Thursday, January 12, with The Enterprise only a few days away, and things certainly not ready for it, Johnny once more asked a day's leave and once more was refused. Fate made it necessary for his mother to go again to the country just at that time.

Mrs. Surratt's worry over the tavern was increasing, for John M. Lloyd's chief occupation seemed to be behind the bar with a personal bottle. Money went out, none came in. Mr. Calvert demanded payment. John Nothey still sidled away whenever mention of payment or even interest money came to his ears.

So matters stood, with Mrs. Surratt caught between Mr. Cal-vert's insistence and Mr. Nothey's disappearances. Perhaps, Johnny said, if they went together and insisted upon action, they might get farther with Nothey. His mother then visited the Express office and explained her need for her son's presence in the country. Still the manager refused. Johnny, his mouth pulled into a straight line and the squire's vein throbbing in his forehead, tossed the Express notices onto his desk and stalked from the room by his mother's side.

They went to the country but had no success with Mr. Nothey. Mrs. Surratt came home by stage, but Johnny remained. On Saturday, January 14, he made his first approaches for The Enterprise.

Bryantown, T. B., Port Tobacco, all saw him that day. Relays of horses and a large boat would be needed on the night of Wednesday, January 18. The week end passed too quickly for all that must be done. An alternate boat was needed. Something might happen at the last moment to change the travel route. Perhaps Tom Jones at Pope's Creek might have one or perhaps the new one owned by Thomas Smoot over in Charles County could be rented. It all took time.

Monday, January 16, Johnny returned to town. Wilkes was sure to be at the New National by this time.

Down in Richmond on that day, Mrs. Nettie Slater applied for a pass through Confederate military lines. B. S. Gaither and James G. Ramsey, members of the Southern Congress, certified they knew her personally and were willing to bond themselves for her loyalty and high social standing. Her purpose in going North, they said in their letter to the Secretary of War, was to join her mother, a French lady living in New York. There, Mrs. Slater could be more comfortable than in her own home in Salisbury, North Carolina. She had lost her only brother in the Confederate Army, the gentlemen wrote, and her husband remained in Confederate service.

She received her pass and a few days later Clerk Bramwell in the State Department entered on his new ledger sheet, "$40 in gold; for courier service to Canada with dispatches."

10

Booth had returned from New York on January 12, and when, a few nights later, Johnny asked permission to bring him to supper his request threw the Surratt household into a commotion.

"Of course, Johnny, of course," his mother agreed.

"Close your mouth, sweetie." He poked Anna's thin waist. "Look out, look out! your jupe's drooping!" He gave her a playful push and she clutched frantically at the loops of her heavily draped overskirt.

"It isn't, either. Not any such-of-a-thing, Johnny Surratt. Mr. Booth? Mr. Booth? Oh, Johnny—oh, Johnny!"

"Oh, Johnny, oh, Johnny!" Lou mimicked her tone, and she whirled angrily away from him.

"Oh, do you think Mr. Booth would really come here? Honora, oh, Honora, come here. Come here." Light as a breeze, Anna's little girl voice eddied into the hall.

"Walk down town with me?" Johnny turned to Lou, "I want to buy some sherry for supper when Wilkes is here."

"Better make it brandy. I've heard Wilkes is a four-bottle man. Four a day, I mean." Lou chuckled at Johnny's irritation.

The wine added a touch of elegance to the basement dining room the following night. Johnny poured it carefully into the heavy glass decanters that had held his father's favorites and placed them where the light from the crystal lamps at either end of the buffet would shine into their color.

"When you're down in the mouth," Lou advised, "always put a swig of something in the same spot," and poured a generous portion into the glass Johnny handed him. Upstairs, Booth's mellow voice said something, and Jinny giggled in reply. Johnny took the steps two at a time.

"Here you are, Wilkes!"

"Ah, Johnny." The actor handed his greatcoat to Jinny and laid a friendly hand on the boy's shoulder. Johnny led him to the parlor where his mother sat, impressive in her new black bombazine.

"Mother, this is Mr. Booth."

"It was good of you to ask me here." The actor's voice gave the trite words dignity. He bowed over her hand.

"Johnny's friends are welcome, Mr. Booth, and we are happy to know you." She turned to the girls quivering by the fireplace. "This is Miss Fitzpatrick, and this is my daughter, Anna."

"I am honored," He bowed gravely again. "Ah, Miss Anna."

Entranced, Anna fluttered her hand toward his, looking up at him through lashes long and heavy. Soft gray eyes like Johnny's were the only beauty in her thin young face. Her childishly inexpressive mouth showed only a pleasant pink softness above a neatly rounded chin. The actor, dark eyes glowing, looked down at her. For a moment her fingers lay supine in his big, firm hand. Her breath struggled through some commonplace word, and suddenly on her lashes a nervous tear trembled. Wilkes would have prolonged the moment but an angry move from Lou broke its enchantment.

"Good evening, Mr. Weichman," the actor turned coldly but with his voice, charm flowed again.

In the doorway Eliza Holohan, one hand on her husband's arm, smiled her remote acknowledgment of the room's occupants. Her crimson taffeta gown snugged a waist fragile as a reed above a skirt draped over widening hoops. She was more suited to one of Mrs. Lincoln's levees than to the shabby little parlor on H Street. Her husband, his eyes bright under crinkling waves of shining black hair, offered her a chair. Parting his coat tails with a flourish, he seated himself, stretched his neck from its collar, and turned an attentive ear to whatever crumbs of conversation his lady might offer in his direction.

Dan entered with the sherry, and taut nerves relaxed as the easy-handed boy moved around the little room serving amber-filled glasses. Mrs. Surratt sat by the fireplace, the white collar of her black dress fastened with a mourning brooch that held a lock of the squire's grizzled red hair. Beside her the bustle and great bow of Anna's dark green dress twitched with her childish movements, and Honora looked more than usually dull in a spiritless blue gown that sallowed her face and dimmed her seeking eyes. Her gaze implored Johnny, who looked over her head to Lou, trim and handsome in his new plaid coat. But Lou turned toward Anna whose eyes ignored him, wordlessly seeking the actor's acknowledgment of her presence.

"Looks at him like he's second cousin t' Jesus," the old squire would have guffawed and his listeners would have joined in his infectious laughter.

The supper bell rang, and they moved down the stairs to the dining room. It was not an elaborate supper that waited them, but the table was laid with well-mended damask, the frail old forks were polished, and Great-Grandmother Jenkins' fat silver teapot sat at Mrs. Surratt's place. On the sideboard the crystal lamps winked and sparkled in the dim gaslight.

Mrs. Surratt crossed herself, and Dan stationed himself behind Johnny's chair as he had done a thousand times when the old squire had headed his table.

All the light in the room centered on Booth. It burnished his blue-back hair, lighted his diamond cravat pin, and glowed in his smile. All life flowed toward him and awaited his word. From behind the teapot, Mrs. Surratt listened to Lou's amusing recital of House of Representatives business, John Holohan's opinion of the draft, the news coming up from Virginia, and Booth's admission that he had no play scheduled for the near future.

He had worked so assiduously, said the actor, that he now deserved a rest. He longed for a southern plantation where he might retire for study of Shakespearean roles to which he planned to give a new interpretation.

"Hamlet, perhaps?" inquired Eliza's cool tones.

"Romeo?" Anna's eager voice fell into a pool of sudden silence, and she looked down at her plate, her blushing vision of herself on a balcony plain to everyone.

Wilkes turned considerately away from her sizzling cheeks. Behind the teapot Mrs. Surratt listened without comment.

Probably it had been a profitable evening. Wilkes swung his cane lightly down the Avenue toward the New National Hotel.

No one ever would give a thought to visitors to a plain little house on H Street.

Always a mistake, though, to ask a young lady if she played the piano . . . usually she would try. But probably the Surratts did not sing every evening.

Probably that Weichman fellow was all right, too. . . . After seven years he must know everything Johnny knew. Kindly Mrs. Surratt . . . childish Anna. God's blood, how green fruit set the teeth on edge! But lucious, ripe Eliza! Her wide skirts rippled round her chair like spilled wine.

He walked on, staring straight ahead.

Back in the Surratt parlor, the ladies talked of him.

Wednesday, January 18, 1865 passed. The president did not attend the theater.

That was just as well, from Johnny's point of view, for certainly the arrangements had not been foolproof. Booth seemed discouraged. It was difficult, Wilkes had complained, to find persons willing to assist their country, willing to take a chance on victory with one simple act.

He had made a long and arduous effort. He had spent his own funds. Now he was beginning to wonder whether he might have to ask Richmond to assist him. Certainly The Enterprise had not failed. It had only been postponed.

It was February before they knew it. Peace negotiations between Confederate officials and the Union president came to nothing. Reports circulated about the Confederate soldiers who had been charged with border raids and the attempted burning of New York grew more alarming.

In Washington, Mr. Booth stopped occasionally at the Surratt home to exchange a word with the girls, sit a moment in the parlor with Mrs. Surratt, or exhibit the formal courtesy with which he invariably treated Eliza. Johnny, engrossed in thoughts of his own, went out frequently with him. Sometimes Lou went too to the theater or to hear the speeches made at night sessions of Congress. Once in a while the young men would remain in the parlor and assist with musical evenings.

Then Johnny went away again. He returned without warning,

accompanied by a guest. Their carriage drew up about dusk, and scarcely had come to a stop before Johnny was out, assisting down the step a smartly dressed young woman. Attracted by the sound of wheels, Dan threw open the front door and, after carrying the lady's carpetbag to the house, returned to drive the rig back to Naylor's.

The guest who entered Mrs. Surratt's little parlor that night was small and trim. She was wrapped in a heavy dark cloak, and a tiny purple bonnet sat atop her dusky hair. A fashionable black lace mask shaded the upper part of her face, making a delicate tracery against a creamy skin that showed almost golden under the feeble gaslight in the room. From behind it flashed bright, intelligent eyes, and below it a smile curved the corners of a mouth full and petulant.

"I am Antoinette—Nettie—Slater." A slightly foreign accent gave charm to her speech.

"I told Mrs. Slater I was sure you would be able to provide her a room for the night," said Johnny over the lady's head. "She comes from down south and is on her way home."

"Indeed, yes," his mother responded. "We're happy to have you, Mrs. Slater. I'll see about your room. I hope we can make you comfortable."

She moved out of the parlor on her housewifely errand. While Lou assisted the lady with her cloak, Johnny divested himself of his wrappings in the hall, and carried the carpetbag into the parlor bedroom after his mother.

Their light supper finished, the family sat in the parlor with their fascinating guest. Lou devoted himself to her. Johnny aired his best French and anticipated her every move, while Anna and Honora watched with envious interest the elegant assurance with which the lady received these attentions.

She was going home, she said, to see her husband who was in the army. He had been wounded. She had lost an only brother. The bleakness that flitted across her face gave way so quickly to a radiance so lavish that her listeners were not quite sure they actually had seen the determined pull that lifted her lips into their heart-twisting smile and the despair that had preceded it.

To change the unhappy subject, Mrs. Surratt commented on

the difficulty of passing through the military lines. The lady replied that if she were stopped she could claim the protection of the French consul because of her French descent. As Lou listened to her conversation, his interest in the lady increased. He commented on the uncertainty of personal mail sent through the lines and mentioned his wish to keep in touch with his patron, Bishop John McGill, in Richmond, but the lady appeared not to recognize his hint.

Next morning, behind a team hired from Pumphrey's stable, Johnny and Mrs. Slater set out for Port Tobacco. That night, after his return, Johnny explained. Mrs. Slater had just returned from Canada. He had been detailed to see her as far as the river, where she was to be met by another escort.

Lou's uneasiness about everything connected with the war and its effect on his personal affairs grew daily. If he could not keep in contact with Bishop McGill, he would lose that gentleman's patronage. He had tried to go down to Richmond but could find no way. In spite of all the information he had given Gus Howell (some of it from his own War Department records), Gus still had refused. He wouldn't even talk about the possibility of Lou's getting a clerkship in the Confederate government. Johnny wouldn't help. He said that, as a courier, he could not be hampered by a traveler who could neither ride a horse nor fire a pistol. Lou saw nothing for it but to stay in Washington.

But he might be trapped in Washington. Memories of his careless talk came back to him at night and worried him sleepless: of how he had entertained his office mates with tales of the $30,000 he could pick up any time he wanted to, of how he had shown them a false mustache just to make them laugh.

Worse yet, he had introduced Mr. Booth to George Atzerodt, who ran his rowboats from Port Tobacco across the river. He might, he had assured Mr. Booth, find Atzerodt helpful. He fretted because he had lent Atzerodt (Port Tobacco, some people called him for a nickname) his long blue military cape to cover his shabby countryman's clothing. By far the worst of all was that in his trunk lay hidden away the ivory cylinder that was the Confederate cipher key. He dared not throw it away, for Gus might ask for it; yet he was terrified to keep it for it might be found. He tried to forget that he had ever let Gus show him how to use it.

He sweated through long and sleepless nights. His torment mounted and at last he could bear it no longer. In the middle of the morning of February 20, 1865 he abruptly rose from his desk leaving the reports and requisitions before him untouched. Beads of perspiration stood out on his forehead as he sought out his office chief, Captain D. H. L. Gleason, and gasped that he must speak to him in private. Behind closed doors he rallied sufficiently to demand protection before he told his story.

He told it all.

After that, days in the office were bad enough but evenings at home were worse. Everybody looked at him strangely, he thought. Even kindly Mrs. Surratt asked questions.

"Your mother's onto something," he said to Johnny a few days later. "She asked me what we were up to, said she knew something was in the wind and she'd find out one way or another. You'd better tell her something before she asks Booth in the parlor in front of everybody. She will, you know, if you don't tell her."

So Johnny sought his mother where she sat by the parlor window, with her mending basket on her knee. This was only a gesture for she could no longer see to darn. She could only sort the articles and lay them aside for Anna or Honora to mend. She picked up Lou's sock as he spoke.

"I think I'll go back up to Canada in a day or two, Ma," he said. "This time I may stay a little longer."

"Canada?" She looked up, two fingers thrust through the sock's heel. "Stay? Why stay in Canada?"

He and Mr. Booth had some business plans together, cotton speculation, Johnny said. Wilkes had made some money in oil investments, but he thought now was the time to buy up cotton, and run it through the blockade before the war ended. That would break the market. An elderly friend had advanced $3,000; this was their capital. Johnny would attend to the buying and convoying the shipment to England, where he would sell it for a terrific price, and then return by way of Mexico. He planned to slip over to Matamoros and find Isaac.

"But, Johnny—"

"I know this is sudden, but it's all arranged now. I signed my share of the property over to you. Justice Pyles fixed this up." He handed her a folded paper from his pocket, and as she stared near-sightedly at the blurred page, Johnny hurried with his explanation. The draft quota, he said. Nearly a half million Yankee volunteers called, but the draft was still closing in.

"Did you tell Mr. Pyles where you're going?"

"I just said I was going away."

"I think, Little Johnny," said his mother, "you'd better give up this idea. Blockade running must be dangerous. It sounds to me as if everything you do is dangerous. I think you ought to try again to find something to do here in Washington, and then pay into an Exemption Club. Lou finished his payments last week."

"Waste money on an Exemption Club? Give up this chance? No, ma'am, not me."

He flung out of the room before he could say more. Behind him his mother sighed as she resumed her work. Johnny was changing but everything now was so serious he was bound to change, too. He would be twenty-one in April; time for him to make his own decisions.

Mrs. Surratt was wrong. The decisions were being made for him for this was February 1865.

II

Saturday, March 4, Inauguration Day in Washington, came in with rain and heavy wind. Umbrellas bobbed up and down the Avenue as sightseers vainly sought accommodations in overcrowded hotels. Mattress and cot space in billiard rooms and halls soon vanished. Republican clubs entertained thousands of visiting vote-producers, and private homes were besieged by room seekers.

Washingtonians remained aloof under shelter as the visitors crowded the streets to watch the presidential parade slither and slosh its way from White House to Capitol where the newly placed statue of Freedom showed through darkening clouds. Aside from the new vice-president's being noticeably unsteady on his feet during the ceremony in which he took the oath of office, nothing disturbed the festivities. The small reception at the White House went off well; the day ended.

At the Surratt supper table John Holohan mentioned the rumors that had flown around town preceding the event. Word had reached the Secretary of War about a plot to abduct the President before he could be inaugurated.

"Abduct?" Lou ran the tip of his tongue over his lips. Who would abduct a man whose only fault was a rough exterior and a taste for low jokes, he wanted to know.

"Like Mr. Wood." Honora snickered heavily and then blushed at the thought of low jokes.

"Who?" Mrs. Surratt looked at Lou.

"Mr. Wood. The one who was here day before yesterday. He had an uncouth exterior. Honora saw it." Lou reveled in the girl's embarrassment.

"That one," Mrs. Surratt said shortly.

The man had come to the house two evenings before. Lou, answering the door, had invited him in, introduced him to Mrs. Surratt, and explained that the visitor needed a room. Some queer people had come to the house after Mrs. Surratt had advertised in the *Evening Star* but none had looked stranger than this one, who said Mr. Booth had sent him.

She had no vacancy at the time, she said, and thought to herself that he did not look like the sort of person Mr. Booth would cultivate, for he was awkward and ill at ease. His clothing was poor and his thick black hair grew low over his forehead in an unkempt fashion. She regretted, she had said again, that she had no room.

"He could stay in my room," Lou had offered. "Johnny won't be home tonight and any friend of Mr. Booth's is welcome to stay with me."

She had looked from one to the other in a puzzled way; Lou was usually so fastidious. "Have you had supper, Mr. Wood?"

She had stepped down to the dining room to see what could be served him. Jinny had carried everything off the table. Would Mr. Wood mind having his supper on a tray upstairs? Lou had come down for the heavy tray, had taken it into his room, and closed the door behind him. Next morning at breakfast he had said that when he awoke, he had found the visitor gone.

This peculiar behavior caused some comment, but Lou could tell nothing further. All Mr. Wood had said was that he had known Mr. Booth for some time. He had met him in Baltimore.

"He certainly wasn't attractive," said Anna. "He had the queerest eyes. I declare, they made me quite nervous." She lifted her fork daintily.

"Everything that reminds you of Wilkes makes you nervous." Lou's teasing words carried an edge recognized by everyone at the table.

The conversation veered to the everyday talk of war. Mrs. Surratt was glad Johnny's work took him North rather than South; things were so bad in Richmond that if a person got down there it was almost impossible to get back. Or so the papers said.

No one commented but Anna and Honora looked at each other. The girls felt perfectly sure that something was in the wind from the way Johnny, Lou, and Mr. Booth talked by themselves.

Another queer stranger, a round little man with an odd name, appeared at the door a few days later and asked to stay the night. The only space available was the tiny attic room where Jinny sometimes slept but because it was late and because this man too said that Mr. Booth had sent him, Mrs. Surratt moved Jinny to a pallet down on the basement floor and made up a bed for the man. He spoke with an accent that no one quite understood but when he said that most people called him Port Tobacco they remembered him by that. He stayed one night.

When later in the week the doorbell rang at supper time, Anna ran to answer it and call her mother. "I think it's a man who was here before. Mr. Payne, I think," she said, "but I'm not sure. He wants a room."

The man gave no sign of knowing Mrs. Surratt when she spoke to him. Well dressed and courteous, he said that he was a clergyman from Baltimore. Later in the evening he inquired for Mr. Surratt and on being told that he was out of town, changed the subject and asked Anna if she would favor the company with music. He opened the piano for her, turned the music pages, and devoted himself to making the evening pass pleasantly.

Early next morning he was gone.

Johnny came home later that day, March 13, and aside from a heavy cold that kept him in bed for a day, he settled down as if he had never been away. Mr. Booth dropped in. He, Lou, and Johnny talked together upstairs. They attended the theater and went to Harvey's for oysters.

On Johnny's return his mother commented on a peculiar young man who had been there for the night, and who had identified himself as a clergyman. The girls had laughed about his unclerical appearance; he would not save many souls, they giggled. In answer to her queries Johnny was noncommittal, but the old squire's stubborn look began to show around his mouth, and the vein in his forehead pulsed. Neither his answers nor his manner pleased his mother.

Wilkes called again. Johnny observed that Mrs. Surratt was thoughtful and that from her euchre board in the parlor she appeared to listen to his conversation in a way she had not done before. At his invitation Lou and Booth again went with him to his room. Sitting on the huge old bed, swinging his penknife chain around his finger he listened, argued, and listened again.

Days passed. Booth and Johnny walked, dined, went to the theater.

A small room at Gautiers Hotel was already smoke filled when on the night of March 17, Johnny and Wilkes made their late appearance. They had attended the performance at Ford's, and by Booth's arrangement had occupied the box usually assigned to the president on his frequent appearances at the theater. This box, No. 8, and adjoining No. 7 were so contrived that their separating wall could be removed to provide ample space for the use of the presidential party's distinguished members. Johnny chatted with Honora and little Miss Dean who was her overnight guest, while Lou and John Holohan conversed together. Following the play, Lou and Holohan called a carriage and escorted the girls home while Wilkes and Johnny went on to the Gautier session.

Up to this time no meeting had been held at which all members could discuss The Enterprise together. Because of this, and because certain of its members were losing interest, Wilkes had called the meeting to determine once and for all what their action would be.

"Goot evening." Atzerodt rose from his chair by the door to allow the latecomers to enter.

Booth smiled at Johnny. "This is Mr. Payne."

The muscular young man who rose to his feet seemed to fill the room. He caught Johnny's hand in a grinding clasp and looked down at him with narrow, obsidian eyes. Stiff black hair fitted like a bristly cap down close to his ears, covering his temples and allowing only a thin line of forehead between it and the brows that met over a thick, wide nostriled nose. A straight, sullen mouth and a massive jaw were supported by a thickly corded neck that rose above powerful shoulders. The hand from which Johnny released his aching fingers swung almost to the man's knees.

Johnny recognized in him the nerveless young giant whom Wilkes said he had found on the streets of Baltimore, friendless and desperate. Booth had helped him, as he had helped countless other stranded young men.

"Here are my Maryland friends, Mike and Sam, known to me since school days."

Michael O'Laughlin stepped forward and bowed from the waist. He was a slight boy with sparkling black eyes and shining straight black hair. His thin nose, closely set eyes, narrow face framed by black sideburns, and his tiny waxed mustache suggested foreign extraction. The money sent him by Wilkes a few days before had quickly turned into clothes on his back. He now wore a long, dahlia-colored coat, opened to show a double-breasted vest. The purple down-stripes of his elegant pantaloons crossed equally noticeable stripes of green. Beside this dandyish young Irishman with a Spanish face waited the pleasant-featured countryman, Sam Arnold.

Johnny's gaze passed over debonair Booth; over Atzerodt, chuckling soundlessly to himself, his bushy hair turned up against the hat he had not removed; over Payne, black-browed and glowering. Queer birds, these.

Johnny must have surprised them, too, as he stood sleek and

slim beside Wilkes. His shoulders carried the gray frock coat well. A matching waistcoat snugged his thin middle. Tight cream breeches, strapped tautly under varnished boots, encased his narrow hips and long legs. His bright hair and thin boyish beard, his slate gray eyes under brows that met above his nose, were deepened by the whiteness of the linen and the prodigious green cravat at his neck. As the final touch of elegance, one of Anna's daintily made handkerchiefs projected from his left cuff.

Anna had given him the handkerchiefs for Christmas. They were made from the fine linen cloth laid away since before the war. She had bleached its yellowing lengths, had drawn threads and cut the kerchief squares, and run their hemstitched borders. In a corner of each square she had embroidered in tiny stitches "John H. Surratt" and under this had placed a number between one and seven. The number, she said, would indicate to him which kerchief he was to use on each day of the week. It would also, according to the ladies' magazines, simplify accounting for the laundry when it was sent out.

A timid knock ushered Davie Herrold into the room. "I thought I'd better see how quiet it's going t' be along the Potomac tonight." Smirking at his own joke, Davie perched himself on the bed's edge.

"Livelier, mebbe, some fine night." Payne answered him, his voice hoarsely pleasant.

"Plans are being perfected." Wilkes shook back the lock that tumbled over his forehead as he pulled up for himself the room's one comfortable chair and motioned Johnny to the next best. "Things are going well. Everyone is eager to assist." He muted his melodic voice to the room's smallness.

"Wilkes'll take care of everything; all we need to know now is when to carry the plan out." This was Payne.

"You mean carry the man out." No one laughed at Davie.

Within a minute all were talking. Mike and Sam engaged Johnny in conversation. What did he think? Could it succeed? Could they indeed capture a man right in a theater? What did he suggest?

"Right at this moment I don't suggest anything. I've never thought the theater plan was practical, but right now I need to stay quiet. For a while, at least. I'm almost sure I've been followed lately."

Instant silence fell. "Tonight our colored boy told me that men have come to our house looking for me. Twice, lately. He says they looked like 'the law' to him. Besides that, there's too much talk going around just now."

"Has anyone actually troubled you?" Booth asked sharply. "About the draft, perhaps? Or the courier business?"

"Wherever I've gone this thing's talked about. Out in our county everybody has heard something of it; there's no more secrecy than if it were a battle about to begin. It's talked about so much and I'm being watched—I can't help but wonder if someone hasn't let the plan slip out."

The boys eyed each other.

"Where's Lou?" Wilkes asked.

"At home, went with Holohan, you know. But Lou's a Southern man!"

Sam cut boldly into the silence that followed.

"I'm not in favor of going on with this, either."

Wilkes looked up, displeased, as Sam continued.

"I'm not in favor of it because I think, in addition to the danger, the time has gone when it could do much good. I think maybe if we'd gone about it when it was first planned, it might have been easy enough, but this sitting back and waiting has ruined the thing. It's too late."

"With intrepid helpers it could be done," Wilkes retorted with more feeling than he yet had shown.

"Intrepid or not, I'm not committing suicide for nothing. I think we'd better agree right now to give it up. What about you?" Sam turned again to Johnny.

"The theater plan's out, all right. No one to handle the gaslights, and I've always said the passageway is too narrow. The smart thing to do now is to give it up."

Wilkes started to speak but Sam cut in firmly. "When we went into this thing, Wilkes, you said it was simple enough to pick the man up, but that was months ago. You sent for me to come here tonight, and even now there's nothing but more talk. I'm through. I've fooled around as long as I can. My family's getting tired of keeping me, and if I get the job I've applied for I'm going on down to Fort Monroe and go to work. You better just count me out."

"Goin' to desert to the Yankees?" Payne's bellow drowned out Wilkes's attempted reply.

Davie, chattering incessantly under his breath, broke the momentary silence with his high voice.

"Desert? I know a man's going to desert. He came home yesterday. He said there wasn't anything to eat, he didn't have any shoes, and his feet hurt. He says Lincoln's promised to give fifty dollars and a ticket to anybody'll go west and fight the Indians. He'll get clothes and Yankee rations. This party," he ducked his head foolishly, "he's going. His whole company's signed up, almost, he says."

A chill fell on the room.

"There's desertion, all right," agreed Johnny somberly.

"That's why we have to free the prisoners." Booth took command again. "Our Enterprise is the only means left. The prisoners we release will more than make up for the cowards who desert."

The capture of one man. Just one man. Booth's mellow voice quieted them. In addition to the need for soldiers, common humanity demanded release of the men in Elmira. Typhus, camp fever, ague, malaria. "With all their talk of Libby and Andersonville our men in Elmira die faster, and unnecessarily."

It was well known, he argued that the North did not want their men back because they served a political purpose where they were. All laws of war demanded the exchange of prisoners but Lincoln and Stanton refused.

"Why," asked Davie, "why wouldn't Lincoln?"

Because the politicians needed horror stories, Booth said bitterly. Horror stories excited soldiers into fighting harder and civilians into furnishing more money and hating the South more and more. When the people had a chance to stop hating each other, after the war ended, they might vote the war administration out; horror stories worked much better than anything else to keep the Radical politicians in office. But, he continued, another more important reason demanded The Enterprise; the addition of the freed prisoners to their army not only would add thousands of

JOHN WILKES BOOTH

"The handsomest man in Washington," the theatre-going public called him. His plot to assassinate Abraham Lincoln began at noon Good Friday, April 14, 1865, when he learned the President would attend Ford's Theatre that night. It ended with the murder of the President at 10:15 that night.

JOHN HARRISON SURRATT, JR.,
in uniform of the Papal Zouaves.

soldiers but it would invite the assistance of all nations in the world. The daring act would prove the valor of the South, that men yet lived who loved their country better than themselves. A few men with courage could end the miseries of the South by the capture of just one man.

An ordinary capture could be made any day at all, with only a carriage, driver, and guards that were not guards at all. On the other hand, a capture in public among throngs of people, under the noses of cabinet officers and military men, say in a theater box, would have a public value that nothing else could achieve. It would set the world on fire. All nations would swerve to the support of the invincible South.

Johnny shook his head. "We don't know," he said thoughtfully, "we don't even know they'd take him down in Richmond. They might send him back again. What then?"

"You mean you asked about the plan? In Richmond?" Booth leaned forward intently, "You told the plan?" A red glow showed deep in his eyes; his facile mouth grew thin and ugly. Davie drew away.

"No." Johnny faced him squarely and Wilkes relaxed a little.

"I heard it talked in general conversation. No one's ever stopped talking about it since Major Taylor said he could bring him in easy as walking across the lawn, that all it needed was to get the man down to the river and a hundred oyster boats would run him South just for the devil of it."

"You see now?" Booth asked complacently.

"That was three years ago." By this time Johnny's replies were sharp. "Mr. Davis said it wouldn't accomplish a thing. He said we couldn't spare an army to guard old Abe, and anyway just holding him wouldn't end the war."

Booth's face went livid. "But it would end the war."

"What do you honestly think, Johnny?"

"Sam, I honestly think—stop now."

Booth's mouth grew taut again.

"Let's ask in Richmond." But Booth broke into Mike's words. The argument flamed into open disagreement. Furiously it rose and fell, Sam stubbornly insisting Richmond should be asked, Mike backing him up, Booth refusing.

"If the War Department would help Conrad, why not us?" Sam wanted to know.

"That was only the secretary telling the Signal Corps to help Conrad across the river—"

Johnny's voice rose above the heated wrangling. "I'm saying this again because everyone of us ought to remember it's been tried too often and talked about too much. Even if we asked in Richmond it's not likely anyone would pay any attention to it any more.

"What if," questioned Johnny, "what if, when you get him to Richmond, no one will take him off your hands?"

Wilkes's pistol clattered on the table. "Then I, at least, shall know what to do."

Johnny rose stifly to his feet. "I've been talking about a prisoner of war, to be delivered up in return for a military advantage. If you have anything else in mind, gentlemen, I—I bid you good evening."

Clapping his hat on his head, Johnny made for the door, stumbled over a chair rocker. He pulled on the door knob. Blindly he fumbled with the key in the lock. Sam and Mike followed. Atzerodt, wakened by the noise, staggered to his feet.

At the sight of Booth's rigid face, Davie drew back the hand he had laid on Johnny's sleeve. Johnny's fingers dropped from the knob.

"I shall know what to do because I have resources, you know." His voice flicked nerves worn raw. "Return to your seats. I have yet one thing to say."

Sheepishly the group at the door turned back. Atzerodt slumped into his chair.

"Say what he will, I won't do it," whispered Sam.

"*Et tu, Brute?*"

Cautiously they sat.

"I had called you here to tell you the time draws near. Now I find you lack the heart to undertake that which you swore to do: The Enterprise on which I expended much time and money." He looked at Mike, who moved uncomfortably in his new dahlia coat. "Still, in spite of this, the time may be near. If not Ford's, then perhaps at Harewood Hospital. He may go soon to an entertainment for the wounded, I believe."

Johnny shook his head doubtfully. "That changes the place but not much else. It's still the same old story."

"An old story?" Swiftly the actor was on his feet, his hands pleading. "Ah, yes. Ah, so it is, an old, old story." For a breathless moment his eyes traveled his audience. "For years we have fought for freedom. For victory. Now our wish is but an old, old story. An ancient, worn-out tale, the fabric of a dream. Perhaps so, but still to be the savior of our country how gladly would I give a thousand lives! A thousand lives, and gladly, if all the hateful scenes of these four years had never been enacted." The pulsating voice bound his listeners to their chairs. Its echoing desolation stopped their speech.

"The deeds of which the Northern flag stands as a bloody emblem, they too will come in time to be but an old and twice-told tale. Past. Unheeded. Forgotten. But oh, should anyone whose love is for the South—and mine is for the South alone—should such a one deem it but honor to capture him to whom she owes her misery? Let doddering impotent old men say what they will, I still shall take him prisoner. Alone, if needs be, but by the great God of Justice, a prisoner.[1] Now who is with me?" He leaned heavily against the table where the pistol still lay. "Whoever is not with me is against me. Payne?"

The gawky youth's wide mouth opened stiffly. "Yes. Yes, Wilkes. I'm with you."

Davie's voice punctured the air. "Yes, I'll do it; yes, I'm with you."

"Yes." Dazedly, Mike agreed.

Sam sat unanswering. In his chair Atzerodt, unconscious of the drama, snored gently.

All eyes turned to Johnny. "How?" he asked hoarsely.

"Harewood Hospital, maybe," Booth said. The room buzzed again. "Across the bridge—Bennings Bridge—out the back roads."

Johnny lapsed into thought. This was March, and the roads south were freezing slush. September's rains had laid Virginia's heavy red dust. October and November had worked it into fine-textured glue, January and February had frozen it into jagged spearheads that crunched under horses' hoofs. February and

---

[1] This speech based on statements in Booth's letter to his sister, Asia, in which he took responsibility for the capture plan.

March had thawed, frozen, and thawed again down to the earth's core. Snow had crusted Virginia's roadbeds above the bottomless mud, over which no wheeled thing could make its way in haste without disaster. And a hostage could not go openly on horseback. A hostage must be transported inside a curtained carriage.

Booth broke into Johnny's thoughts. "By overnight we could get almost to Richmond."

"Of course we can do it—who does Johnny think he is? So gawdamighty smart?"

It was four o'clock in the morning before they wore him down. Then, Johnny consenting and their decisions made, the group parted.

12

The early spring sun shone pale and warm as the small band of riders trotted briskly out of Washington. Houses spaced out and woods began to crowd close to the roadside. They met few travelers, only an occasional soldier hurrying toward town or returning unsteadily to camp.

Yesterday's rain had left the roadbed soft under the horses' hoofs; deep, narrow channels had been cut by the wheels of mule ambulances hauling the wounded to Harewood Hospital. The dead wagons, too, had passed this way, laden with ghastly freight.

Presently the riders glimpsed far ahead the staggered rows of overflow tents clustered around wooden barracks. Above them, bright against the azure sky, floated the Stars and Stripes. Wilkes cursed under his breath; there would be guards, guns, riders on swift mounts.

Johnny pulled up and motioned to the others.

"We'll go no closer. Payne, you and Mike hide over there behind those shrubs. Sam, get out your handcuffs. When Mike pulls the driver down, clap them on him quick."

"Yes."

"Payne, soon as we s'round the carriage, you jump. Keep the man covered."

"Yeah."

"You two watch from behind the trees." He pointed with his crop. "The rest of us'll ride on slow, but we'll be watching you. Give the signal and we'll be there in a twist. Booth'll get the guard. May take you a minute t' mount and catch up to us once we've turned the carriage around and started back toward town."

"This is it, boys!" Wilkes's face lightened. "This is the moment—!"

"Do it now and talk later." Johnny cut gruffly into his words. "Come on. Ride slow till we get the signal. Ready?"

Sam and Payne slid from their horses, led them behind the pines.

"Not much shelter." Mike shook with nervousness.

The slow-paced walk was unbearable. Doggedly Johnny pulled his eyes from the road ahead, looked down at the ditch water covered with sickly yellow pollen from newly budded trees. Booth reined in the little mare with a heavy hand.

Mike heard it first, the faint, low-pitched call. "That's Sam." His face paled until his black hair and mustache, his heavy brows seemed patches on a putty man.

Wilkes leaped in his stirrups. Lacking a sword, he waved a gallant hand: "On! On!" The mare rose like a bird, reared, whirled on two feet.

"Down!" snarled Johnny, and furiously Wilkes reined in beside Mike. They moved slowly forward. Behind the pine trees, hidden from the curving road, Sam motioned caution.

"Talk," whispered Mike hoarsely. "Talk till they get here. Look like we're just out for a ride."

The carriage was approaching at a sedate trot. They heard the jangle of metal-mounted harness, rattle of wheels, creak of leather. Then they saw it. Alone on the box sat the driver, the single guard following behind.

"He's got the curtains up, how's that?"

"For God and country," whispered Booth, "now—"

Johnny gave the bay his head. Booth's mare mounted high into the air. Pounding as one body the horses stretched forward.

Sam and Payne, pistols drawn, leaped from the shrubs. The man in the carriage leaned out inquiringly.

Even as his blue spurs raked, Johnny sawed savagely on the reins. The big bay slid to his fetlocks, regained his balance, plunged away. The mare, shivering under Booth's big cruel hands, whirled against the carriage horses as they fought their traces.

Sam and Payne stood incredulous in the road. The carriage lumbered through spattering mud. Mike clamped desperate knees on his dancing saddle.

"Get out of here, quick. . . ." Johnny barked the words as he fought to control his plunging horse.

"What's the matter?" goggled Payne, "why didn't they stop him?"

"Stop who? Who knows who the bastard was?"

The carriage rattled on. One more attempt had failed.

Lou came home late that afternoon. He was often late these days, for he preferred to linger in the security of his office and then to stroll leisurely through the spring-touched streets. The first warm days had greened Washington lawns, brought jasmine flowering in yellow sprays and japonica flaming along bare stems. The sweetness of opening lilac leaves scented the air.

As he strolled this afternoon he tried to concentrate on the reports on his desk. They and the dispatches coming to the Commissary of Prisons suggested that the end of the war was very near. He and his office comrades pictured to each other the Rebels, huddled miserably behind clay embankments, hatless, barefoot, shivering from cold, weak from hunger. The Rebels could not hold out much longer, the warm and well-fed War Department clerks told each other.

Lou hated to think about it. Indeed, he hated to think at all, hated to remember how he had passed information on to Johnny, to Gus Howell, and how he had then betrayed them to Captain Gleason. Trouble, nasty trouble was sure to come of it. Each night on Mrs. Surratt's doorstep he hesitated to enter, wondering what news would greet him; afraid to open the door.

This night he forced a low whistle as he went into the hall and started downstairs to the dining room. No cheerful buzz of conversation, no giggling girls busy laying the table, no romping children met him. From somewhere above came the sound of low sobbing. His scalp crawled. He was straining to hear, poised for flight, when Dan appeared from the kitchen.

"What's wrong?"

"Where's Li'l Johnny? You know where-at he gone to?"

"No. No, I don't." He ran his tongue across suddenly dry lips.

"Li'l Johnny gone away somewheres. Gennelmen rode up leading him a horse and swear like anything, and away they goes. Miz Mary 'Genia, she call him but he don't even look back."

"Who?" Lou could scarcely frame the words. "Who were the gentlemen?"

"I don't know, rightly," Dan looked at him queerly. "They's the one says he's a Baltimore Baptist, and the one Miz Mary 'Genia say cain't come here no more on account of how he drinks too much."

"Who else? Who else?"

"Mista Wilkes. I don't know who else. There something wrong. Miz Mary 'Genia's crying! If Lil Johnny's catched—"

"I don't know. I really don't." Dan, looking at him so strangely, made Lou nervous. He took an uncertain step backward but Dan followed. Something in the rigid, dark features, in the catlike tread of the advancing man, drove Lou backward, step by step, toward the stairs.

Anna woke him from his nightmare as her light feet skipped down the steps followed by Honora's clumping tread. Dan disappeared into the kitchen.

"We had the most marvelous afternoon. We found wonderful pictures of Mr. Booth at the Daguerrean's. I'm going to ask him to sign mine. Ma says we're to go on and have supper. She has a headache and won't come down till later. Maybe when Johnny comes in—if he's late again. What's the matter, Lou?"

"Nothing. Nothing." His voice quivered. A loud slam of the upper hall door made him draw in his breath again. Dan appeared somberly in the doorway.

"My Lawd-and-Mawster, what's the matter with Johnny now?"

Anna stepped back to the door to listen, then giggled at the sound of boots furiously stomping up the stairs, spurs clattering. "Is Johnny ever in a rage!"

Without a word to the girls, Lou scuttled like a spider past Mrs. Surratt's door and up the stairs to the room he shared with Johnny.

Johnny's mud-spattered hat lay on the bed, his pistol belt crossed a chair, boots and spurs sprawled on the floor. Already his riding breeches, torn off, lay in a heap in the corner. One by one, three pairs of woolen underdrawers joined them in little mounds.

"Thought I'd have a long ride in the cold," he kicked the drawers aside, "but I'm not going any place, it seems. That fool!" He clambered into fresh underpants, furiously bundled the discarded garments under the ruffled petticoat of the big bed. "Risked our necks." A white linen shirt swished out of a drawer. "All this time and work lost." Breeches climbed up over the shirt tail. ". . . everything ended." Socks. Boots. Collar. Cravat.

"What went wrong?" Lou rested his shaking body on the bed while Johnny told the story.

It looked like old Salmon P. Chase in the carriage. Who wanted that damned goldfish? They had galloped all the way to the tavern and back to get rid of the rope, the carbine, other things. Lloyd had hidden them in the ell room. Johnny ran a comb through his shining hair and wiped the sweat from his lip with one of Anna's handkerchiefs.

"Crazy. Wilkes is clean crazy." Who, Johnny wanted to know, had said that Old Abe would be in the carriage? Where were the people so eager to help—so influential their names couldn't even be mentioned, but so infallible they could be counted on to the last moment? Huh! Out saving their own necks, Gawd blast their souls to hell! The good old Anglo-Saxon words that had served his father well seemed suddenly puerile; he lapsed into French that left Lou gasping. "They're after us right now."

"Oh—no!"

"Oh—yes! I'm on my way. I'll stay at the Ebbitt House if I can get a room; if not, the Herndon. Maybe I'll go back to the country. Or Baltimore. Someone talked, Lou. That's the only way this could have happened, unless Wilkes is a complete idiot. What did Ma say? She saw them at the door."

"Dan said she was upset. She saw the pistol."

"Now what do I do? If they catch up with me for this, I'm gone. Maybe I'd better take a clerkship and lie low. Know where I can get one?" He leaned, shaking, against the dresser and stared at Lou. "If ever I find the one who talked—" Lou shrank back.

Johnny banged the dresser shut, caught up his shawl, and made for the door, looking an elegant city gentleman who'd never touched a muddy boot. Tilting his hat at a rakish angle, he stormed into the hall. "Tell Ma I'll see her later."

Behind him Lou collapsed on the bed. He pulled at his collar and sank deeper into the pillows. He wanted no supper this night.

In the days that followed fear sat with Lou where he went. Johnny did not return. Wilkes sent no word. On March 23 a wire came from Wilkes in New York asking Johnny's address. Lou did not know, nor did Mrs. Surratt. Then, two days later, Johnny came home again.

"Regular trip North," he answered his mother briefly. In their room, he explained to Lou. He had been in New York and Montreal with messages he had picked up from Gus Howell down in the country. The Yankees nabbed up so many couriers these days it required duplicate letters, each sent by a different messenger, to assure that at least one copy got through.

"Where's Booth?" Lou asked.

"I don't know. I haven't heard from him since I told him it was all over. Sam's down at Fort Monroe. The jig's clear up and over."

The doorbell rang, and Johnny started from his chair, then motioned to Lou to listen at the door. He remained back in the room until he heard the voice. "It's Mrs. Slater," he said, relieved.

In the front hall the lady explained to Mrs. Surratt that she was in Washington on business and wondered if she might spend the night again.

"Yes, indeed. Come right in. We're pleased to see you again. Anna, take Mrs. Slater's cloak. I wonder where the boys are. Have you a carpetbag, Mrs. Slater? I'll send Dan out to the carriage for it."

Honora and Anna swarmed to the lady's side. Her fashionable garments gave off the scent of violets, the gloves she had removed retained the imprint of her long, trim fingers. Honora stared, fascinated. Anna carried in the tea tray and set it before her mother.

She regretted to disturb Mrs. Surratt at this hour, the lady smiled over her cup, but she must meet a relative in Port Tobacco the next morning.

"We'll be pleased to have you go with us," offered Mrs. Surratt. "Johnny and I have to go to my brother's and then I think I'll try again to find Mr. Nothey."

The next evening Mrs. Surratt returned by stagecoach to Washington. Mrs. Slater had missed her appointment and since she had no means of travel in the country, Johnny had kept the hired carriage to help her, if he could, explained his mother.

But out at Port Tobacco, where they went immediately, Johnny found no trace of Gus Howell. This meant more delay and in an upstairs room of the rackety little hotel, Mrs. Slater peered anxiously from the window and mustered such patience as she could. Late in the afternoon Johnny rapped at her door, and she came decorously into the hall. With him waited a plainly dressed countryman.

"May I present Mr. Barry? He lives close to us in the country. He's come over looking for word from his boys."

She nodded to the man and turned back to Johnny.

"Mr. Barry says he's just heard Gus was captured on the other side of the river."

She looked at him with apprehensive eyes. "Get some men, please, and a boat. I must go on."

"But there isn't—"

"Right away. Not a moment's to be lost." She gathered up her gloves, her bag. She held its pins in her mouth while she settled the little purple bonnet on her head. She tied its bows under her chin and jabbed the pins fiercely into her hair.

"I'll take the horses back to town," offered Mr. Barry.

"Thanks. Tell Ma, will you, I'll be back in a few days. The horses came from Pumphreys."

Mrs. Slater hurried Johnny toward the door.

At nightfall he returned with transportation arranged.

"It's an awful boat," he apologized, as he led her to the wharf where an old man bent over his oars. Darkness lay across the river, lighted by a thin moon shining in fitful whiteness from behind scudding clouds. Johnny added his strong pull to the old man's strokes and they moved steadily away, against the current, toward Mathias Point. A carriage usually waited there to carry travelers to the Rappahannock where, crossing by rickety ferry, they could quickly reach the open road to Richmond. No carriage awaited them this time.

"Too many Yanks aroun'," the ferry man explained. "Nabbed a couple of runners last day-so, and now a whole company's hangin' aroun', watchin'."

Mrs. Slater picked up her long skirts and motioned to Johnny. After only a moment's hesitation, he started off beside the slender little lady in the purple bonnet. The first drops of chill, penetrating rain began to fall.

They traveled along the roadside, without speaking, leaping at times from hummock to hummock of lightly frozen grass. Other travelers before them had done the same. Shoes and hoofs and wheels had widened muddy tracks that passed for a road so that often they must circle into open fields. Water splashed to their knees, but they ploughed slowly forward, Mrs. Slater clutching long skirts that dragged above her ruined high-heeled shoes. At midmorning, March 28, they reached Pole Cat.

At noon the next day the crazy old cars pulled by a feeble old wood-burning engine carried them into Richmond. Mrs. Slater took a carriage to the home of friends and Johnny sought the Spotswood Hotel.

"Well, you back again, Mr. Sherman?" Clerk J. B. Tinsley greeted him by the name he used for his trips south. Nice to see him again. What with everybody moving farther south, surprised to see him. Oh, yes. Some officials and lady clerks had been gone for some time. Chief Clerk Bramwell would leave pretty soon. No telling, now, what would happen to Richmond.

The uneasiness these words brought to him increased as he walked toward The Bureau. Surely on his last trip streets had not been so deserted; not so many stores had stood empty with windows locked and barred. Even the Capitol with its white marble columns and steps showed bleak above its hill, which led down to Bank Street and the Department offices.

On the second floor of the Customs Building, about halfway down its center hall, President Davis and Secretary of War James Seddons maintained their offices. Between them lay a suite of rooms whose outer door bore the modest sign "Signal Bureau." From this door a public reception room guarded an apartment to which only trusted employees and high officials were admitted. From this inner room, known as The Bureau, flowed correspondence that couriers carried to agents outside the Confederacy's borders. Here the couriers delivered the letters, ciphered messages, and detailed accounts of what went on in Washington for which they daily risked their lives. Johnny did not know it, but Mrs. Slater had been received even before he reported, and the large buttons were slashed from her heavy cloak to reveal fine silk linings covered with cipher messages.

Inside the door Harry Hall Brogden rose to meet Johnny. "Better start back quick as you can. Not much time to lose." In the face of Johnny's shock he added, "Before you go, Mr. Davis wants to see you."

"See me? Mr. Davis?"

"Yes. Mr. Benjamin, too. Messages to go back."

Jefferson Davis sat at his desk, thin shoulders hunched over his work. He managed a smile, a listless handclasp and a few spiritless words. His messages would be ready the next day. His lined ascetic face showed no wish to continue the interview beyond that moment and even before Johnny left the room the President turned back to the papers on this desk and his forehead sank again into his frail hand.

In the Secretary of State's office, Judah P. Benjamin waited, jovial and complacent. Under his genial manner the boy relaxed.

"He must have better news," said Johnny to Brogden as they left the room, "something he hasn't yet told Mr. Davis."

"He's always like that." Brogden shrugged. "I used to think that too, but—well—he'll get through all right. Some people say he's already made his separate peace with Washington. I only say that," he hastened to explain, "to show how people talk. They say anything now, blame anybody."

"What will happen next?"

"Depends on how long Petersburg holds. We're trying to get everything down to Montgomery. The Capitol will be kept there as long as it's necessary."

"But I heard he said Richmond wouldn't be evacuated."

"Hope not. The next thing to do is get word to Colonel Thompson in Canada. Get our money into English firms, where it can't be touched, no matter what happens."

Johnny nodded. The dispatches he would carry already burned in his consciousness.

13

On the evening of April 3, Johnny came home spattered with the red clay of Virginia and lashings of Maryland mud. Physical fatigue deepened the dejection that rode with him and weighted his heart. Everyone at the Surratt supper table that night had his own reason for dismay.

Mrs. Surratt worried over the mortgage. During the week she had tried again to obtain some word from John Nothey but he slithered away from under her eyes. Mr. Calvert had been patient so long he could not be asked for further tolerance, but she was no nearer settlement than when the squire was living. This and her unceasing concern for Johnny left a look of uncertainty on her usually placid countenance.

Lou, next to her at the table, tried to tell himself he had no cause for fear. Everything was over, and nothing had happened. Anna moped. No word had come from Mr. Booth and a suspicious brightness in her eyes was more disturbing than the hurt they sometimes showed. She fretted audibly over the actor's neglect.

Eliza smiled nastily at her conjectures, and John Holohan glared at his wife as she did so.

The family rose from the table as Johnny came in the hall door. He was not ill, he answered his mother's hasty inquiry; he felt tired and his head ached. He had not had supper.

In the parlor he threw aside his hat and sank to the sofa. Anna ran for slippers while Dan tugged at his boots.

"Honora, have you any eau de cologne?" asked Mrs. Surratt. "Perhaps that might help his head. Make yourself comfortable, Johnny. It'll be a minute or two before we have supper for you. We have a new cook, Susan Ann, and she's slow. She's not used to things here just yet."

Anna went down to tell Susan Ann to lay a fresh place. Honora, returning with the cologne, stood helplessly by, longing to be useful but not knowing what to do.

"You don't suppose you're taking down with malaria, do you, Johnny?" she asked timidly.

"No."

"Honora, would you go down and measure out the tea for Susan Ann? She's still so unreliable. Tell her to be sure it's steaming hot. She can bring it in after everything else is ready. Will you, Honora?"

The girl moved slowly away. Anna called, and Johnny and his mother went down the stairs, followed by Lou.

"We'll sit with you, Johnny. We haven't seen you around for a while." Lou's comment brought no response and he fell silent.

Susan Ann came into the room, teapot in hand. Johnny looked up without curiosity. "New cook?" he inquired languidly.

His mother nodded.

"This is my son, Mista Johnny, Susan. Doesn't he look like Miss Anna? Set the pot right here by me, please."

Susan grinned her reply, "He shore do. He shore do." She ducked an awkward acknowledgment to Johnny.

"Evening, Susan," he spoke mechanically. "I see you're quite a cook."

The girl grinned again and slouched out of the room.

She wasn't much of a cook, Mrs. Surratt went on placidly, but better than no help at all. She had been there only a few days;

she might improve. Too bad they couldn't have Rachel with them. None of the Washington Free-Issues were much good. They came and went, never staying long. Probably they hadn't yet learned they must now support themselves.

Johnny, not listening, turned to Lou. "Is John Holohan around?"

"He went upstairs, I think, after he finished supper. Want to see him?"

"If he's here. I thought he might exchange some gold for me. Greenbacks go farther."

"Maybe I can. How much is it?"

"Forty dollars." Johnny pulled two twenty-dollar gold pieces from his pocket.

"Can't do it. Too much for me, even at pay day."

"Where'd you get all that money, Johnny? Where'd you get all that?" Anna giggled. "Now we're rich again. I'll just buy that sweet little bonnet down in Harper and Mitchell's."

Her brother crumpled biscuit and preserves on his plate without touching his ham and salad. He drank his hot tea. His mother poured another cup for herself and sipped it, noting his lack of appetite.

"Where'd you get all that money, Johnny?" Anna persisted.

"Lawd, Annie, I've had it quite a while. You're a pest."

"Never mind, Annie," his mother said quietly. "Where he got it isn't important. The important thing is that now he can pay for an exemption with it. Then we won't have to worry about him any more." She smiled directly at him but her words flicked him on the raw.

"I shall not—" he began, but stopped before Honora's listening ears and Lou's plain curiosity.

Lou commented on the advantage of the exchange, greenbacks over gold. Anna sat abashed at her brother's sharpness, and Mrs. Surratt started to relate something Eliza had read that afternoon about the draft in Maryland.

"Never mind the draft. I'll never be drafted now." Shoving his chair away with such force that it clattered against the wall behind the table, Johnny bounded to his feet. "Come, Lou," he turned savagely, "we'll take oysters."

Without a word Lou followed him up the stairs. Johnny pounded on the Holohan door.

"Oh, halloo, Johnny." John Holohan slapped him on the shoulder.

"Can you accommodate me with greenbacks for gold?" He held out the two double eagles.

Holohan closed the door behind him. From his vest pocket he removed his wallet and handed Johnny five ten-dollar bills. "Is that enough for your purpose?"

Johnny hesitated. "Sixty would be better. I may go North." He jingled his coins in his hand.

Holohan disappeared within his room, closing the door carefully behind him, and returned with another bill.

"Don't bother about the gold now; you can give it to me another time. I guess you're good for that amount." He smiled at Johnny's rigid face. The boy, relenting a little, smiled in return before turning away with perfunctory apologies for his haste.

At the street corner they heard the news. Richmond was being evacuated.

"Hoor-a-ay-Ho-ho-ray. Rebels're licked. G'ddamum. G'ddamum, we done it," sang two victors staggering a bias path toward town.

Lou and Johnny stopped, paralyzed.

"Evacuated? Peace, maybe, Lou; but not licked. Not Richmond evacuated."

Lou looked with pity at his friend's stricken face.

"Why not?"

"Mr. Davis said, Mr. Benjamin said, they'd never evacuate. They'd never give up Richmond. The dispatch said—"

"It's true." A gentleman on the corner offered details. Word had come in by telegraph. It had begun yesterday morning. Mr. Davis had been in church when the first news came that Petersburg had fallen. Richmond must be abandoned." Tears ran down the speaker's face. "Poor Mr. Davis. Oh, Richmond, Richmond."

Lou listened, white lipped. Johnny's throat closed.

The town had gone mad, the speaker went on—rioting, looting, warehouse supplies turned into the streets. Confederate officials had fled carrying with them the treasury gold . . . the War Department building had been fired . . . The bureau was gone. Government buildings gutted . . . hotels stripped . . . streets white with flour and puddled with liquor from smashed hogsheads of commissary stores. Solid masses of carriages and vehicles piled high with household goods blocked the roadways as civilians, soldiers, politicians and profiteers fled the doomed city. In the river, ships blown up to keep them from the Yankees had fired the waterfront with their sparks. Main Street was a holocaust, its buildings dynamited to stop the flames. Tears ran down the speaker's face.

"There'll be nothing left," the telegraph had said. "The rebel capital will perish from the earth."

Yankee troops were in the town, the inexorable voice went on. Nigger troops, too. Lou stood irresolute beside his anguished friend.

"But that couldn't happen. They said—Mr. Davis said—"

Yet it had happened. The Yankees had won.

Singing and shouting came loudly down the Avenue. "Come on," said Lou. "Let's go see it."

A torchlight procession flared in the distance, wending its fire-fly way through the dusk. In the town's outlying batteries, guns began to bark. Above the musket rounds, the rattletrap old cannons in the parks blasted forth the news.

Johnny stopped. Mr. Benjamin was gone; Mr. Davis was gone. The bureau had been fired. The dispatches in his pocket—

"I'll leave you here," he said thickly. Lou looked at him questioningly, but Johnny spoke first. "Tell Ma I'll go on out of town. Tell her I'll see her later."

Lou came up the steps and through the front hall to the parlor where Mrs. Surratt waited.

"Where's Johnny?"

"Johnny's gone out of town."

"Where? He didn't say he was leaving again tonight."

"He didn't say where; just out of town." At the look on her face he asked quickly, "Have you heard the news? Petersburg has fallen and Richmond's being evacuated. That means the war's over."

"Over? The war over? Thank God, thank God. Anna, Anna, Honora—Eliza—come quickly, the war's over. Oh, Mary-Mother, Blessed Mother! But Lou, Lou, if the war is over, where's Little Johnny?"

14

Johnny spent the night of April 3 at the Kirkwood House. After leaving Lou he had slipped deftly through the crowds to the shelter of the hotel where he occasionally stayed in seclusion. The desk clerk assigned him a room and he hastened away from the groups crowding into the lobby and bar to celebrate the news of victory.

Early next morning he took a cab across town to the station, stopping only long enough to swoop down on an early-bird bookstore. He picked up and paid for a book in a single move and jumped on the New York cars as they pulled away. As the ramshackle outskirts of Washington fell behind he eased back into his seat and opened his book. With its title carefully exposed he settled down to the *Life of John Brown* and immersed himself in the writer's contention that the murdering old zealot actually had been a martyred saint.

In lulls between the train's rattling he heard fragmentary exultations. Rebels destroyed. Richmond in flames. Jeff Davis'd made off with the Confederate treasury funds.

Gradually the monotonous clatter of wheels eased his tension. Wrinkles knotted between his heavy brows smoothed out as he leaned his head back on the chair rest. His fine light hair spread over the prickly fabric, and his spare, boyish beard trailed down his cheeks as he lay with closed eyes. Under the shawl across his lap rested the book. His long fingers between its leaves assured him of its precious content, the tissue pages of closely written dispatches.

In the afternoon he stepped gratefully into the anonymity of New York and by cab hastily crossed the city. Mr. Wilkes was not at home, the Booth butler explained; he had gone to Boston on a theatrical engagement. Mr. Edwin was at home. It was not Edwin that Johnny needed to see. Strange that no word had come from Wilkes since the failure of The Enterprise. What place could be safe for them now that the Yankees had won? Certainly they had been betrayed. If not, why had the president's carriage arrived at the right time, at the right place, but with a decoy passenger? He must talk to Wilkes. But where was Wilkes?

With his shawl close around him, for Washington's spring had not yet reached New York, Johnny sought the station again and once more caught northbound cars. As the miles rolled away behind the swaying coach and the night wore on, the coal fire in the small iron stove died out. The air grew chillier. Johnny, huddled inside his shawl, clutching his book, stared sleeplessly into the darkness.

Once over the Canadian line he drew a breath of relief, and early on April 6, weary and disheveled, he stepped from the smoke-laden car into Montreal's biting cold. He caught the charabanc waiting at Windsor Station and wheeled away to the St. Lawrence Hall hotel on St. James Street, where he registered as John Harrison.

The men to whom he reported within the next few minutes were like himself red-eyed from late hours, grim-mouthed and noncommittal. Colonel Jacob Thompson, impulsive and irascible, waited for instructions from his government. General Edwin G. Lee, frantic with anxiety over the Southern armies' need for men, paced the floor. Professor Holcombe, hastily arrived from Halifax, worried over the hundreds of men whose transportation home he had just arranged. John Porterfield, guarding Confederate funds in Canadian banks, shivered at the implications of his government's defeat.

By contrast, Johnny's own troubles seemed very small.

The day passed in a haze. Men came and went from the suite at the St. Lawrence where Johnny's verbal reports as well as his dispatches were eagerly received. Endless conferences endlessly repeated lost import and vitality. The cause to which these men had given their unflinching devotion now verged on collapse. The end of their nation might be in sight. How did men face such a catastrophe?

A day sufficed to show what some of them would do. Among non-officials who daily crowded bar and billiard room, formerly vocal patriots now listened intently to every word but were, themselves, conspicuously silent. By evening some of these had been seen in steamship offices whose clerks grinned at the upturn in European sailings.

Hourly the news grew worse. The clacking telegraph brought in astounding stories. President Davis and his party relentlessly pursued. Members of his cabinet had abandoned their chief when defeat overcame him. Confederate officials arrested right and left as they tried to escape Richmond. It was only a matter of time . . . all would be behind bars.

At the hotel the hardiest Confederates put on confident faces. The capital was being moved to Alabama, they said, because Virginia was so vulnerable—so close to Washington. It had been planned for many months. President Davis was certainly well guarded and safe.

In the meantime, ordered Jacob Thompson, all assigned duties would be carried out. The army probably was only making a strategic retreat and would re-establish itself in a better locale, said the little group in General Lee's room. No matter how critical the situation, insisted the General, means must be found to liberate the prisoners held in the North.

That night Johnny received a visitor. Would Mr. Harrison consider a mission to the United States? Remembering, of course, that it presented an unusually dangerous undertaking? If, said General Lee, Elmira Camp prisoners still could be freed and returned south, it might yet be decisive. But before an escape could be arranged, specific information was needed. A number of scouts had been sent on this mission but had been unable to obtain the details necessary for an operation of such obvious difficulty.

Promptly Johnny accepted the assignment. Danger had been his daily bread. "It seemed I could not do enough," he was to explain years later.

General Lee required the location and condition of prisoners confined near the town; sketches of stations of the guard, prison approaches, roads, and nearby exits; the number and type of arms used by the guards. Most of all, he must know the number of federal troops in the vicinity.

After the general left his room Johnny thought it over. If, as the general said, the assignment had been hazardous for other men, it would be doubly so for him since he was already sought by the federals. His missions around Washington had not been complicated by his personality but in the North his tongue might betray him for try as he might he could not conquer the Maryland drawl to which he had been born.

After some thought, he decided to appear in Elmira as a Canadian traveling down to New York. With the right clothing and general appearance his accent might be taken for that of a West Canadian. With a bit of luck he might even pass for an English visitor to the States.

On his first visit to Canada, Confederate friends had introduced him to the young priest Father LaPierre who served as canon to the Bishop of Montreal, and he had been invited to the priest's home. He now called on him for advice. Early on the morning of April 7 he arrived at the shop of John J. Reeves, Notre Dame Street, explained who had sent him, and his immediate needs.

Reeves set about at once to make up a Garibaldi jacket and Canadian style pantaloons.

The new outfit contrasted strangely with Johnny's long double breasted frock coat and heavy plaid shawl that fell to its skirts. The Garibaldi, a dashing product of the tailor's art, was a gay little jacket of blue-gray tweed, single breasted with a small round collar that buttoned tightly at his thin young neck. From its shoulder yoke soft pleats fitted into a snug belt; four buttons marched from the collar down to a fifth that held the belt in place. A slightly flared skirt, also pleated into the belt, reached to mid-hip, and full sleeves ended in bands buttoned neatly around his bony wrists.

The light gray trousers, which typed him as a Southerner, were replaced by the dark blue pantaloons Reeves had turned out in no time. A round bowler hat now topped his face. His straggly beard and thin mustache were now closely clipped. Heavy British-made shoes, awkward after the elegant, highly polished boots he affected in Washington, gave the final touch. With them he no longer was the young American whose shining beaver perched at a jaunty angle above his silver gilt hair. Now he was a traveling Canadian in garments of undoubted British origin.

On the morning of April 10 devastating news came in. General Robert E. Lee had surrendered the Army of Northern Virginia the day before at Appomattox Courthouse, a small village not far from Richmond.

Grimly the Confederates reassured each other. Fortunes of war. Temporary only. There still were armies in the field. Johnston's great army in the deep South could not be vanquished.

Johnny paid his hotel bill but delayed his departure. He wrote a letter to his mother, cheerful in spite of his worries. He had attended Mass at the Cathedral. He had bought a new jacket. Board was high; it cost him $2.50 a day, in gold. All was well.

The letter reached his mother on the morning of Good Friday, April 14, and as she read it in her parlor, annoyance that he stayed away from home, that he lingered in Canada when the war was over, all combined to cause her dismay.

Even before the letter reached her, Little Johnny had arrived in Elmira, had registered at the Brainard House as John Harrison, had eaten a hearty supper, and retired to his room.

This was April 12 and anger over prisoners of war and their treatment was at its height. Northern papers printed horrifying stories about Andersonville prison and its conditions. Southern editors retaliated with reports on Elmira. In spite of the low sanitation standards of the day, the violent attacks on Elmira were justified, for its tents had been pitched below the level of the nearby river and were bordered by lagoons of stagnant water. Prisoners' letters smuggled out told of starvation diet, of lack of beds and blankets, and of patients dying on hospital floors from smallpox, typhoid, pneumonia, and scurvy. All this, the Union doctors reported time after time, was confirmed in reports to army authorities, but still the death rate rose and Southern hatred swelled.

On April 13 and 14 little Johnny wandered around the town familiarizing himself with its streets, the prison-camp road, and impressing on his mind details for the pencil sketches he would

make. On April 14 he strolled through the town's business section. On Lake Street he peered into the windows of a gentlemen's
furnishing store and after looking for a moment stepped into
Ufford's and inquired for white shirts.

Joseph Carroll, the salesman, grew loquacious. Cotton, he explained, was difficult to obtain because of the war. White shirts?
He shook his head. Almost a thing of the past. However, Mr.
Ufford was in New York buying merchandise and on his return
might have shirts of the kind and size the gentleman required. He
hoped by tomorrow. Merchants found war times difficult; very
difficult indeed.

Undoubtedly so, agreed Johnny. He would return Saturday to
see if Mr. Ufford had found the shirts. Certainly, now that
General Lee had surrendered his army, the war would soon be
over. Things would ease a little.

The salesman eyed the jaunty Garibaldi jacket his customer
wore. From an Elmira firm?

No, from Montreal, a Canadian garment, Johnny explained.

Ah, Canadian? From his accent he would have taken the gentleman to be from the South.

Through the open doorway Frank Atkinson the bookkeeper
listened. Johnny thanked the two employees and repeated that he
would drop in the next day, which would be Saturday. Possibly
the shirts might be available at that time.

Mr. Charles B. Stewart, who attended to hats, suitings, and
tailoring in the next department, also observed the Garibaldi with
a professional eye, noting the skill with which it had been fitted
to Johnny's wide shoulders and lean waist. He too apologized for
the depleted state of his inventory. Mr. Ufford would buy merchandise for his department. If the gentleman would call again?

On the street, Johnny turned his mind back to work. Camps One
and Three in the prison area were two miles apart and would require two liberating parties working simultaneously, a difficult
matter to arrange. He attracted no particular attention as he
walked along the prison roads, for curiosity seekers haunted
these areas hoping to catch a glimpse of the horrors described
in print.

Returning late to Brainard House, Johnny stumbled over the
crutches of a crippled man who sat on a sofa in the reading room.

He offered an apology and sitting down by the man, entered into aimless conversation.

Johnny's easy manner, his pleasant speech, and his obvious wish to atone for the accident brought immediate response. In a moment or two they were discussing the city of Elmira, its surroundings, and the news relative to the war's end. Johnny asked if the man's injury resulted from war service but his innocent question met with such sudden coldness that he wondered once more if his accent had given him away. He excused himself and passed on to the dining room.

On Elmira's streets that night exultation over Richmond's fall and General Lee's surrender continued. Little else was discussed in any public place. The sooner his mission could be completed the better pleased Johnny would be, for although he patronized the hotel bar and chatted about national affairs, he longed to be away. Too often his soft speech brought the comment, "You sound like a Southerner."

At night he completed the crude sketches indicating approaches, guard stations, and locations of the prison camps.

Next morning he came down to the dining room where a gentleman breakfasted alone, his newspaper propped up in front of his plate. Johnny seated himself across from him, took a sip of water and was unfolding his napkin when the man spoke. "Have you heard about the President? Assassinated last night."

Johnny smiled his slow smile. "It's a little early for joking, isn't it?"

The man spread his paper on the table. There in black and white towered the words, PRESIDENT LINCOLN SHOT . . . STRUCK DOWN IN FORD'S THEATRE . . . ASSAILANT ESCAPES . . .

Johnny swallowed hard and when his companion continued to read aloud, replied automatically. He rose, walked out on the street, not quite knowing where he went. Who? Who? Not anyone he knew, certainly, but who? He crossed the street to a store on the corner of Water and Baldwin Streets, where proprietor John Cass talked to his clerks.

"The wire just came in," Cass was saying. "Close the shop. Put crape on the door."

"There's another bulletin." Excitedly a clerk pointed at the telegraph office. In the window of Western Union, a telegrapher still stood beside the notice he had just pasted on the glass.

Cass came forward and when Johnny asked him for white shirts, he produced a box from under the counter. "There are all I have, but we are closing now. . . . Death of the President."

Johnny's reply was unintelligible as he bent over the box.

"What did you say?" Cass straightened suddenly. "What was that?"

His antagonism vanished in the quiet friendliness of Johnny's reply. He had not meant to question the great loss occasioned by the President's death, Johnny said. The shirts were not quite what he was looking for.

John Cass stood back to watch Johnny recross the street to the hotel. "Canadian," he muttered. "Little thing like the president's murder doesn't bother him."

Bells began to toll. Flags floated down to half-staff. People milled restlessly around, repeating over and over the inane things mouthed by persons under stress. Johnny walked slowly, intent on his question. Who?

An inquiry to Washington or Baltimore would betray his Southern connections. Montreal? But officials there would know no more than anyone else who read the papers. He stepped into the Western Union office and pulled forward the pad of blanks on the counter.

"John Wilkes Booth," he wrote, then destroyed the blank and began again. "J.W.B.," he wrote, then followed it with Edwin Booth's address. "If you are in New York, wire me Elmira. John Harrison."

The telegrapher looked at the blank. "J.W.B.?" he asked, and Johnny nodded.

The outside door opened bringing in a rush of noisy voices.

"There's three-four of them, I think," a loud voice shouted. "There's Edwin, and Junius Brutus. The youngest is John Wilkes."

"My God!" Johnny's moan stopped in his throat. His long fingers clawed at the message before him, but the clerk was quicker.

"We keep and file all telegrams, sir."

Johnny stumbled from the counter, through the hotel lounge,

up the stairs, to the temporary shelter of his room, tossed his few garments and his sketches into his carpetbag. He forced himself to descend the stairs composedly, pay his bill and call a cab. He must go. He must find out.

Cold-blooded murder. Not Wilkes. Certainly not Wilkes.

At the station, the Harrisburg to Baltimore cars had pulled out; no more southbound cars that day. A train left for Canandaigua where it connected with New York cars, by a longer, roundabout route. Johnny wanted only to get away from Elmira. Elmira was no place for a man with a Southern accent and a pocketful of prison sketches.

In Canandaigua no trains were scheduled before Monday morning. He sought a hotel, the Webster House, where business was brisk that day. The register was already half full when it was placed before him; he signed in the middle of the page, John Harrison. Striving to appear composed, he attended Easter Mass, took his meals in the hotel dining room, and spent Sunday afternoon with the New York newspapers.

Their accounts alarmed him beyond measure. Washington had become a bedlam of crape, tears, hysteria, and panic. Streets were hung from one end to the other with mourning. Government offices had closed down. Secretary of War Stanton had announced the murder was part of a huge Southern conspiracy to assassinate all the heads of government. Secretary Seward, stabbed by a member of the group, lay near death. Arrests had been made; more were expected momentarily.

Monday morning, April 17, as he left for the railroad station, Johnny stopped long enough to pick up an early paper. Its pages bannered that along with John Wilkes Booth, police sought the notorious Southern spy, John Harrison Surratt, Jr. Tensely he waited for the Montreal cars but once aboard felt little better. At every stop swarming guards searched for fugitive assassins with impressive rewards on their heads. Tuesday, April 18, he arrived in Albany in time for breakfast. At St. Albans, Vermont, the cars pulled into a depot thick with detectives.

In Garibaldi and bowler hat, swinging his rattan cane with a jaunty air, Johnny entered the depot with other passengers, and looked the detectives over while they looked over him. In the dining room he ate a hearty lunch and joined with other men in discussing the nation's tragedy. After his meal he lighted a cigar and took off for a brisk walk uptown. A detective walked too, and catching up just as Johnny wheeled to return to the station, stared at him with an appraising eye. Johnny returned the gaze unabashedly. The detective looked away and the fugitive boarded the cars in safety.

The hours before crossing Rouse's Point bridge over the St. Lawrence River to enter Canada seemed interminable. On reaching Montreal he registered again at the St. Lawrence Hall hotel as John Harrison, and hurried with his reports to General Lee.

Unconcealed consternation held the Confederates. Men whose names now accompanied those of Booth and Johnny in the reward lists fumed with resentful alarm. To General Lee, Johnny explained his contacts with Booth and confided the details of the abandoned Enterprise.

At the general's urging he returned quickly to his room, removed his carpetbag, paid his bill, and caught a cab to the home of John Porterfield. That evening he kept to his room in the Porterfield home, not venturing down to the tea table, where the ladies smiled about the distinguished looking gentleman who had slipped upstairs.

"Is it John Wilkes Booth?" roguishly asked a pert young miss, and the family joined in her laughter.

Johnny's Confederate friends worked fast. A few hours later a curtained carriage whisked him through the dark streets of Montreal to Father LaPierre, canon to Bourget, Lord Bishop of Montreal. Scarcely had he arrived in the small back parlor of the Bishop's Palace where Father LaPierre entertained his guests than the priest was called away to answer the door.

Barely inside the front hall's massive door stood Stephen F. Cameron, former chaplain with the First Maryland Regiment, C.S.A., but now a courier for its War Department. He went sharply to the point.

"I have come, father, to ask whether the young man has gone back to Washington."

The priest raised a deprecating hand. "We have been advised it is better for him to remain here."

"To that I cannot agree; his mother is in deadly danger."

The priest's hands folded themselves under his black-robed arms. "I know only what is told me by my Lord Bishop. The matter is decided."

"But the note I sent you—didn't you read it? He must go back to save his mother. No matter what the officials say, he must go back."

The canon leaned forward and whispered softly, but Cameron shook his head. "No," he said coldly, "I have no wish to meet nor talk to any man who abandons his mother in her danger."

The heavy door clanged shut.

Father LaPierre walked slowly down the hall but when he reached the little parlor where Johnny waited, he hid his disturbed feelings from his guest.

15

Throughout the rest of his life the days that followed remained an incredible nightmare for John Surratt. Newspapers filled him with consternation. On Wednesday, more than 30,000 persons had watched the president's funeral procession. The dreaded Secretary of War Stanton, for the moment in charge of the government, promised trial by military commission for the murderers. They would be executed before the body of the president could be buried. Samuel B. Arnold and George Atzerodt of Maryland had been arrested. John, James, and Henry Clay Ford, theater owners, with all their employees, lay under arrest in Old Capitol, where the actors babbled, cackled, sobbed hysterically, or cursed according to their sex and temperament.

From the pages of the *National Intelligencer* came information that a stout, middle-aged man arrested in Prince George's County had tried to commit suicide. In his room Johnny paced the floor and wondered. John M. Lloyd? Had the things in the ell-room been found?

Porterfield added to the reports. Refugees arriving from Richmond via the underground to Washington and then north contributed their share. Arrests continued to mount daily. Hundreds of persons had disappeared. Where? No one knew unless into the Old Capitol.

Anyone who smiled on a Washington street courted arrest. A woman who had hung a gray jacket on the clothesline to air had been hauled off to prison as a traitor. A Mrs. Surratt who operated a genteel boarding house and her young daughter, Miss Anna, had been arrested because Booth had called at their home and because the lady's son was a blockade runner. The ladies had been taken to the Old Capitol. Wednesday nights, rioting crowds had surrounded the prison, demanding death for all its prisoners.

It was horrifying. Johnny's Canadian friends soothed him. He must remember that everyone who had known the actor, or had spoken to him, or rented him a horse, or had a black mustache, all, all of them were under surveillance. Innocent persons would not be held after the first hysterical outbrusts had calmed down, the Canadians said: Johnny, not his family, faced danger. He should avoid arrest and questioning until after Washington had returned to normal. But he paced the floor, stared out the window, and determined to return to his mother's assistance at the first moment. The knot of wrinkles on his forehad grew deeper, and unaccustomed lines framed his mouth. Wretched and distraught, he glanced out the window into the street.

Three men stood on the corner. John Holohan, grim and silent, hands thrust deep in his pockets, stood unmoving. James A. McDevitt, a Washington detective, looked up at the Porterfield house while Lou Weichman leaned toward him, directing a steady flow of words in his direction. Johnny stared incredulously, but even as he stared he knew his betrayer. Lou had known everything. Now McDevitt knew too. Now everyone knew everything.

At noon Porterfield reported a visitor that morning. A man came to tell him that a $25,000 reward would be paid to the man who would turn over John Surratt to him. One word and the money was his; how about it, Mr. Porterfield?

"That's a lot of money." Johnny grinned bravely. "Why not get it and divide with me?"

That afternoon Johnny slipped away from the house he endangered. At the corner he caught a cab and gave the address of a tailor shop on Notre Dame Street. There he asked for Mr. Reeves; the collar of the Garibaldi buttoned too tight around his neck. Could it be changed?

"Promptly," Reeves replied. While he waited would Mr. Harrison join him for dinner? The conversation extended. Mr. Reeves seemed fully aware of the trend of events. Would Mr. Harrison stay with him for a day or two?

That night police gave the Porterfield house a thorough going over.

American police and detectives swarmed into Montreal on every train. Canadian detectives, too, trailed every man with waving black hair and looked piercingly at every light-haired six-footer. They worked fast but Johnny's friends worked faster. The next night a carriage drove up to the Reeves home with Mr. Mettevie and Mr. LaPierre, the priest's brother. While police patrolled the street, Reeves and Johnny slipped into the carriage and drove away. Behind them, another carriage stopped at the door, a thin young man in a Garibaldi slid in, and was wheeled rapidly away in the opposite direction.

Johnny's carriage trotted briskly through Montreal out to Long Point on the St. Lawrence River eight miles away. At the Hochelega Tavern they stopped for supper. Later, Reeves and LaPierre returned to town breathing easier than they had in some hours, and Johnny and Mettevie strolled along the shadows of the river bank. A short time later a frail little canoe bearing two huntsmen in Canadian garb swept out into the current of the river. As the lights of the tavern faded behind him, Johnny faced the night with only the clothes on his back and the word of a stranger who carried him with swift strokes over the dark water into an unknown future.

Across the river, Joseph DuTilley beached his canoe and guided Johnny to where a two-wheeled cart waited. All night they jogged along the narrow country roads, hiding behind bushes when sounds of wheels or horses' hoofs alarmed them. Between times, Johnny dozed a moment or two, but stiff from the cramped seat, aching from fatigue, weak from shock and apprehension, he rested little. All day they rode, and by noontime a fierce headache that came from tension and fatigue held Johnny sick and at times half conscious. He could feel a fever rising. Helplessly he clung to the cart, broke into sweat, then chilled until he shivered with cold. Late the evening of April 22 they reached the home of Father Charles Boucher, parish priest of St. Liboire, whom they aroused from his bed.

"This is indeed the Mr. Charles Armstrong of whom Canon LaPierre has written," DuTilley said. "He is the American who comes here because of his health and because he has been compromised in the war in which he has been engaged."

The priest nodded, then turned to look at Johnny who, unable to stand alone, leaned weakly against DuTilley. One look told the priest he had a sick man on his hands. Quickly DuTilley helped Johnny into the room off the little sitting room and onto its bed. For the next few hours chills shook him. When the recurrent shudders finally died away he lay inert, colorless, and his hands motionless on the heavy woolen blanket DuTilley had thrown over him.

"Wine, wine, he must have the restorative," whispered the priest, but already color was flushing back into the bloodless face and the thin hands were pushing feebly against the smothering blanket.

"*Fièvre tremblante*," muttered DuTilley. All night they watched and at daybreak, exhausted by their vigil, they left him in a stupor more like death than sleep. For the next weeks his life wavered from one attack to another.

Father LaPierre came out from Montreal. Johnny roused enough to ask for news from St. Lawrence Hall, to read the reports that 1,500 detectives, 10,000 soldiers were patrolling the Maryland peninsula, where Booth had been seen. Among the persons arrested were Lewis Payne Powell, who had tried to assassinate Secretary Seward but had failed. He had been apprehended at the home of Mrs. Surratt, mother of the notorious blockade runner and spy. Michael O'Laughlin, Samuel B. Arnold, George Atzerodt, and Ned Spangler, a Ford's theater employee, were now in custody; they were known to have been implicated in the murder of the president. Booth and Surratt remained at large.

Every few days Father LaPierre returned with more newspapers. Between his visits, Johnny lay unmoving on his bed. On April 27 came the report that John Wilkes Booth, murderer of Abraham Lincoln, had been captured. Johnny roused enough to read the words. The assassin, trailed to southern Maryland, across the Potomac into Virginia, had been found in the barn of a rebel family, the Garretts near Port Royal. From inside the barn his famous golden voice had resounded: "Give me but fifty feet—I will come out and fight you all!" The crackle of fire, a slight black-clad body in brief silhouette against the leaping flames, a shot—and on the burning floor lay the crumpled body that had been the gay, the irresistible, lovable, and unpredictable Wilkes, idol of the theater crowds and of his friends.

On May 3 Canadian dailies bannered the news of rewards, thousands of dollars for Jacob Thompson, Clement C. Clay, Nathaniel Beverly Tucker, and other gentlemen well known to Montreal. High on the list appeared the name and description of John Harrison Surratt, Jr.

Father Boucher read the news. He waited until his patient reached an interval of improvement and spoke to him.

"There are things to consider, my son," he said. Johnny's eyes sought the priest's stern face.

"There is the mystery of the young man, one John Surratt, who has disappeared." Johnny waited. "There is then the mystery of you hiding here; ill, it is true, but hiding, is it not?"

The boy nodded and closed his eyes.

"Could it be then that you are truly Charles Armstrong, compromised in the war, or that you are indeed this Surratt?"

The boy opened his eyes tiredly and looked at the priest. Tonelessly he replied, "I am John Harrison Surratt."

Johnny, at the priest's side, staggered across the rectory yard and entered the village church. In its austere quiet he knelt on the stone floor before the plain little altar. In the confessional the priest waited.

Later, when they emerged together, unshed tears shone in the eyes of the boy but his face was washed clear of its torment.

"Now we must plan together, my son," the little priest spoke briskly. "We must now assure your safety."

In the next few days Johnny improved slowly. Father LaPierre

SAMUEL B. ARNOLD

Hooded for his arraignment. No record has been found of men hooded
and chained in an English speaking court since medieval days. Official
records show that Secretary Stanton designed the hoods. Although this
picture shows the lower part of the hood open, Arnold's description
says there was only a slit for breathing and another small slit for eating.

SAMUEL B. ARNOLD

Arnold attended St. Charl
school in Maryland with Joh
Wilkes Booth. A member of th
plot-to-capture he soon bro
away from it and went down
Fortress Monroe to work. H
was not in Washington at th
time of the assassination, but w
sentenced to life imprisonme
largely on guilt by associatio
He was pardoned, released fro
Dry Tortugas, and lived to wri
down his story.

DAVIE HERROLD

Although he was twenty-two
years old, physicians described
Herrold as having the mind of
"about an eleven-year-old." He
had hunted and fished in lower
Maryland and so was thought
useful to the capture plan for his
knowledge of its road systems.
There is no evidence that he ever
visited the Surratt house. His affidavit says he saw Booth on
horseback, the night of the assassination, followed him across
the Navy Yard bridge and accompanied him on his flight. He
was hanged.

General Wallace seems to
have thought him not worth a
sketch.

frequently brought American newspapers, which Johnny devoured for hopeful word from home. There was none. There was only word that eight persons had been accused of Lincoln's murder and their trial would open May 10. The accused were Arnold, O'Laughlin, Atzerodt, Herrold, Payne, Spangler, and Mrs. Surratt. There was now also Dr. Samuel A. Mudd who had set Booth's injured leg after he fled from Washington.

National criticism met the announcement that a military commission would try the accused persons. Such commissions had been frequently held during the war, although there had been general dissatisfaction over trials of civilians in military courts. In such a court no defendant might speak in his own defense nor for any other accused person, and the American public found that displeasing.

But Secretary of War Stanton had demanded it, and on the opening day the men appeared in the courtroom in heavily padded hoods that cut off their sight and hearing and, in that torrid Washington spring, permitted them to breathe only through slits cut in the canvas. Stiff shackles bound their hands, and huge metal balls weighted their ankle chains. Mrs. Surratt in black dress and bonnet wore lighter ankle chains and no handcuffs, a benevolent prosecutor's consideration for her age and sex, explained the papers.

Suddenly the newspapers grew scarcer or were delivered to Johnny with whole pages missing. In the sections left for him he read of chaos in Washington, turmoil and hysteria. No longer could he accept his friends' advice: "Stay quiet. You will only harm your mother if you are found."

Desperately he demanded to be returned to Washington, but his friends refused. Once arrested, as he would be the moment he set foot in the United States, nothing he could say would help his mother, they argued. It had accomplished nothing for other Confederates to offer to return to Washington and stand trial in an honest civil, not military court. He wrote a letter to a Montreal daily paper, and gave it to Father LaPierre to mail. The priest destroyed it.

When he could no longer be trusted to remain quietly inside the Boucher cottage, his protectors sent a message to Washington. There the emissary conferred with Mrs. Surratt's lawyers, talked with Father Wiget, learned the details of a military commission's procedure, and the progress of the trial. He attended one day's session and from a distance viewed Mrs. Surratt as she sat in bonnet and black veil in the far corner of the prisoners' box. On his return he brought from John W. Clampitt and Frederick Aiken, his mother's lawyers, a message to her son:

> Be under no apprehension as to any serious consequences. Remain perfectly quiet, as any action on your part would only tend to make matters worse. If you can be of any service we will let you know, but remain quiet.

To Johnny the letter brought comfort. The knowledge that his mother knew he was safe, that he had sent funds for her needs, and that he remained away on the advice of her lawyers eased his anxiety.

He alone received the message with confidence. Stephen F. Cameron continued to disagree. He believed that young Surratt should, above all, return to Washington. If he could not save his mother he could die with her. In St. Lawrence Hall, Confederates with prices on their heads argued with him. Nothing could be accomplished by Johnny's return; he would be bound and gagged, tried and convicted, with no more opportunity to tell his story than those now on trial. Moreover, he might be forced to endanger other refugees. The word *torture*, which traveled from mouth to mouth along Washington streets, had reached Montreal.

By this time news accounts were full of testimony of Sanford Conover and his associates, who reported meetings in Montreal and in Richmond at which the assassination of Lincoln had been planned, discussed, and eagerly anticipated. Letters from Jefferson Davis encouraging the murder had been brought by John Surratt, swore Conover, along with $300,000 to pay the murderers.

Days of torment racked Johnny, and then early in June he suffered a severe relapse of his malady and for days was scarcely able to rise from his bed.

Life was dull in the bleak little village of St. Liboire, and even minor departures from the usual routine invited endless discussions by its citizens. The buxom wench who cleaned the priest's house, washed his clothing, and did other homely tasks about the womanless household itched with curiosity over the room she was forbidden to enter. For days she pondered the fascinating mystery and its solution. Then, on an afternoon when the priest was away from home, she investigated. The locked door baffled her, but there remained a small opening in the wall behind the stove. It had been cut to allow warm air from the stove to enter the small bedroom, but now it accommodated curious eyes.

Tiptoeing into the corner and holding her voluminous skirts in a modest clasp, she up-ended herself until she could peek through the opening. On the bed, a few feet from her popping eyes, a thin body scarcely swelled the heavy blanket that covered it from head to foot that warm June day. She did not see the face turned away from her, but she could see the soft yellow hair that touched the blanket's edge.

Screeching, she tore from the room, out of the house. Excitedly she babbled to the nearest neighbor the horrid news that their village priest harbored a woman who lay all day behind a locked bedroom door.

Her shrieks reached Father Boucher who, to calm his scandalized flock, suggested that Johnny show himself in the village and visit the home of Joseph DuTilley. Within a few days Johnny had recovered strength enough for Joseph to carry him in the priest's carriage to the DuTilley home. There the family conversed garrulously with friends about the young American student who visited them to improve his idiom and who needed only a short stay for his French to become, of a truth, remarkable.

Late in June Johnny returned to Montreal to the home of Canon LaPierre's father on Cemetery Street. In a rear room whose windows overlooked the small yard that joined the back garden of the Bishop's Palace he paced the floor and waited for news of his mother and Anna.

Once he ventured out at night. Reveling in the luxury of freedom, he strolled as far as John Reeves's house, across from the gray limestone post office with its mansard roof, on the corner of St.

James and St. Francis Xaviar Streets. Mrs. Reeves answered the door.

"Mr. Harrison, oh, Mr. Harrison." Her husband would so regret that he had not been at home to meet him. Please do come in.

The courtesies exchanged, Johnny asked hesitantly if she had come across his walking stick in her house? A small rattan stick, of no value except for sentiment, but he had mislaid it.

Yes, she remembered it. She had found it and had laid it carefully away, but where? At the moment she had no idea but when her husband returned, he would know. Kindly though she was, her relief was apparent when Johnny rose to go.

Other than crossing the garden to the Bishop's Palace, Johnny went out no more. Palace visitors were frequent, for the Bishop was accustomed to offering the most generous hospitality to the officials of the Confederate Consulate. With them came clergy, prosperous businessmen, foreign diplomats, but only a few could Johnny meet, and with only a trusted few could he converse.

June came to an end, and the final days of his mother's trial drew near. His protectors' reluctance to sit with him for any length of time or to converse on any but the most trivial topics and the scarcity of newspapers delivered to him became more obvious. His anxiety deepened.

July 1 came. Verdicts of guilty for all eight defendants sounded throughout the world, but not the faintest whisper penetrated the second floor room in which Johnny so agonizingly waited. July 2, 3, 4, and 5 passed. A small group of agitated men whispered together. "Send him to the country. A hunting trip, maybe. . . . Get him out of the way until we see what comes of this. The president will surely intervene for her."

So, on July 6 they sent word for Johnny to meet them at the Bonaventure Station for the next night's train to the country. It would be safe enough, said the group in St. Lawrence Hall; they would be there a few minutes ahead of him.

On the night of July 7 Johnny in his huntsman's dress, stepped lightly into the station and bought his ticket. His friends had not arrived. He sauntered across the street to the Queen's Hotel. The clerk at the news desk looked up. "Good evening."

"Good evening," Johnny replied.

"Hear about the conspirators?"

Johnny looked down at the newspaper thrust under his eyes. MRS. SURRATT HANGED TODAY. The sheet fell unnoticed to the floor. He stared unseeing at the man who went on talking although the words fell on deaf ears. Blindly he turned away, not knowing that he moved. He came to his senses on the Bishop's threshold and opened the door unannounced. Father LaPierre, newspaper in hand, sat frozen to his chair.

"You thought this—this deception—the part of a friend?" Johnny's hoarse whisper was scarcely intelligible.

"We thought," mumbled the priest, "all of us—we thought it best."

Johnny swayed forward. Only his hand on the door frame kept him from falling. "I forgive you. I forgive you."

Still babbling, he sank unconscious to the floor.

16

A hint of snow chilled the Canadian air when the *Peruvian*, pride of Montreal Ocean Steamship Lines, sailed out into the Atlantic. In the lee of her smokestack, sheltered from biting winds, a tall man with a pale, despairing face watched the shoreline disappear. As the bluffs of Quebec faded in the darkening clouds, he moved restlessly to the railing, where he leaned for support and shrugged closer his long frock coat and plaid shawl. In his forehand a pulsing blue vein thickened.

Much of what had happened between July 7 when in one horror-struck moment he had learned of his mother's fate and the present day, September 16, remained unremembered by John Surratt the rest of his life. On that July night, racked by bitter self-denunciation, he had wept himself into exhaustion. As daylight neared he had stumbled to his feet, feebly collected his few possessions, and attempted to leave the house in which he had been deceived. The door was bolted against his nerveless fingers. He paced the floor until weakness felled him. He refused food and walked again until he dropped.

For days he lay unmindful of his surroundings. Father Boucher came in from St. Liboire and when the illness became most critical stayed the night to take his turn at watching. Never was the patient left alone behind an unlocked door.

"She didn't know . . . she didn't know. Oh, *mea culpa, mea culpa, mea maxima culpa*," he muttered endlessly. The watching priest shook his head and counted an almost imperceptible pulse in the wasted wrist.

He had a mission to perform, encouraged the priest; he must live to tell of his mother's innocence. But even as he listened Johnny was torn between disgust that he lived and agony that because of him his mother had died.

Because he had been a credulous witling, she had died. She had died on a scaffold, and he, a fool, lived. A fool, yet not so great a fool as to believe that he could in any measure persuade a duped, condemning world of her innocence. He beat his breast and cried his shame, but he found no release. He buried his head in the shelter of his pillow and longed for death.

But his youthful vigor could not be destroyed. Reluctantly he returned to life, gained strength, and as the weeks passed the desire to live faintly stirred itself.

He listened to the friends who had saved his life by endangering their own. He must go away, they said; he must join those who sought safety in Europe until the aftermath of war and hatred died out. When justice under law had been restored, he could return to his own country. Then he might be believed. He grew passive, and after a time the locked door swung free on its hinges.

For more than two months he remained hidden, and then Father LaPierre arranged with a college friend, L. J. A. McMillan, who was now ships' doctor for the Montreal Ocean Steamship Lines, for help with passage to Europe. Johnny walked one night to John Reeves's shop to say goodbye. Reeves returned to his listless hand the little rattan stick that once had swung in rhythm with Wilkes' gold-headed cane as they stepped down the Avenue. The memory sickened him.

Then, a few days later, he emerged from a rear room of the LaPierre house, no longer a pale, sickly boy with silver gilt hair but a mature-looking young man with short brown hair and mustache, his eyes circled by small, steel-rimmed spectacles. On the afternoon of Friday, September 16, Johnny, Father LaPierre in nonclerical garb, and Father Boucher in his shabby black cassock drove in the bishop's carriage to the mailboat landing. Waiting to take the little mail steamer up the St. Lawrence to Quebec were General R. S. Ripley, C.S.A., William Cornell Jewett, and Nathaniel Beverly Tucker. The latter would see the travelers aboard the *Peruvian* and then with Father LaPierre return to Montreal. Dr. McMillan received Johnny cordially, introduced him to the other gentlemen as Father LaPierre's friend, Mr. McCarthy, who would be a fellow passenger across the Atlantic.

For the first few days aboard the *Peruvian,* Dr. McMillan viewed Johnny's hair and mustache with uncomfortable attention, and then he exerted himself to be agreeable. His convictions with regard to the American War, said the doctor, were definitely slanted toward the Confederacy, and this congenial topic occupied hours during which he sought companionship.

If in their conversations in the lee of the steamer's smokestack he observed that Johnny invariably placed himself in a location from which he could view all angles of approach, the doctor failed to mention it. If he deliberately led their conversations toward the war and the assassination, Johnny appeared oblivious of his maneuver.

Early on the morning of the eighth day, Sunday, September 24, Johnny sought the shelter of the aftersquare as he waited for the first glimpse of land. Through the low-hanging clouds, heavy with unspent rain, the Irish coast came slowly into view. As he watched the lights of Londonderry draw slowly nearer he stood lightly poised, hands tense on the deck rail, an impulse to flight in every line of his sinuous body.

Suppose that, when they docked, men were waiting on the wharf? Suppose—and he was sure now that he could tell a detective from a hundred other men—they boarded the ship the moment the gangplank dropped? There would be no place to go, water all around and only the narrow walkway by which the men approached in front of him. His breath came fast. He felt the old tension that, years before, had presaged the presence of bluecoats. The pulse in his forehead quickened.

Along the deck came Dr. McMillan. He flashed a smile, and Johnny fell into step for their morning turn.

"It's been a pleasant crossing, thanks to you," said Johnny; then hesitantly, "I believe instead of going on to Liverpool I'll land here. This morning."

"Here? Not go on to England?" Something more than surprise showed in the doctor's tone.

Johnny surveyed the wharf, low and indistinct in the murky light. Mist hung over the clustering warehouses, making them only a blur lighted by dirty yellow arcs on occasional lampposts.

"Yes," he said. "I can come on to London later."

"I'll see you in Liverpool, then?" His eyes searched Johnny's face and the boy nodded.

The only passenger to land, Johnny soon was lost among the shadowy workmen whose disembodied voices sounded through the ghostly murk.

The *Peruvian* docked Monday night in Liverpool. Early Tuesday morning McMillan hurried to the U.S. Consulate. There he confided to the surprised vice-consul, A. Wilding, that he had just crossed the Atlantic in company with that notorious murderer John Harrison Surratt.

If Johnny and his friends believed that his presence anywhere could be concealed from other Americans, they were wrong. Within two days of his landing at Londonderry, Vice-Consul Wilding relayed to Washington the information provided by McMillan, and asked that evidence be forwarded on which to base the fugitive's arrest.

On September 28 he followed up his dispatch with a letter to Secretary Stanton:

> *Surratt has arrived in Liverpool and is staying at the Oratory of the Roman Catholic Church of the Holy Cross. His appearance indicates him to be about twenty-one years old, tolerably good looking. According to reports Mrs. Sur-*

ratt was a devout Catholic, and I learn that clergymen of that persuasion on their way to and from America frequently lodge at the Oratory. . . . I can of course do nothing without further instructions, but if this be Surratt, such a wretch should not be allowed to escape.

While the vice-consul waited, Johnny roamed over Liverpool under McMillan's guidance and discussed his plans for the future with the solicitous doctor. He estimated that it would be two years before he could go home again, he said, and in the meantime he must find a way to support himself.

On October 10 Mr. Wilding once more notified Washington that the fugitive could be easily picked up. Three days later came a dispatch informing him that, on the advice of Secretary Stanton and Judge Advocate Joseph Holt, no warrant for arrest would be issued.

Not having experienced the hectic hours of Washington during the Conspirators' Trials and Mrs. Surratt's execution, Mr. Wilding could not appreciate the reluctance of any politician connected with that event to face a revival of its contentious days. The Secretary of War had forbidden all participants in the affair to talk about it; he was more than willing to let the matter die.

Not so Dr. McMillan who, while Johnny sipped his tea with the protecting clergy at the Oratory or walked Liverpool's foggy streets, paced the deck of the Canada-bound *Peruvian*. The fugitive might not stay where he was, as he had promised; someone else might cut in on the reward money. Tormented by the nightmare of dollars winging away, McMillan, as soon as the ship docked again in Quebec, sped to John F. Potter, U.S. Consul General in Canada.

Potter's wire on October 25 informing Secretary Stanton of Johnny's whereabouts brought the noncommittal reply: "Information received and properly availed of."

Meanwhile, Johnny spent his small funds sparingly as, idle and restless, he roamed the streets. The chill of early fall penetrated his very marrow. Against the sea damps of the city he wore over his coat a long, dark cape that, if he felt curious eyes upon him, he could throw across his face as if seeking protection from the weather.

The *Nova Scotian* sailed from Quebec on October 28, carrying its full quota of Confederate refugees, among them a spare, tall man of ascetic countenance, and Dr. McMillan.

By the third day out, Dr. McMillan had made the acquaintance of Stephen F. Cameron, former Confederate courier. Since Mr. Cameron was a close friend of Father LaPierre and had visited him in his home, and had received his assistance in sailing arrangements, no doubt he knew John H. Surratt also? Cameron quickly denied it. He had never seen nor talked to Surratt. Father LaPierre had suggested a meeting and he had refused. He did not, he said, care to know a young man who had abandoned his mother and left her to die while he saved his own cowardly skin.

"You're mistaken, sir," McMillan replied. "I got to know Mr. Surratt on my previous trip. He was hidden by friends, restrained, kept in ignorance of his mother's danger until after her execution." Cameron shrugged and made no reply.

As he had sought out Johnny, McMillan now sought Cameron and returned to the subject. Frequently he mentioned the Canadian Confederates and their activities, but no subject seemed so close to his heart as that of young Surratt and his tragic experiences.

Cameron, listening to the doctor, began to wonder. As they neared port on November 3 he asked the doctor for his English address so that he might keep in touch with him. Leaning over the ship's rail as Johnny had done a month before, Cameron entered McMillan's Birkenhead address in his notebook. As he returned the pencil he had borrowed the doctor suggested, "Write 'always in after 6 P.M.' " and Cameron noted that too.

A few hours after landing, Cameron arrived at the Oratory, presented his letter of introduction and immediately asked to see Johnny.

Johnny listened incredulously to Cameron's warning. Dr. McMillan? Friend to Father LaPierre? Betray him? Surely not. Surely not.

But $25,000? He lay back in his chair depressed.

Once more he had been a credulous fool. He had lived with Lou for seven years and had not really known him. Father LaPierre to whom he had entrusted his life had saved it, but at the expense of his mother's. Why should he believe McMillan a better man than they? Even the Confederacy had had its traitors. Bitterness overcame him. As he turned the matter in his mind Cameron sought McMillan in his boarding house.

"I understand," he said casually, "that the reward for Mr. Surratt's arrest is to be lifted at once."

"Lifted?" The word escaped McMillan before he could collect himself. "Why?"

Embroidering his account, Cameron discussed his information, which he said came from sources close to the United States government. Washington politicians, he said, had no wish to revive the public fury that had attended the trial of Mr. Surratt's mother; it was still too sore a subject with the American public.

Johnny met Cameron once more; after talking with him again, he packed the carpetbag and moved hastily from the Oratory to a small hotel. There, if arrest came, he would not endanger the priests who had befriended him.

His situation grew increasingly precarious. He could not follow General Ripley's instruction to call on his London banker for funds, because he had no way to repay such a loan, and although Judah P. Benjamin and other Confederates now in London appeared to have ample means, he could not ask them, he thought, for help. As a volunteer courier his expenses had been paid by the Confederate government, as agreed, and the vanished nation owed him nothing.

Among his letters of introduction was one addressed to the Rector of the English College in Rome; perhaps a minor teaching post or scholarship might be obtainable there. He made brief farewell calls on a few London Confederates and then, with other letters and a few more pounds, he crossed France hastily and embarked for Italy.

At Civita Vecchio, seaport of the Papal States, he was still fifty miles from Rome, but the coins in his pocket were gone. Reluctantly he dispatched a note to Father Neve[1] and uneasily waited

---

[1] The Reverend Alfred Isacsson, editor of *The Scapular Magazine*, has identified for me the rector of the English College, Rome, between 1863 and 1867.

Father Isacsson gives as his source of information Stock's *U.S. Ministers to the Papal State* in which the name NEANE shows in a dispatch and is corrected in a footnote to NEVE.

for a reply. It came promptly and with it fifty francs. With this advance he reported to the college early in the winter of 1865.

For a short time he remained under the protection of the priests in an atmosphere reminiscent of his school days at St. Charles, but his wartime training would not die, and he began to lay lines of communication. He cultivated the friendship of E. T. Conner, a clerk in a bookstore. Here, in his free hours, he lingered to hear the news of the city and of the world. He guarded his tongue. He had been a Confederate, he admitted, but further than that he gave no word of his past. The papers carried long columns of American news. Why, they asked, did the President's assassin remain unapprehended? Why had the reward for his capture been withdrawn?

Johnny grew restive. Winter gave way to spring and his uneasiness deepened. Now travel into Rome would increase. Any man passing him on the street might be the one to stretch out a hand and tap him on the shoulder.

In March, able to bear the uncertainty no longer, with the consent and possibly the help of his friends at the college he enlisted in the Papal Zouaves. Surely in the service of the Holy Father an innocent man might find refuge from his pursuers.

Besides, Vatican City had no extradition treaty with the United States.

17

Pope Pius IX ruled as both temporal and spiritual monarch in Vatican City. The King of Italy maintained his government in Florence. Each monarch maintained his own army and each court was attended by United States diplomats of equal rank. But

---

The name NEANE without a Christian name appears consistently as that of the priest who aided John Surratt with money to reach Rome. It now appears to have been the Reverend Frederick Neve.

the Vatican's lack of an extradition treaty with the United States assured Johnny's safety, at least for a time.

The Papal Zouaves were a light infantry corps and their uniform had been adapted from that worn by the early Arab fighting corps from which the regiment had evolved. In its blue jacket and waistcoat, scarlet sash above baggy blue pants with red striped seams that fell to midcalf, its white gaiters and scarlet fez with long dangling tassel, Zouave Johnny Watson stood out in barracks and street. His height, for he towered inches above most of his comrades, and his bright hair from which the brown dye now had faded, his soft light beard, and his deep gray eyes distinguished him from the Latins around him. His American look caught the attention of another Zouave, a small dark man with bright, seeking eyes, straight black hair, and French Canadian accent.

The man seemed familiar and Johnny therefore observed him carefully. Watching, he kept to himself, sought no friends, and made few. He was twenty-two years old but felt a thousand.

Only a few weeks later when one morning the man entered the guard room, Johnny suddenly realized why he looked familiar, and as he walked purposely forward, saw in a flash why danger came with him. Time rolled back, and he stood in jacket, cap, and dusty shoes, his face flushed from the heat of the Maryland spring and the long walk to Pikesville, and heard Father Walton saying, ". . . and this is Mr. Ste. Marie . . . Mr. Surratt and Mr. Weichman."

The Zouave stepped up to where the company trumpeter lounged at the table beside Johnny.

"Zouave Watson, he spik Anglish?" The trumpeter nodded, jerking his head toward Johnny so that the tassel on his fez swung gaily.

Ste. Marie looked at Johnny's expressionless face and narrowed his eyes thoughtfully.

One year and one week after Lincoln's death, Zouave Ste. Marie wrote to General Rufus King, the United States envoy to the Vatican. General King communicated with Secretary of State William H. Seward. According to information in his office, Surratt was at Sezze and had admitted his identity and his participation in the plot against Abraham Lincoln. The plot, he explained, had been instigated by Jefferson Davis. Surratt was well supplied with money. King enclosed Ste. Marie's letter.

It is lost time to require further proof. . . . I have known him in Baltimore. . . . I desire to leave here as soon as possible. . . . I think I can do it if I receive five or six thousand francs. . . . In writing me, use ordinary paper and envelope and take a turn and form of expression that none but myself will understand.

Two weeks later, Ste. Marie wrote again, giving his own background. He had joined the Union Army as a substitute for E. D. Porter, principal of Newark, New Jersey, Academy and had been captured near Orange Courthouse, Virginia. While a prisoner in Richmond's Castle Thunder he had met several forgers and for informing on them to the Confederate General Winder he had received his liberty. He had gone by blockade runner to Nassau, from there to England, and then back to Canada. When he had read of the assassination he had hastened to the Consul in Montreal to tell him what he knew of Surratt and Weichman.

Here he embellished his first story and charged that Johnny had admitted instigating the president's murder. Washington made no haste to answer, and the delay alarmed Ste. Marie. The funds he had so confidently expected did not arrive. He was on edge, anxious to keep from his comrades his betrayal of a fellow Zouave, and aware that any increase in correspondence excited jealous attention; even in an "ordinary envelope" a letter from Rome was sure to be noticed.

General King, perplexed at Washington's indifference, sent a personal letter on June 30. In official correspondence on July 10 he forwarded Ste. Marie's second statement in which he corrected some inaccuracies of the early version that had been caught by United States officials. He corrected Lou's name, which he had given as William J. Weichman. He admitted that after teaching at St. Matthews Institute in Washington he had left because of a quarrel with Lou. He accused Lou of providing information for Surratt to take South.

His new mixture of trivial truth and heavy fabrication gave the U.S. War Department pause. The last thing it wanted now was evidence that Weichman, who would of course be the government's star witness against Surratt (if it prosecuted him) had participated in Johnny's missions to the South. Certainly it did not want a statement that Johnny had been "in New York prepared to fly when the deed was done." The government needed him at the scene of the crime. Unaware of his errors, Ste. Marie continued to plead for passage money home in letters dated July 14, 16, and 20.

In August, General King wrote the State Department that if the United States demanded the return of Surratt, it probably could be arranged despite the lack of an extradition treaty. Also, the Zouave commander would gladly discharge Ste. Marie to go home as a witness. On August 16 Secretary Seward forwarded a photograph of Johnny for identification.

More weeks passed, and Ste. Marie fumed and waited. Johnny waited too, his apprehension unrelieved. He wrote to Conner.

> *Veroli*
> *August 30*
> *1866*

> *Dear Sir: Will you be so kind as to send me a French and English grammar? I think Allendorf's is the most in use. When I come to Rome I will settle with you, which I shall in the course of two or three months.*
>
> *If you should have time to reply, please give me all the news you can. By doing so, you will greatly oblige your friend,*

> *John Watson*
> *3rd Compagnie*
> *Veroli.*

A few days later the trumpeter came running to Johnny and thrust a letter into his hand. The shock of the first word rooted him to the ground. It was not from Conner. His thoughts raced but he kept his face carefully blank as he turned the letter back to the trumpeter. "It's not mine. It's for Ste. Marie."

The trumpeter shook his head emphatically. It had come to him, he chattered. He had opened it. He could not read it. Zouave Watson should please to read the Anglish.

Johnny read it again, the words burning into his mind. Slowly he replaced the letter, written on ordinary paper, inside its plain envelope. "It's for Ste. Marie," he repeated, and handed it back to the little man. Nodding violently, the trumpeter caught it and hastened back toward the barracks.

General King's turn and form of expression had not prevented Johnny from understanding that Ste. Marie would be paid and immediately discharged to be a witness against him, and that his own arrest was imminent. The bugle sang out, and as he hastened to obey its summons, Johnny debated again what to do. His company had been ordered to Veroli for short duty and as it returned to Velletri, Johnny marched with it, but his thoughts roamed far away.

Back in Velletri, Lt. Colonel Allet, Commanding Officer of the Zouave Battalion, received a message.

> *Cause the arrest of Zouave Watson and have him conducted under secure escort to the military prison in Rome. It is of the utmost importance that this order be executed with exactness.*
>
> *General pro-Minister Kantzler.*

Within minutes Sergeant Halyeril and six men took off for Tresulte, where Zouave Watson had been ordered on detachment. When Halyeril learned that Johnny had returned to Veroli, he left a corporal and two privates to await the missing Zouave, and himself returned to his company.

In the end it was simple, for Johnny returned on the evening of November 7 and found the corporal and guard waiting. He submitted without protest and, flanked by his guards, walked quietly to the barracks atop the mountain.

John slept very little in his tiny cell, for early next morning he would go back to Rome and the military prison. To go home manacled for trial had not been his plan, and once inside the military prison he could have no plans.

Nor could he break out of Veroli. Even if he could overpower the sentry at his door it would accomplish nothing, for at the end of the long stone hall the outer door stood barred and guarded. Windows and doors all had been examined before he had been locked in his cell. He could not get out, and if he could, there was no place to go.

The great stone prison with its two high towers topped a steep hill down which a narrow roadway led to the valley below. A stone platform joined the towers in front and its gate opened onto the roadway but its rear was edged by a low balustrade that followed the top of a precipice whose sides, flush with the prison wall, dropped a hundred feet to the rocky gorge below.

Many an evening the Zouaves, gathered in little groups until night bugle, had leaned over the balustrade to look down into the shadowy abyss, whose sheer walls were dotted here and there with scrubby little bushes clinging perilously to its fissured sides. Certainly the rear of the Veroli Barracks prison offered no escape route.

From the front gate, his blue pants and scarlet fez would be the brightest of targets against the white roadway. No matter how fast his long legs went bullets would travel faster. Yet he had outrun and outwitted the Yankees many a time; he had hidden in places that had seemed impossible.

Back home he had hidden in haystacks while bluecoats passed within inches. He had lain in underbrush while their horses' hoofs had broken twigs by his side. He had crossed the river in a rubber canoe, snugged in the lee of the gunboat that searched for him. A cornfield had sheltered him many a time. Here were no cornfields but he recalled Prince George's laughter that fall, so long before, at the Yankee officer sitting on a fence waiting in vain for the river runner who had asked permission to step a moment behind the rows of waving corn. Here was no such escape. Here, the orders of the General pro-Minister Kanzlter would be carried out with exactness.

Before daylight, the guard called him. He rose from his bunk and donned his gaudy uniform. It was only four o'clock, and the first streaks of dawn were still some hours away. The guard stepped back to allow a soldier with a tin of coffee to enter.

Johnny drank the coffee as the guards moved up on either side, then marched with them down the long stone wall. On the platform outside the door he nodded inquiringly toward the privy next to the barracks wall. Obligingly the guards halted.

But as they eased their carbines to the ground, Johnny, one hand, grasping the balustrade top, vaulted over it and disappeared into the gorge below.

In the darkness he lay still, remembering. He had fallen—no—leaped into the gorge. Through the bursting pain in his head he forced his eyes open.

Above him, the rising sun touched the first mountain tops. Below, miles down, lay the unending rocks, an abyss of merciless gray spears. If he closed his eyes he would fall through endless space until on their jagged points he would burst, to lie like a torn garment loosely flung. He lay still on the narrow ledge of rock on which he had landed, thirty feet from the top, in slimy refuse from the barracks and privies.

The humming lifted from his ears and he shrank back into the darkness to listen. Above him sounded the familiar cries of assembling troops; in a minute they were down the roadway, and the noise of their departure faded out. Morning lighted the mountain tops but in the gorge below night covered his motley garments. He slipped from his ledge and slithered down the wall, holding to shrubs and projecting stones.

Once through the gorge and onto the rocky roadway, he headed toward the Italian border. As he moved, the sick stiffness of his bruised body eased. Now his long tramps over Richmond roads to Washington stood him in good stead. The nights of steady walking broken only by catnaps, the disciplined muscles and the disciplined mind that had trained them moved him along his way.

Twenty miles he covered that first day, seen by no one save a peasant working his fields outside Casa Maria. Late that afternoon with almost the same sense of safety he had felt whenever he crossed into Canada he stepped over the border of the Pope's domain into the area ruled by Italy's King. Here, where the papal Zouaves might not follow, no one could stop him save United States officials. He could depend on red tape to slow them down.

That evening he entered Sora. Straight south the Mediterranean waited. A hundred miles still lay between him and the sailing ships of Naples, but he was free. What could stop him now?

But as he trod the white roads lined with gray-green cypress trees and birches golden as along the roads at home, his pursuers pitted their efforts against his ceaseless vigilance. Exasperated messages flashed back and forth between military men, papal government, and American ambassador. Between that annoyed gentleman and Washington.

> *Cardinal Antonelli has apprised me that Surratt has escaped. I sent a confidential message to Florence. I did not feel sure that a message would escape surveillance or possible interruption by Papal authorities.*

Down the road toward Naples went Johnny. Silver-green shrubs offered hiding places familiar and safe as the undergrowth lining the Potomac's shore.

On November 14, seven days after his escape, he entered Naples. His homespun political education served him as well here as in Washington. With hard feelings between Pope and king, who would be more likely to shelter a fugitive from the papal government than the king's loud supporters, the Neapolitan police?

For three days he remained in their custody, receiving treatment for his injured back and arm. Occasionally the police questioned him, although ostensibly they accepted his statement that he was English, that he had enlisted in the papal army but had found the discipline too severe, and that after being arrested for insubordination he had run away. All he asked was to be allowed to rest. He had only twelve scudi (dollars) and he preferred the hospitality of the police to the expenditure of his small funds on lodging.

When the questioning became too harsh, he demanded to be taken to the British consulate. There, having been freed by the police as a British subject, he excited considerable sympathy by his good appearance and his lack of money. English gentlemen provided him with funds to continue his travel.

On November 19 the American consul, Frank Swan, called on the Naples police.

True enough, he was told, the one he sought had stayed three days. Unfortunately he was now gone from Naples, having sailed on the British ship *Tripoli* two days before. The assistance of the British consulate gentlemen had been so considerable that even his lack of a passport had not prevented his sailing on the first British ship to leave port. Under the name of Waters he had gone.

One chance remained. *The Tripoli* must stop at Malta for coal. The American consul there, William Winthrop, was alerted to request the assistance of the British Governor. The governor's office replied that no one by the name of Waters was aboard the *Tripoli*.

Yes, admitted the governor's secretary, there was a Zouave aboard, but his name was John Agostina, and he came from Candia. No, the consul would not be permitted to go aboard for a personal investigation. No, the ship would not come in to shore because of a fog.

As the *Tripoli* steamed away toward Alexandria, Egypt, another message came from the British governor's office for Consul Winthrop. It was believed that possibly the Zouave aboard might be from Canada, not Candia: a clerical error, regrettable. General King, also informed of this possibility, instructed Mr. Winthrop to cable Mr. Hale, the American consul at Alexandria.

So sorry, replied the British office, most unfortunate and all that, but the cable between Malta and Alexandria was not working.

There was still the possibility of contact on land. General King's message, routed via Constantinople, said: "Arrest the Zouave the moment he sets foot on land."

Obediently Mr. Hale sought the ship. Again there was delay, this time because of a plague. Third class passengers were in quarantine. There was no third class passenger list. Mr. Hale stalked to the quarantine station and looked over the passengers. Walking up to the tall, blonde Zouave, he asked, "What is your name?"

"Waters, sir."

"I believe your true name is Surratt?"

The soldier made no reply.

Speedily the Director of Quarantine provided a guard of soldiers, and they escorted Johnny and Mr. Hale off the pier toward a prison cell.

"When you are questioned," Mr. Hale advised his prisoner, "you are not required to say anything that will incriminate you."

"I have nothing to say," replied Johnny somberly. "I want nothing except what is right."

18

On February 19, 1867 the S. S. *Swatara* steamed up the Potomac under clear cold skies to the Washington Navy Yard where throngs of curiosity seekers waited.

In manacles and ankle chains Johnny returned home for trial. During those long nights and days on shipboard he had told himself that he would disbark with head held high and face the world so that no man might believe him cowering in fear of judgment, yet he may not have counted on that first moment when Washington waterlines first moved into view and the grim brick walls of the Arsenal loomed up before him. Within those walls his mother had been tried; within its grounds she had been hanged.

If to avoid that blinding vision he dropped his eyes, he must have seen instead of his own manacled wrists his mother's shapely hands, browned by Maryland suns, imprisoned as his own now were.

So perhaps not so much facing the world but oblivious of its staring eyes, he walked down the narrow gangplank, staggered from the shock of motionless land after days of pitching seas, crossed the wharf, and entered the waiting police wagon.

Turning sharply at the gate, the wagon headed for the city. Familiar landmarks greeted him as he rode, wordless, between his guards. The wagon angled northeast down the mud-bound roads he had ridden with Wilkes, bordered the narrow walks he had strolled with Lou. In the distance, *Freedom,* visible through leafless trees, topped the Capitol building. A few blocks away, the comfortable brick home on H Street now housed strangers.

The streets unwound in a muddy ribbon behind the wagon's wheels. Monotonously the horses' hoofs clacked off the blocks. On Fourth Street they stopped at the dark entrance to the District Jail. Warden Brown received the quiet group in his small front office and made the entry in his book: "John H. Surratt, No. 2164. Entered February 19, 1867. Committed by David S. Gooding."

Bell V. Coleman, Captain of the Guard, led the way down the central hall. On the east wing's second floor he stopped before a vacant cell. Engrossed in the depressing business at hand, Johnny did not see the three pairs of eyes staring at him from behind the grated door across the way. Coleman motioned to Johnny to precede him through the door.

Inside the door, Johnny shuddered in his short Zouave jacket, useless against Washington's bone-cold winter. Coleman removed the manacles and clanged the door shut behind him. Johnny closed his hands, opened them, stretched his long fingers to warm them and sat down slowly on the one available article of furniture, a narrow iron cot. He tossed his fez down beside him, flicked away a few grains of sand that spattered his baggy pantaloons, and waited.

Slowly the afternoon passed, the night, the next day and night, and still he waited. On the third morning, he asked for pen, ink, and a newspaper.

"No." His guard, old Robert Waters, shook his head. "You're incommunicado. Special order of the president, or so I hear."

The chill down Johnny's spine was not all due to the unheated room. The implication was clear; guilty or not, he would be allowed no more chance to defend himself than his mother had been. His trial would be no more a trial than hers had been; it would be an arena for contending political interests, not for legal or moral issues.

Scarcely had the door clanged shut behind old Waters when a voice called softly from across the hall: "John! Hello, John!"

"Who are you?"

"Cleaver! Don't you remember? The stable where Booth kept the horses?"

Johnny recoiled. At the Conspirators' Trial, Cleaver had made much of the friendship between Johnny and Booth. A Negro came in with a tin plate of food now, cutting the conversation short. As Johnny turned the unappetizing food over and around the plate with no wish to taste it, he remembered the testimony printed in the newspapers and the comments about Cleaver. As a witness, Cleaver had sworn how Wilkes and Johnny had come to his stable for their horses, how Wilkes had joked, and playfully flicked Johnny's arm with his elegant riding gloves. Cleaver had sworn that Wilkes had once shown him a folded letter that he claimed bore Jefferson Davis' signature. Smooth, artful, deceptive testimony Cleaver had given, based on enough trivial truth to be convincing.

The voice called again across the corridor, but Johnny did not answer. He stared idly through the barred window at the jail yard, where yesterday's brief snowfall drifted aimlessly before a gusty wind.

As he stood pondering his situation, two things puzzled him. He was incommunicado yet the men across the hall, Cleaver in particular, kept trying to get in touch with him. The heavy traffic from Cleaver's cell to a room down at the end of the hall seemed very strange. The sound of footsteps in the hall alerted him. Isaac? Anna?

It was neither. A smartly dressed young woman was clicking swiftly toward the opposite cell. Waters shuffled along behind her and unlocked the door, his keys clanking. It was not Cleaver who emerged, but a well-dressed, amiable-looking young man who kissed the lady lightly on her cheek and gallantly offered his arm to squire her up the hall. He wore no hat. Obviously he was not leaving the jail. Presently they returned, he kissed the lady once more, and humming a tune, waited confidently for Waters to unlock the cell door. The lady, with a gay little laugh, touched his cheek with gloved fingers, and as the door clanged shut moved quickly away.

The second day and night passed without incident except for a visit from the prison doctor and a second excursion down the hall for the smartly attired inmate of the cell across the way. Johnny could just glimpse the black-coated figure of a man waiting at the end of the hall, and then the two of them disappeared together into the room.

The third morning as Johnny listlessly stirred his bitter, watery coffee, footsteps approached and stopped outside his cell. Behind Waters stood an elderly, stern-looking man.

"That's Surratt." The key rattled in the lock, the man stepped inside, and Waters stationed himself in the hall, his back to the door.

"My name is Bradley, John." The man held out a thin, firm hand. "I'm your lawyer. Your brother and Miss Anna want me to talk to you."

"Where are they? Incommunicado, too?" John rose to his feet, set down his tin coffee cup, and offered his own long fingers. He looked down to meet the lawyer's blazing blue eyes.

Bradley appraised his client. He missed no line of the thin young face, the deep-set eyes that looked straight into his own from under their heavy brows, the sensitive mouth. He took in at one glance the slender, muscular frame in the absurd foreign clothing, the silver gilt hair bright against the dark cell's one window. He smiled slightly, and John relaxed.

"They'll be here soon." Bradley's voice was soft and drawling, his accent pure Washington D.C. "How do you mean to plead?"

"I'm not guilty, sir."

"Yes, I know. No one ever is, but can you prove it?"

"I don't know."

The door swung open and Waters thrust a small, straight-backed chair into the cell and disappeared. The older man sank onto the chair, and Johnny perched on the cot's sharp edge.

Waters leaned against the door frame, shifting from foot to foot as inside the cell the low-toned words went on and on. At midday he saw the lawyer out, and then returned to Johnny's door, thoughtfully scratching his chin. "That's Joseph Habersham Bradley. He going t' defend you?"

"I'm not sure yet."

"If he do," Waters shifted his tobacco cud, "I reckon you got some kind of a chance. Mebbe."

Johnny scarcely heard him. He was still hearing the lawyer's parting words. He was incommunicado not for punishment but for his own protection.

Sometime during that afternoon Anna was admitted. Two long years had passed since the night she had run for his slippers and their mother rubbed his aching head with Honora's cologne. Two years less a month since word of Richmond's burning had sent him hastily north, dispatches in his pocket. In all that time there had been no direct word exchanged. No record now remains of what was said in that first visit when death and the loss of all they had loved stood between them. But surely, as they wept in each other's arms, Anna must have told them their mother had been thankful he had not returned to die with her.

"John, John, take care of Anna," she had whispered as she tottered to her death on the gallows. Hearing his mother's charge to him, something of his bitterness must have given way, something of his grief must have eased. Not once in all the anguished weeks that preceded their mother's death, Anna must have told him, had she been tricked into any word that could be distorted and used against him.

Anna gave him their mother's wedding ring, the little brooch with the lock of their father's red hair she had worn at her throat, and with them the message that they carried her dying love. Sometime during the next few days Anna provided him with clothing, and his motley Zouave garb disappeared.

On the morning of February 23, preceded by U.S. Marshal Gooding and flanked by two District of Columbia police officers, John crossed the yard to the District Criminal Court. Curious onlookers lined the path and stared at the bright-headed young man who would surely hang like his mother, and then, their curiosity satisfied, turned away without entering the court.

Standing before the bench where sat Judge George P. Fisher, John heard the long indictment read. Only a few understandable words came through the ancient Clerk of the Court's legal verbiage: " . . . and the said John H. Surratt did with gun feloniously shoot, kill, and murder Abraham Lincoln . . . did conspire, aid, assist, comfort, and maintain . . . Mary E. Surratt, Lewis Payne, George T. Atzerodt, David Herrold . . . to kill and murder . . ."

"How say you, guilty or not guilty?"

"Not guilty."

"How will you be tried?"

"By a jury of my countrymen." John faced the bench head erect.

"Then may God send you safe deliverance," dismally intoned the clerk.

John needed that prayer, as he soon learned, for this jury would hear not only evidence legally acquired and presented, but much obtained by influence and pressures.

Three days later the prison doctor penned a letter to a patient of his, Andrew Johnson, President of the United States.

> *Mr. President: I was yesterday approached by the Reverend W. B. Matchett (444 Eighth Street), who says he is connected with the Judiciary Committee, and asked if I often saw John Surratt. I replied that I saw him in a professional way as physician to the U.S. jail.*
>
> *Mr. Matchett then requested me to mention to Surratt there was a means by which he could save his neck, have the shackles struck from his arms, and have his mother's name rescued from odium if he would give the name of someone high in position who might have prompted the assassination as he and his party were no doubt tools in the hands of more important personages and that he need not look to Andrew Johnson for pardon as he dare not do it.*
>
> *Mr. Matchett said he approached Miss Anna Surratt but old Bradley, her brother's lawyer, had prevented his communicating with her. . . .*
>
> *Yours respectfully*
> *W. I. C. Duhamel*

The power behind these and other events that preceded Johnny's trial was Edwin M. Stanton, Secretary of War, and leader of the Radical faction of the Republican Party. He had been the power behind the military trial of the alleged conspirators, and his determination to convict the defendants had brought about Mrs. Surratt's death. Both the methods and the verdicts that had sent four civilians to life imprisonment and four others to the gallows still generated intense public feeling. Stanton had a double interest now for unless John Surratt was found guilty, thus upholding the verdicts of that earlier trial, the whole Radical faction might be destroyed politically.

Since long before Lincoln's death, Stanton had aspired to the White House and had made no particular secret of it. Northern and Western votes could keep the Radical Republicans in office, and so strengthen his chances, only if Southern votes could be reduced to a trickle. The strategy devised to accomplish this had been to disfranchise Southern white men and bestow suffrage on the Freedmen, who would support their Northern liberators at the polls, thus preserving the Radicals.

But to their discomfiture the Radicals discovered that the new President, Andrew Johnson, would not follow blindly where they led. At first they threatened him with party power but when he continued to pardon Rebels and to revert to many of Lincoln's conciliatory and personal vote-winning policies, they cast about for means of getting rid of him.

Johnny Surratt's trial could, perhaps, be a great assistance.

At the Conspirators Trial in 1865 a large part of the prosecution's testimony had been procured by Charles A. Dunham. An agreeably mannered young man, Dunham had once been, or so he claimed, a roving correspondent for the *New York Tribune*. When the trial had opened he had offered himself as witness. Calling himself Sanford Conover (for reasons best known to himself) he had given damaging testimony against the accused and had furnished seven other persons, his wife included, who obligingly swore to whatever the prosecution needed.

Then Conover had volunteered and had been employed by Stanton to supply evidence implicating the Confederate officials in Canada and also John Surratt. He began to submit regular reports to Stanton, enclosing with each one a request for more funds with which to seek witnesses.

While Johnny had traveled Europe, Conover had covered the United States on paper. He had reported to Stanton with total dishonesty that he had gone from Canada to New Orleans, from Washington and New York to the far west, trailing witnesses who would establish the fact that Jefferson Davis, assisted by John H. Surratt, had planned, animated, and financed the murder of Abraham Lincoln. He had produced one Farnum N. Wright, a voluble New Yorker whose deposition in Stanton's office said that in Montreal he had met Confederate Commissioners Clement C. Clay and Jacob Thompson, who had sent Surratt down to Richmond to fetch back Davis' written approval of the assassination. He had sworn too that he had been present at an interview in Richmond during which Jefferson Davis had heartily endorsed the murder plan.

In December, 1866, a short time after Johnny's arrest, Representative James H. Ashley of Ohio had introduced before the House of Representatives a resolution to impeach President Andrew Johnson. The House Judiciary Committee thereupon had launched the necessary investigation. When the Committee began its search for evidence useful in removing President Johnson from office, it first of all requested the Secretary of War to supply copies of all information in his possession concerning persons accused of complicity in the murder of Lincoln. After the astounded Committee read the Conover material, they immediately tried to locate the witnesses at the Conspirators' Trial and bring them in for further questioning.

The first of these, William Campbell, broke down under questioning. "This is all false," he cried miserably. "I must make a clean breast of it. I can't stand this any longer."

All the testimony given by himself and the seven others had been manufactured, he confessed. Conover had written it out and coached the witnesses in delivering it. His pupils had then traveled to Washington, made depositions at the War Department and, using their assumed names, had testified at the Conspirators' Trial.

As a result of his resourceful activities Conover was arrested, convicted of perjury, and sentenced to eight years in prison. When Johnny Surratt entered the District Jail in February 1867, there was Conover in the cell right across the hall waiting to be transferred to the Federal Penitentiary in Albany, New York.

Even in jail Conover was not idle. He attempted to interest President Johnson in a pardon in return for his promise of 5,000 New York votes in the next election. This effort failed. Then, one happy day in February, his attractive young wife reported jubilantly that she had been approached by two Radical politicians of very high standing, General Benjamin F. Butler and Representative James H. Ashley. These gentlemen felt Conover's freedom could be obtained if he supplied a little evidence against President Johnson. Reviewing the possibilities, Conover realized that what he needed now was someone whose name had been linked with the assassination.

Providentially, in the cell across the hall sat John Surratt.

On March 17 Mr. Ashley paid his first visit to Conover in the District Jail and found it sufficiently worth while to justify coming back. Many an evening, then, the black coattails of the Congressman whisked into the room at the end of the hall, to be followed by Conover and frequently by his wife.

Johnny too had his visitors. Young Joe Bradley came with his father and with them at times came Dick Merrick, junior member of the firm. Young Joe had made a successful trip to Canada to verify Johnny's story. The three lawyers were now prepared to undertake his defense.

From their new home on Massachusetts Avenue Isaac and Anna brought daily baskets of food. Shortly after this, overtures from the cell across the way began again. This time Cleaver was not the caller but a third inmate of the cell, who lay hour after hour on his cot with his face turned to the wall. The Negro who brought the meal trays told Johnny the man was sick, so within a day or two Johnny offered food from Anna's basket to sick William Rabe. Rabe gratefully accepted the friendly gifts. Later as he overheard conversations between his cellmates, Conover and Cleaver, a decision began slowly to formulate in his mind.

Johnny grew cheerful as plans for his defense progressed. Across the hall Conover was cheerful too, confident of his approaching release. Cleaver said very little to Johnny now, but often joined Conover in his conferences with Ashley. When these two visited the room at the end of the hall, Rabe recovered enough to write feverishly.

A visit from General Butler swelled Conover's assurance. He would never serve his term, he told his cellmates: powerful interests would secure his release.

Conover and company underestimated Andrew Johnson and his few friends. Before the *Swatara* had arrived with Johnny, the president had talked with the only cabinet member who had his complete confidence, Secretary of the Navy Gideon Welles. He had disclosed his fear that Ashley or some of his henchmen might suborn Johnny into a lie to save his neck.

"The man's life is at stake," he had said, "and the more reckless Radicals would, if they have access to him, be ready to tamper with him." He had suggested barring all unauthorized communications, with the result that Johnny found himself denied all company except his family and lawyers, and refused all contacts.

Anna Surratt's indifference to his scheme had surprised Conover. Also, he had never imagined that Ashley's aide, the Reverend Mr. Matchett, could be so mistaken in the prison doctor. Nor did Conover ever dream that the frazzled little Dr. Duhamel would record Matchett's confidential message and report it promptly to the President of the United States.

While Andrew Johnson in the White House meditated on the turn of events that had entangled his official life with a Confederate prisoner in the District Jail, John Surratt meditated too. A connection between him and the president? Fantastic. Yet it seemed that the House Judiciary Committee was in all seriousness investigating the charge. Why, the Committee asked, had not the accused murderer been brought home promptly for trial? The crime "is still mysteriously unfathomed," editorialized the Radical press, "and its benefits are being reaped by the President of the United States."

How could they imagine, Johnny asked himself, any possible connection between him and the one man who could have saved his mother's life simply by lifting a pen, but who had not lifted that pen? What bond could he have with the man who had refused even to hear a plea for mercy? Anna had thrown herself on the stairs outside his office, sobbing: "Oh, help me, for the love of God—oh, hear me, for the love of Christ—" War-hardened soldiers had dashed tears from their eyes, but Johnson had not moved.

Andrew Johnson, pacing his study floor, also must have asked a question: what should he, the President, expect from the son who now, with one word, might free himself and avenge his mother?

While President and prisoner wondered, the latter learned some details of the two years just passed; how Lou, terrified, had betrayed his closest friends; how the Prince George's neighbors had come to Anna's aid; how the Holohans had stood staunchly by her. They had helped her clean and repair the house on H Street, which had been left a shambles by the federal soldiers who had occupied it as guards during her mother's trial. John Holohan had helped her sell it, advising her to accept the $4,000 loss as inevitable. She had then lived with the Holohan family, who had taken a house on Massachusetts Avenue, between Sixth and Seventh streets. They had returned to Baltimore and she and Isaac had kept the little home together. From its kitchen came the baskets she carried to Johnny each day.

Isaac[1] had come home a few weeks after their mother's execution. Jingling in his pockets the few coins his company could get together, he had trudged the weary miles from San Antonio, Texas. "Go home," the penniless Confederate soldiers had said. "Go home and kill Andy Johnson."

Others had helped too. Friends, acquaintances, even strangers had contributed to John's defense fund, which now totaled $1,500.

A different kind of help came from William Rabe. The interviews of his cellmates interested Rabe so strongly that he wrote to Johnny. Using a pencil and lined paper, he filled four pages.

---

[1] Records of the Adjutant General's Office, War Department, show Isaac D. Surratt enlisted May 4, 1862 in 33rd Regiment, Texas Cavalry (Duff's Partisan Rangers, 14th Battalion [Cavalry], Confederate States Army, and that in August 1864 he was Acting Q.M.S. He was paroled at San Antonio, Texas, September 18, 1865.

Because of its explosive contents, he headed the letter with a warning:

NOTE. Be very careful how you use this information.
NOTE. Select good and true men.

Monday, March 27, 1867

My dear John

All letters you receive from me by mail are carried out of here and posted by the wife of a prisoner in the same cell with me. This prisoner has the privilege of seeing his wife in a private room or in other words not under surveillance as I am when I talk to you through the grate.

Give my sincere thanks for the last kind gifts from your house but such good things unfit me for my prison and jail fare. One other thing send me no more whiskey. It is nearly all drunk up by the keepers and others who are below. I got a drink or so out of each bottle (small ones at that) but not more than eight out of both bottles. I think I am getting stronger now and shall need no more.

Now I wish to give you a piece of information which you must be very careful in the use of. None but very discreet men and men of probity and character should be entrusted with it and I believe if the right persons get ahold of it they can use it to my benefit with the President.

My two cellmates were witnesses in the Assassination Trials (I mean Mr. L.). One is named Sanford Conover and one is called Dr. Cleaver. He is connected with the livery stable on 6th Street near the Canal. Conover is here for perjury in some matter connected with the attempt to implicate Jefferson Davis with the assassination and I believe Cleaver is here for rape on a young girl thereby causing her death. I rarely sleep day or night I am so nervous I cannot, and thus I have heard them talking when they thought I was asleep. I am satisfied their intention is to have President Johnson implicated with knowing to Mr. L's death.

Cleaver says Booth once showed him a letter to Jefferson Davis which Booth alledged was written by Mr. Johnson and this was just before the murder. Again, Cono-

DR. SAMUEL A. MUDD

Awakened from sleep early Saturday morning, April 15, 1865, this gentleman farmer and physician dressed the leg Booth had injured in his fall from the Ford's Theatre box. For this act he was sentenced to life imprisonment. When an epidemic of yellow fever caused the death of the prison doctor, he volunteered to serve. President Andrew Johnson pardoned him in February 1868.

ABOVE: As General Wallace saw him.

NED SPANGLER

A stage hand at Ford's Theatre, Spangler had known Booth for years. He was accused of helping Booth get out of the back door of the theatre after the murder, and spent four years in Dry Tortugas for it. Note the stiff-shacked manacles.

ver tells me tonight he will be out of jail, although in-dicted for perjury within a few days and that it will be brought about by General Benjamin F. Butler and Mr. Ashley of Ohio. His wife brings that information this eve-ning.

Butler and Ashley will both be here he says tomorrow evening to see him again (they have both been here several times and had private interviews with him last week). He remarked to Cleaver tonight "My wife will see them both tonight and inform them what you know about the matter. I have no doubt they will put you right."

From all I can learn and it is but little I firmly believe this to be a made-up thing and in the possession of men such as Butler and Ashley it will be used in the impeach-ment of the President. Conover remarked a few days ago that he meant to get out of this if he could and if those that ought to help it did not work for him he should do the best he could for himself. He seems to rely strongly on Judge Fisher's ignorance.[2]

To whom Rabe addressed this letter is not shown, but surely no envelope bearing the Surratt name or the Bradley street address or that of anyone else connected with the defense of the prisoner could have traveled any distance in Mrs. Conover's reticule with its seal unbroken. However it traveled, it reached Johnny while its author, a few feet across the halls, cast a quick, knowing look at Joseph Bradley, who smuggled it out of the jail once more. It reposed for a time in the Bradley law office, and then went on to join other letters preserved in Andrew Johnson's desk.

Duhamel, busy with his own Doctors' Line, wrote again.

PRIVATE

March 27, 1867

Mr. President:

Whilst on my visit to the jail Miss Surratt asked me to prescribe for her after which she told me that General But-

---

[2] The original letter in the Manuscript Division, Library of Congress, ends here.

ler and Mr. Ashley had sent for her and she told them it was the instruction of her lawyer, Mr. Bradley, to see them only in his presence to which Butler and Ashley declined seeing her.

I spoke of the announced attempts to implicate the President by evidence of her brother John and Miss Surratt repeated in the most earnest manner that her brother knew nothing in the least against the President, and could say nothing and she knew John could not be induced to swear away his own soul.

> *Believe me your devoted friend*
> *W. I. C. Duhamel, M.D.*

March passed in flurries of activity in the War Department, White House, and jail. In the latter, Johnny passed his twenty-third birthday while Mr. Bradley petitioned for an early hearing of the case. Newsmen filled their columns with comment and complaint as they labored to keep their public pitch hot until the trial stories could begin. They missed the story on April 19 that sleepy William Rabe had received an unconditional pardon from President Johnson.

Meanwhile the able hand of Joseph H. Bradley guided more letters and affidavits toward the slowly accumulating file in the presidential desk.

On May 8 Dr. Duhamel gave the correspondence fresh momentum with a note to Colonel Robert Johnson, private secretary to the president. Two days later a statement arrived from Bell V. Coleman, captain of the jail guards. On that same day the crowning accomplishment, a full affidavit provided by Rabe, topped off the memorable collection the good doctor had begun.

On one side of the hallway Ashley, Cleaver, and Conover laid their plans, and the latter hastily scribbled down outlines of the testimony that Ashley considered necessary to hang John and remove the president. A few feet away, across the corridor, Johnny, the Bradleys, Dr. Duhamel, and the jail guards scribbled equally hard on the evidence that would blow Conover and the prosecution sky high.

19

Judge George P. Fisher entered the courtroom and the spectators rose. With the slow gait of a sick man he approached the bench, swept the room with a glance, and seated himself. The assembly sat down.

"Oyez! Oyez!" called the crier. "The court . . . now . . . open."

Judge Fisher lifted a glass of water from his table to his lips, dabbed at his mustache with a folded handkerchief.

"Gentlemen," he addressed the attorneys inside the bar space. "This is the morning assigned to the trial of John H. Surratt for the murder of Abraham Lincoln. Are you ready on the part of the prisoner?"

"Your Honor, the prisoner is ready and has been for weeks."

"Are you ready, Mr. Carrington?"

"If it may please Your Honor, I am happy to announce that we are ready to engage in the trial of John H. Surratt for the murder of Abraham Lincoln, late President of the United States, on April 14. 1865," replied E. C. Carrington, Washington's District Attorney.

It was the morning of June 10, 1867. The warm, humid day promised rain, but that had prevented no spectator from attending what the papers said would be the most sensational trial of the century. Three times the defense lawyers had pressed for an opening day, three times the prosecution had obtained a delay. Was this, the newspapers asked, because the government attorneys felt unsure of winning?

The crowds that had watched Johnny, manacled and guarded, led along the path from jail to courthouse, followed. Johnny no longer appeared the romantic brigand in baggy pants and jaunty fez. The ancient jail's squalid gloom had made him pale and somberly listless. His eyes were shadowed in their deep sockets and his hair fell unevenly over the collar of his neat, dark suit.

Inside the courtroom he sank into a seat beside Isaac, already at the defense table with young Joe Bradley. Marshal Gooding removed his handcuffs. Dick Merrick bestowed a friendly slap on his shoulder.

The courtroom hummed with underbreath conversation. Newspaper correspondents seeking to present a picture for avid readers over the nation wrote of a dingy room, miserably ventilated, of dirty, smoke-clouded windows, of spider webs in corners, of a sanded floor spattered with tobacco juice. Before the judge's high bench sat the ancient clerk of the court; near him waited the court reporter, impatient to begin his flowing shorthand. Just beyond, the witness stand awaited its first occupant. In the corner close to the judge's bench stood the uncomfortable jury benches.

Officers in uniform, a few women in long dresses and wide bonnets, a handful of men with the air of congressional halls, and an occasional smartly dressed Negro exercising his new status as freedmen filled the seats. Somberly clad Prince George's County neighbors scattered through the room, and on all sides familiar faces from town and country sought out the squire's son.

Edwin C. Carrington seated himself at the prosecution table and Johnny suddenly remembered that years ago the squire of Surratts' had counted this man among his acquaintances. A grizzled red beard fell a full fifteen inches down Carrington's white shirt front; his body, spare and angular, moved abruptly as he turned to speak to his colleagues.

They were an imposing lot, the prosecution attorneys. Beside Carrington stood Edwards Pierrepont, who affected English side whiskers and Bond Street frock coat. One of the nation's toughest courtroom operators, he was a member of the Radicals' inner circle, and every Washingtonian there knew his mission; to fight to the death to win this case and so preserve the political supremacy of the Radical faction.

Bombastic Carrington, full of sound and pointless fury, often had shown himself to be no match for Joseph Habersham Bradley, and so Pierrepont had been detailed to head witness examinations. The District Attorney, Carrington, would then sit like a glorified office boy doing little beyond taking notes in a small black book.

With them sat Albert G. Riddle, whose massive skull, covered with sculptured curls, roofed a brain brilliant as it was devious. Months later Riddle would reluctantly admit under pressure that Stanton had assigned to him the "general management of the case." In other words, the war secretary had arranged to dictate the trial of a civilian in a civilian court, as he had dictated the trial of civilians in a military court. Assisting the prosecution, the House Judiciary Committee worked night and day on plans to remove the president, and turned over to the War Department any information its members thought would help to unseat Andrew Johnson and hang John Surratt.

Almost lost among such eminences sat Nathaniel Wilson, nebulous young assistant district attorney.

Defense counsel showed up well. Dick Merrick, in light gray suit and maroon cravat, besides being the best dressed man at the Washington bar was an able hand with juries. Joseph Bradley, at the height of his legal career, also impressed them, for his snapping blue eyes missed nothing. His firmly set jaw and assured manner seemed forbidding, yet his attitude toward the defendant was almost fatherly.

A forty-year veteran of the District courts, Bradley had watched administrations come and go, and he viewed with a jaundiced eye political machinations in judicial affairs. He had become the champion of the politically oppressed, and he knew every soul in Washington. Washington, wrote the newsmen, worshipped at his shrine.

Johnny had Anna to thank for Joseph Bradley. The $1,500 she had collected with the aid of neighbors and friends from the sale of Johnny's photographs would barely cover basic trial costs, but because of her plea Johnny would be defended by Bradley, young Joe, and Dick Merrick.

During the preliminary formalities, Carrington fired the opening shot. The law's requirements, he said, had been ignored in drawing the jury. A jury illegally drawn could not give a legal verdict. Here Pierrepont interrupted bluntly, ". . . on such a verdict, no man could be executed. . . ."

Johnny flinched slightly and looked down at his hands. Mr. Bradley's voice rose. The customary procedure, legal or not, had been observed. "It's a very nice question," he continued drily, "whether or not every man hung under the jurisdiction of this court has been illegally hung."

Hastily the court remanded the prisoner into the custody of the U.S. marshal and adjourned the session.

On Wednesday, twenty-six freshly chosen talesmen appeared, and suddenly evasion of jury duty became front page news. A hundred were called; they begged off on grounds of poor health, trips to Europe, no one to open the store mornings, or wives in delicate condition. The next hundred were no better. They didn't hear very well, they had stomach ailments that made them fall asleep when other people talked. They had sons who had served in the Confederate army. They had kidney trouble, or they had supported General Lee. They were Catholic. They were Protestant. Chiefly, they had opinions that nothing could change.

The session adjourned, and again newspapers hinted that the prosecution was seeking every means of delay. More than a week was required and more than two hundred talesmen were called before twelve unhappy men found themselves assigned to the uncomfortable benches, with the prospect of a long, hot, contentious session before them.

Joseph Bradley asked that defense witnesses be summoned at government expense. The court agreed. Isaac whispered to Johnny, who nodded. Isaac, wrote a reporter, with his bold, black eyes and devil-may-care manner, appeared a better murder prospect than his scholarly-looking brother. Anna's absence disappointed the spectators but her brothers refused to subject her to this second trial agony. They watched Johnny. Only those who knew him well understood the import of the vein pulsing in his forehead as the court asked,

"Are you ready, gentlemen?"

Reporters and listeners settled back in their chairs as Nathaniel Wilson rose and bowed to judge and jury.

May it please Your Honor and gentlemen of the jury, the Grand Jury of the District of Columbia have indicted the prisoner at the bar as one of the murderers of Abraham Lincoln. It has become your duty to judge whether or not he is guilty of that charge..... You are to turn back

*the leaves of history to that awful scene in Ford's Theatre
. . . hearts were throbbing with the newborn joy of peace
and victory. Above them sat him who had borne the nation's burdens through many and disastrous years. . . .
Persons present will tell you that about twenty minutes past
ten that night of April 14, 1865, John Wilkes Booth, armed
with pistol and knife, ascended to the dress circle, entered
the President's box. By the discharge of a pistol, he in-
flicted a death wound, leaped to the stage and, passing rapidly across it, disappeared into the darkness of the night.*

*We shall prove to your entire satisfaction that the
prisoner was then present, aiding and abetting the murder,
and that at twenty minutes past ten he was in front of the
theatre with Booth. We shall prove to you that the butch-
ery was the result of a long premeditated plot in which the
prisoner was the chief conspirator. In the years 1864 and
1865 he passed repeatedly from Richmond to Washington to
Canada, weaving his nefarious scheme. It will be proved
that he made his home in this city a rendezvous for tools
and agents whom he called to his bloody work. . . . We
shall prove as clear as the noonday sun that he was here
that awful April 14, contriving and assisting in the awful
deed . . . present at the theatre that night. Then when at
last the blow had been struck, he turned his back on his
home and began his shuddering flight.*

*We shall trace that flight to Canada, where he volun-
tarily absented himself from his mother during the time
the Conspiracy Trials were in progress here and when it
was within his power to give testimony which might have
shed light on that transaction.*

A poorly muffled snort in the back of the room half interrupted him. Washingtonians remembered the hooded, blinded,
gagged men who had been held speechless during their trial,
and remembering, their faces became grave.

Wilson continued.

*Before we are through the public mind will be set to rest
on a great many subjects about which there have been*

*numerous and unfounded reports. It has been circulated in
nearly all the journals of the country that the United States
dared not bring forward a diary found on the body of John
Wilkes Booth because it would prove things they did not
want known. This will be proved false. It has also been
stated that after the conviction of the prisoner's mother, an
effort was made to get to the President for pardon but that
men active at the seat of government prevented the President from being reached to see if he would exercise clemency. The truth is, the matter was brought to the President
at a full Cabinet meeting, that it was discussed, and that
condemnation and execution received the sanction not only
of the President but of every member of his Cabinet. This
and a thousand false rumors will be set at rest.*

*When the facts which I have stated have been proved,
and when all the subterfuges and contrivances of the defense have been removed, we shall demand of you that ret-
ribution be done upon the shedder of innocent blood.*

Wilson sat down. Although Johnny had been prepared for
the charge, the very sound of the words unnerved him, and he
held himself rigid lest onlookers observe his reaction.

Unmoved, Mr. Bradley obtained the court's permission to delay
the defense's reply until the prosecution had presented its case in
full. Next, he requested a list of the prosecution's witnesses. During the Conspiracys' Trials, he said, the defense had found itself
greatly handicapped by the prosecution's refusal of this customary procedure. The defense, he said, would gladly submit its
witness list.

After a sharp debate, Judge Fisher said he would take the matter under advisement and ordered the prosecution to proceed.

"Joseph K. Barnes, Surgeon General of the United States
Army," intoned the clerk. "Be sworn." The officer stepped forward.

He had been called to Ford's Theater the night of April 14, 1865,
said General Barnes. He had found the president dying of a gun-
shot wound and had remained with him until he died.

The ball had entered the skull at the left of the middle line and below the ear. The president had not been conscious at any moment after receiving it; he had lived until twenty minutes past seven on the morning of April 15.

A woman sobbed, and the judge turned his eyes toward the back of the room. Offered a packet, General Barnes received it, examined it, and identified its contents. This was the pistol that had killed the president. This, the ball that had entered his head. He had probed for the ball, and he would know its flattened edges anywhere. He had found it behind the orbit of the president's right eye, buried in the president's brain.

"This," he held up the fragment for the jury to see, "this is a piece of the shattered bone I removed from the skull of the President, Abraham Lincoln." Women peered over heads of persons in front of them. In back rows, people crowded to their feet, anticipation showing on every face.

"Won't miss a trick," someone near the defense table muttered. "Not a damn ghoulish trick."

"Major Rathbone," called the clerk.

The blue-coated officer mounted the stand, and was sworn.

"I was well acquainted with the late president," he testified. "I was present in the theater the night of the assassination. I went with him and Mrs. Lincoln and Miss Harris to Ford's Theater." Clearly he sketched the picture, the entrance, the actors halting the performance, the band playing "Hail to the Chief," and the audience rising to greet the president with vociferous cheering. They had moved along the dress circle to the box that had been prepared, Number 7. The president had occupied a large armchair, the one nearest the audience. As he watched the performance he had heard a pistol shot behind him, had looked about, and had seen a man, indistinct in the pistol smoke, between him and the president and the door. He had heard the man shriek some word such as *Freedom;* he wasn't sure what it was.

"I sprang toward the man, seized him. He wrestled out of my grasp and made at me with a large knife. I parried the blow by striking up and received it on my left arm between elbow and shoulder. The man sprang toward the front of the box. . . . I cried, 'Stop that man!' "

The measured tones fell on breathless quiet as the horror of the night was re-enacted. Johnny could almost see the theater, the presidential box with gold damask curtains over fine lace veiling its front, chairs pulled close to the polished ledge. Only this time an extra chair, a deep, comfortable rocking chair, in which relaxed a worn and wearied man. A pistol crack, and from the fat, brightly dressed woman in the box an unearthly scream: *He has killed the president!*

Vividly listeners saw Booth poised lightly on the ledge, heard the whisper of shredding cloth, saw on the stage his falling body with a wisp of bunting caught in a spur. Pound of feet, slam of door, beat of hoofs.

Released breath sighed through the room.

"I looked toward the president," Rathbone said tonelessly, as if repeating a lesson. "His head was bowed forward and his eyes were closed. Seeing he was insensible and believing the wound to be mortal, I rushed to the door, and found it barred with a heavy piece of wood propped against the center of the door about four feet from the floor. People outside were beating on it. With some difficulty I removed the bar and they came in."

Tense bodies sank back into seats as the speaker stepped down from the witness box. Johnny dried wet palms on Anna's daintily stitched pocket handkerchief. The clerk called the next witness, and listeners leaned forward again.

Joseph B. Stewart, Washington resident and lawyer, had seen a flash, heard a gun, seen a man climb over the balustrade, a curl of smoke behind him. The man had crouched, then leaped from the box onto the stage. Stewart jumped onto a chair, up onto the stage shouting, "Stop that man! He has shot the president!" He heard a door slam, and actors crowded the doorway.

"He's getting onto a horse," someone yelled, but Stewart had seen it for himself.

"I followed him. He was so near that another step and I could have put my hands on him," he mourned, "but he crouched over the pommel and the horse dashed away. It kicked mud into my face. I still ran after him. I don't know why. It was a feeling of desperation. I heard the sound of the horse's feet going out of the alley . . . in the direction of the Patent Office. It happened in less time than I am telling it."

"Who was the man you saw come onto the stage and cross over?" asked Pierrepont.

"He was John Wilkes Booth."

The next witness, John B. Pettit, was a nondescript little man who said that on the date of the murder he had lived in a building whose rear was a few feet from the rear of Ford's Theater. He had spent that night in his room reading by gaslight. As he read, he had heard several whistle calls. They sounded as if they were signals and seemed to come from a vacant lot behind the house.

"I stopped reading once or twice to see what was going on," he said, and his attention had been attracted by a horse that had acted very uneasy, changing position on the paving stones of the alley leading to the theater.

"State whether you heard a horse retreating."

"Yes, I did. A very short time after. All of this passed in a very short time. Say, a quarter of an hour. The whistlings appeared to be all together. The last one was a very loud whistle."

The horse had been uneasy, he went on, and it had run down the alley. He had heard its hoofs very plainly. It had been, he replied in answer to Pierrepont's query, immediately after the shrillest whistle.

Joseph M. Dye, in army uniform, took the witness stand. He was twenty-three years old, he said, a sergeant in the Philadelphia Recruiting Office. During the war he had been in the Union artillery, and had been in Washington on the night of the murder. With a friend, Sergeant Cooper, he had stood in front of Ford's Theater, watching the crowds. It had been about 9:30 P.M. They had sat on some planks placed in front of the theater to "alleviate people getting in and out of the carriages." A large lamp had lighted the front door of the theater.

As they stood there, Booth had come out of the theater, conversing with a low, villainous-looking person at the end of the passage. In another moment a third person joined them. This person had been neat in appearance, neatly dressed. A rush of persons had come out of the theater, and Booth had said to this person, "He will come out now," referring, Dye thought, to the president.

Booth had entered a nearby restaurant, then appeared again. The third party (the neatly dressed one) had stepped up in front of the theater, looked at the clock, and called out the time to the other two.

"Where was the clock?"

"In the vestibule of the theater." The neatly dressed man, he continued, had gone up toward H Street, come down again, calling the time. He had looked excited. Sergeant Dye's suspicions had been so aroused that he had unwrapped his pistol. The man had stood in front of the theater, and the light had shone on his face. There was a picture on that countenance of great excitement, exceedingly nervous, he was, and very pale. Then he told his companions for the third time it was ten minutes past ten.

"Did you see the man's face distinctly?" Pierrepont asked.

"I did." Dye turned toward the prisoner and pointed, "It's there."

"Where did Booth stand?"

"He faced the space the president would have to face in coming out."

"Did he come out?"

"No. The president did not come out."

"What did Booth do then?"

"He talked to the men, walked up and down, and examined the president's carriage."

"What did the neat appearing man do?"

"He called the time, walked up and down, then toward H Street, returned, looked at the clock in the theater, and called the time to Booth and the other men. It was then 10:10."

"Do you see this man in the courtroom?"

"Yes, I do."

At a signal from the bench, the marshal prodded Johnny and he rose to his full height, looking the witness square in the face.

"Is that the man?"

"Yes, it is," said Dye. "I have seen his face often since then."

"When have you seen it?"

"While I have been sleeping."

Pierrepont could not quite control his surprise at this answer, and a small ripple of laughter went through the courtroom.

"You say it was the prisoner at the bar?"

"Yes, sir, and I say I have seen that face while I have been asleep." He stared at the smiling listeners, "It was so exceeding pale."

"Did it make a great impression on you?"

"It did, sir."

Judge Fisher rapped sharply to still the whispering in the room.

"Where did Booth go?"

"He entered the theater."

"How soon did you hear of the murder?"

"We had gone into an oyster saloon but we hadn't had time to eat our oysters. We hurried back to camp."

"State what happened as you were passing up H Street."

A lady had hoisted a window, he replied, and had asked what was wrong uptown. He had answered that the President had been shot and that he had heard that John Wilkes Booth had done it.

"Describe the woman."

She was elderly, Dye responded; he didn't remember whether she was stout, but she resembled the lady on trial with the conspirators, Mrs. Surratt. He remembered the house from which she called was 541 H Street; he recollected its appearance. The front steps were very tall.

"Will you state what was the manner of the woman who addressed you?"

"Well—she just asked—"

Amid disappointed murmurings, the court adjourned the session for the day.

Tuesday, June 18, the courtroom filled long before the opening hour arrived. Fans waved, straw hats moved lazily in the air, and persons with pages of the *National Intelligencer* or *Washington Chronicle* brought themselves up to date on developments and then folded the papers into fans for practical use.

"You stated yesterday," Pierrepont said to Dye, "that you and Sergeant Cooper hurried up H Street. What did you see on H Street?"

Dye repeated amiably that as they had passed along the street a lady had called out the window of 541 H Street and asked what was wrong uptown.

The room buzzed like a swarm of bees while minor repetitions of previous testimony were reviewed and Pierrepont turned the witness over to the defense.

Up to this time Mr. Bradley had not cross-examined the prosecution's witnesses as so far their testimony had not included any reference to his client, but now that Johnny's name had been introduced, and his mother's also, the defense attorneys moved in.

Dick Merrick asked his first questions pleasantly and in a few minutes drew from the witness that he would be twenty-three years old the next August, that his home was in Washington, Pennsylvania, and while there he had worked for a newspaper, the *Washington Examiner*. On the night of the murder he had come into town to see the torchlight procession and had sat on some planks in front of Ford's Theater with his feet in the gutter. After the president's murder he had told about this and the first thing he knew he had been called to testify at the Conspirators' Trial. He had been sent to Old Capitol Prison to see if he could identify the villainous-looking man and the neatly dressed man and had not been able to do so.

"Now, Sergeant," Dick Merrick went on, smiling with suspicious gentleness, "You have given us a succinct narrative of that night. You mention Booth, a low, villainous-looking person, and a person neatly dressed. In what order did these men stand?"

They had stood in the way the president would have had to pass had he come out to his carriage; the villain nearest the theater, then Booth, then Surratt.

"Now, this man you call Surratt. Had you ever seen him before?"

"Never to my knowledge."

"When did you next see him?"

"In prison here."

"I take it you have seen him in your dreams?"

"Yes. But when I saw him in prison I saw the same excited face. That convinced me this is the man I saw at Ford's."

Pinned down, he said he believed that Surratt by calling the time had regulated the moment for Booth and Payne to strike. He agreed with Merrick that in such a terrible undertaking it would be more natural for men to whisper, but it seemed to him that Surratt was in such a hurry he hadn't time to whisper; he had just stood there and hollooed it.

Surratt had been neatly dressed, very neatly dressed. Yes, it did seem that most gentlemen so prettily garbed carried a watch, but he had seen cases where they didn't. There had been great nervousness on his countenance. He was positively the man. No doubt.

Sergeant Dye remembered details about the theater episode better now than when he testified at the Conspirators' Trial two years before because he had thought the matter over so many times since.

Over and over the questioning went. Yes, he positively identified Surratt; he had seen him in his dreams. Yes, he had seen Booth in his dreams but always with Surratt. He often dreamed of Surratt.

"What is your religious faith?" asked Merrick and loud calls of protest came from the prosecution attorneys. Nothing that concerned religion could be dragged in here.

"I have no wish to drag religion in here," said Dick Merrick lightly, "I just thought perhaps he was a Swedenborgian."

Judge Fisher rapped loudly to still the tumult that arose. "I hope we shall all avoid such controversies," he said, "and try this solemn case in a solemn way."

"Well," said Bradley, "now that we're all solemnized, let's get on with it."

On it went. The witness did not believe in dreams that foretell events—he never let them bother him—still he once had dreamed he was married—and he later was. Yes, the girl he married was the one he had dreamed about, and a flurry of questions and answers brought snickers from listeners.

"Mr. Merrick," interposed Judge Fisher, "do you propose to examine all witnesses like this? You've wasted two hours—"

Dick attempted to answer, "Your Honor, I think this time was profitably spent—"

Abruptly the court adjourned the session for lunch.

"I understand," said Dick after the session re-opened, "that you saw Mrs. Surratt at the Conspirators' Trial, about three weeks after the night of the murder. It didn't strike you then that she resembled the lady who looked out her window that night?"

"No, sir."

"Not until two years later?"

"Yes, sir. Then I remembered she was an elderly lady."

With a satisfied smile he released the witness.

Eyewitness evidence that Johnny had been in Washington the night of April 14 came as a surprise to most of the listeners. Following the assassination, public opinion at first had placed him in the theater with Booth and fleeing with him, but in the weeks and months that followed, a revulsion had set in against the hasty execution of four accused persons. By the time John's trial was called, most Washingtonians would agree that maybe, just maybe, the boy had been misjudged. But here now was proof positive of his guilt, and to add weight to the story, David S. Reed, a local resident, took the stand.

He had known John H. Surratt, the prisoner, all his life, he swore.

"Stand up," ordered Marshal Gooding and Johnny rose to his feet, towering thinly above the men seated around him.

"That's the man," said Reed. He had seen him in Washington on April 14, on Pennsylvania Avenue just below the new National Hotel, where Mr. Steers keeps the sewing-machine store.

"What attracted your attention to him?"

"The appearance of the suit he wore," replied the witness. "It was something very genteel, nothing like country-made goods, but got up in very elegant style, the coat, the vest, the pantaloons."

"Was there any particular reason to notice his clothes?"

"Only that Mr. Surratt's appearance was so remarkably genteel." He had worn black boots with blue-steel rowels, and a felt hat, not one of those low-crowned hats but a rather wide-brimmed hat, a sort of drab color, stiff brimmed, you know. The witness was a tailor by trade. True he ran a faro bank on the side, but he was a tailor and so the prisoner's clothes had impressed him.

Cross-examination by Mr. Bradley only confirmed Reed's opinion that on the day of the murder Johnny had been a most dressed-up young man.

For fifteen years, he swore, he had seen the prisoner coming into town. He had often seen him with his father at Pumphrey's stable, where the old gentleman had put up his horses. He had visited Surratt's home in 1851. At that time the prisoner had been a chunk of a boy, about that tall; he held his hand about three feet from the floor.

"If you have known John Surratt since he was about 'that tall,'" demanded Merrick, "and that was only sixteen years ago, how could you have said at the Conspirators' Trial, in 1865, that he was between thirty and thirty-five years old?"

Feebly he doubted that he had said that.

Reed had only mildly interested the listeners but now they perked up at the entrance of Susan Ann Jackson, freedwoman. Susan Ann, however, was not happy to be there. Only a few days before she had undergone another questioning by Judge Advocate Holt. For her part Susan Ann was ready to be done with white folks' questionings. Still, for her testimony in the other trial she had been paid $250 in folding money. Probably these gentlemen would pay as much.

So she testified, as before, that she had lived with Mrs. Surratt in April 1865, and she remembered the day of the president's murder, Good Friday. Mrs. Surratt had gone down to the country. Mr. Weichman had gone with her. They got home about eight or nine that night.

"Did you see the prisoner that night?"

"That one?" She pointed a stubby finger at Johnny. "Yes, sir. I seen him in the dining room." She had lived in the house for about three weeks but that was the first time she had seen him. His mother said he was her son.

"What else did she say about him?"

"Nothing. I was gathering up some clothes for the wash and I asked her if they was for Mr. Weichman and she said no they was for her son."

"Did she say whom he looked like?"

"She asked me didn't he look like his sister."

"Did you bring anything else into the room?"

"Just a pot of tea."

"Do you see anyone now who she said was her son?"

"Yes, sir. I'm lookin' at him now." Again she pointed.

"Your Honor," explained Pierrepont after Susan Ann's dismissal, "our next witness being out of the jurisdiction of the United States, we are obliged to go a little out of our order and examine him so that he may return home."

Pierrepont's examination quickly brought out that James Sanger of Montreal had been bookkeeper of the St. Lawrence Hall hotel in 1865. The witness identified the hotel's arrival book and departure book; the latter gave the room number of departing guests and the boat or train they had taken.

These exhibits, he swore, showed that one John Harrison had registered at the hotel April 6, 1865, had paid his bill four days later, but had not left, since an entry "not gone" showed on the page. On April 12 he had paid again and had left at 2:45 to catch the 3 P.M. train to New York. His signature appeared again on April 18, when he had arrived at 12:30 in the afternoon.

"On the eighteenth, how long did he stay?"

"He didn't stay at all. He just came into the house."

Pierrepont rested the inquiry, and Joe Bradley rose.

"Can you identify this Harrison as the prisoner at the bar?"

Sanger shook his head. He recalled Harrison only because after the assassination parties had come to the hotel inquiring about Harrison, and he had recalled Harrison's Garibaldi jacket.

Joe Bradley displayed a garment. "This is not the jacket worn by Mr. Surratt, but it is similar. Is it the kind of coat worn by Harrison?"

"It is," agreed the witness.

To the obvious dissatisfaction of the spectators, the court adjourned the session for that day.

20

On Wednesday, June 19, Judge Fisher denied the defense request for the list of names of prosecution witnesses. To Mr. Bradley's protest that access to this list was customary and that its denial handicapped the defense he turned a deaf ear.

The first witness that day swore he had been a conductor on the Vermont Central Railroad on a run that ended in St. Albans, Vermont. At six one morning a man had tried to bum a ride on his train. A man with him had urged their need for getting into St. Albans at once. Listeners showed little interest for few of them could recognize the prosecution's need to prove that Johnny had fled to Canada after the murder. They listened carelessly to Charles Blinn, night watchman in the Burlington depot where travelers caught the cars for St. Albans on their way to Montreal. Two men had slept in the depot the night of Tuesday, April 18, and after they left, Blinn had found a handkerchief on the floor.

"Is there a name on the handkerchief?"

"Yes, sir. John H. Surratt, No. 2." Blinn identified the linen square marked with Anna's neat stitches.

Having traced Johnny out of Washington to St. Albans, the prosecution now confidently showed him there on April 17 and registered in Montreal on the next day.

John T. Tibbit of Prince George's was called. Certainly he was a Union man, he swore. In 1863 he had carried U.S. mail and he had then known John Surratt for about twelve years. Well, he never had heard John say much but he certainly had heard his mother say she would give a thousand dollars to anyone who would kill Abraham Lincoln. This had been in 1863.

Mr. Bradley had cross-examined the preceding witnesses in an indifferent fashion but Mr. Tibbit aroused his interest. "Did you tell anybody about it then?" he asked firmly and the witness hesitated a moment.

"I don't think so."

"What?" Bradley demanded incredulously. "You never told a soul that she would give a thousand dollars to anyone who would kill the president?"

"Well, not until about two months ago," admitted Tibbit. "Then I told my uncle here in Washington, William J. Watson. I suppose he let the cat out of the wallet."

In obvious disbelief, Bradley released the witness, without remembering until too late to ask where Mrs. Surratt would have got the money for the project when she couldn't make a mortgage payment to save her property.

In came Sergeant Robert H. Cooper, friend to Sergeant Dye. Cooper could remember very little about April 14, 1865, other than that he had gone downtown with Sergeant Dye that evening. Vaguely he confirmed the statement that Booth had gone into the saloon. Then, his face turned a sickish green, he wobbled a little, and without warning pitched forward onto the floor in a faint.

In the hubbub that followed, chattering onlookers waved fans over him and one brave lady grabbed the judge's glass of tepid water and dashed it into his twitching face. He revived and in a few minutes resumed the stand. He didn't remember anything about the incidents in front of the theater described by Dye. He did recall walking up H Street and seeing a lady stick her head out of a window. He couldn't tell in the dark whether she was black or white, young or old; well, maybe middle aged. Yes, stout. He didn't know whether she had worn a cap, whether her hair was brushed back in curls; he thought perhaps it was plain.

Except for the fainting fit it had been a dull day for onlookers but they overflowed the room next day, just the same. Carrington took over the examination of lesser witnesses.

E. L. Smoot, Charles County farmer, testified that Johnny had spent the night at his home about four years before. He had joked the boy about his trips to Richmond. Johnny had admitted nothing but had joked in reply, "If the Yanks knew what I'm doing, they'd stretch this old neck of mine." Smoot's gesture for neck stretching brought loud guffaws.

John Lee of Vicksburg, Mississippi, stated that as a detective in

Washington during the war he had known practically everybody in town. He had known John Surratt by sight then; he recognized him now. He had seen him along the Avenue, at about Sixth Street, on April 14, 1865. All he'd ever known about the young man was a suspicion that he ran quinine, calomel, and other medicines through the lines. Of course, everybody knew he was a Rebel.

Recalled for cross-examination in the afternoon session, Lee could not remember a thing about the personal appearance of the man he swore he had had known for years. He didn't remember the color of his hair, whether he had worn a beard, anything about his clothing, whether or not he had gone about on horseback or in a carriage. All he could remember was that on the afternoon of April 14, 1865 he had passed him on the Avenue. Joseph Bradley gave him severe treatment.

"Can you tell me how he was dressed on April 14?"

"No, sir."

"When you were a witness at the Conspirators' Trial did you say a word about seeing John Surratt that day?"

"I wasn't asked."

"You haven't told anyone connected with the government that you saw Mr. Surratt on the day of the murder?"

"I—I told the district attorney now."

"Ah-ha, so you did tell the district attorney?"

"Yes."

Further questions elicited nothing of interest or value. Lee simply couldn't remember anything Mr. Bradley wanted to know about.

On the following day attendance at the trial attracted comment from reporters who pointed out the number of women who were present. In addition to that, the morning papers said that all the prosecution had established so far was Surratt's presence in Washington on the day of the murder.

Then that afternoon, William E. Cleaver went on the stand. Yes, he knew Booth; Booth and Surratt had boarded horses at his stable. He had known Sam Arnold. On January 25, 1865 Surratt had come to the stable for horses for himself and Booth.

They had sat in his office while the horses were being saddled, and Surratt had explained that they were going out to T.B. to meet a party who would help them across the river; they had dirty work to do; they were going to kill Abraham Lincoln, the damned old scoundrel who had ruined Maryland and the country. If no one else would do it, he would do it himself, Surratt had said, and he had pulled a pistol from his pocket and laid it on the table.

Joseph Bradley rose for cross-examination. According to his statement, then, Cleaver had seen Surratt on the day of the murder? Surratt had worn a rust-colored coat? A muffler, something like a lady's Victorine? A jockey cap? Cleaver had not told this story to the Military Commission? He had known that the purpose of the trial was to find out who was involved in the murder, yet he had not previously told the things he had offered today?"

"Well," replied the witness, "I wasn't asked."

"Now, I ask you, are you the same Dr. Cleaver convicted in this term of court for rape upon a poor little girl of this city, and have you, since this trial began, received an order for a new trial?"

"I cannot answer the question."

"The record of conviction may be brought in, Mr. Bradley," suggested the judge, but the defense wished the full impact of the information to hit the jury.

"I have the right to question, and the witness may answer or not. Now," he looked the witness squarely in the face, "where have you been the last month or two?"

"In this city."

"Where in this city?"

"In different places."

"What different places?"

"I—I have been in Philadelphia," parried the unhappy Cleaver.

"Then you have not been in this city?"

"Yes, I have. I have been in this city."

"Where have you been for the past three weeks?"

"I cannot answer that question."

"I hope the court will instruct the witness that he must answer." Bradley turned to the judge who leaned wearily over his desk.

"If the witness chooses not to answer, he may do so."

"Can he decline unless he states that it would tend to degrade or incriminate him?"

"Tend to 'criminate or degrade him," feebly assented the judge.

Bradley resumed. All sound other than the questions and answers had died down.

"Have you recently seen a man, Sanford Conover, otherwise known as Dunham?"

"Yes."

"Have you been in daily intercourse with him?"

"Sometimes."

"Have you talked about this case?"

"Yes."

"Did Conover write it down?"

"Not in my presence." Then, apprehensively, he added, "He is a man I seldom spoke to."

"Then how did you come to tell him about this case?"

"We were in conversation about Surratt's hiring a horse from me."

Mr. Bradley sat down and Dick Merrick rose. "Where did you see Conover?" he asked.

"I decline to state."

"Was it, perhaps, somewhere around Fourth Street?"

"Well—perhaps."

"On the corner of the street?"

"No—no."

"Near the corner of the street?"

Titters began in the back of the room.

"Yes."

"Just around the corner from G Street? On the left-hand side as you go up Fourth?" The giggling increased.

"Er—well—yes."

The room rocked with laughter as Dick pinpointed the site of the District Jail.

"Is that where you have been staying for several weeks?"

Sullenly the witness admitted it was. Merrick turned the questioning back to Bradley, and the room quieted to listen.

"Were you at large when Surratt was arrested?"

"No. I was in the city jail—" He stopped abruptly. People in the room remembered the excitement of that time, the newspaper reports of the rape of a minor girl, and the consequent abortion that had caused her death.

"Up to that time had you told anyone of this thing?"

"I might. I cannot say."

"You knew it was important during the Conspirators' Trial to ascertain whether or not John H. Surratt was in town, and you still didn't tell this?"

"Yes. And I wouldn't have told it now if it hadn't been for Conover." Rustlings around the room revived, but hushed at the next words. "Conover told someone, and the first thing I knew, someone came to the jail to see me. I got very mad at Conover. I told him I didn't want to answer that question."

Cleaver's eyes sought Johnny, sitting motionless at the table, but quickly turned away from the look they met.

"Did you say it was in jail?" Bradley asked significantly.

"Who came to see you?"

"I think it was Mr. Ashley, a stoutish gentleman. I wouldn't answer a question until he told me how he knew it. Then I went back and didn't speak to Conover for six or seven days."

"Who was the Mr. Ashley who called on you in jail?" Mr. Bradley's tone remained gentle but no one mistook its dangerous tenor.

"I believe he is a member of Congress. I never saw him before."

Mr. Bradley ran an appraising eye across the jury and, apparently satisfied that he had made his point, released Cleaver with only a word or so. The prosecution, content to go no farther with this information, made only a slight attempt at cross-examination and let him go.

Eddy Martin succeeded Cleaver. As a New York cotton broker, he testified that he had gone down to Richmond in the fall of 1864 to consult with Confederate authorities about buying up the South's entire cotton crop. On his return, accompanied by personal and political friends of Mr. Lincoln, he had conferred with the President about his plan.

"You don't need to go into any of that," interrupted Pierrepont.

"It will take only a moment. I think it is right to state the circumstances under which I went. I think you promised me," Martin protested.

"We have no objection." Bradley offered the smile his opponents distrusted and courtroom hangers-on welcomed. "When
he smiles like that," the latter whispered to each other, "he's
about to slit a gullet."

The witness continued. "Mr. Lincoln expressed a desire to see
this thing consummated, and he suggested a course in which our
government would not be directly connected with it. The Confederate government wanted to treat directly with Mr. Lincoln
but he said he couldn't recognize nor treat with it, but if any association of individuals entered into an agreement to purchase
tobacco and cotton in the South, he would guarantee the protection of the government and every facility for carrying out the
arrangement. These parties asked me to take hold of the deal and
complete it, and I agreed, believing I acted with the consent of the
president."

An ominous buzz greeted this statement of business-as-usual.
Two years had not erased the memory of the South's blockaded
seacoast and the favored few who had benefited.

"I went to Richmond. I bought six million dollars' worth of
cotton and obtained the refusal of fifteen million more. I came
back to Washington and reported what I had done. There was
nothing irregular about it. It was done with the consent of President Lincoln. I employed a man by the name of Atzerodt to get
me across the river. I saw Surratt on one occasion." He continued,
sketching broadly, perhaps, his travel south. He had heard, he
said, that Surratt was going south and had asked to be introduced.
Surratt did not go across. He was employed by the Adams Express Company and must get back to Washington that night.

"How long did you stay?"

"I stayed three or four days. Atzerodt kept holding me off, although I was paying him, well, liberally. Finally he said a large
party would be crossing Wednesday night and that he had been
buying extra boats. He said there were horses waiting along the

road from Washington to Port Tobacco. I asked if that meant a jail break of Confederate officers; he thought a moment and then said, Yes, that was it."

Friday morning's crowd was larger than usual. Spectators gathered to see the prisoner brought across the yard, and then hustled into the building and scuffled for seats. The room became stifling. Southern men in cotton clothing were scarcely more comfortable than Pierrepont in his heavy frock coat.

Early in the day it became clear that the judge advocate general's name must not be introduced by witnesses. Unhappy Mr. Smoot, who had been recalled to open the session, stated flatly that he did not know Judge Holt by sight; he had only been told that the man who had questioned him at the War Department was the judge advocate general. Dick Merrick asked for a description of the man, but the court interrupted impatiently.

"Too much time is being taken up." Then, tartly, "Any government officer who did not use every diligence to find what could be proved by witnesses would certainly be derelict in his duty."

Bradley, waiting his chance, jumped quickly at it. "The government has abundant means in its judicial department without bringing in aid from other departments. I protest any secret tribunal to investigate, and probably create, proof. In matters connected with the army, Mr. Holt undoubtedly has authority, but under what authority has he the right to examine in a case pending in civil tribunal? If there is such authority, then let us see the statute. We must have some reason for Holt's investigating such matters!"

Wearily the court waved Merrick on.

"Describe the gentleman," repeated Dick Merrick.

"An old gentleman," said Smoot. "White hair, he had, and gray beard."

"In what room were you examined?" Bradley wanted to know.

"When I was looking about, I saw over the door, 'Judge Advocate General's Office.' "

Mr. Carrington cut in here. "Your Honor, I think it proper to state that the judge advocate general is not examining witnesses, not assisting us at all."

"If that is true," snapped Bradley, "state it under oath!"

He paused, waiting, while the prosecution lawyers looked at each other. He smiled significantly at the silence, and then resumed his questions.

After the noon recess Pierrepont assisted Honora Fitzpatrick as she moved awkwardly toward the stand and stumbled on its step. Most gently he questioned her, for, as anyone could see, Honora was no willing witness.

She had been boarding with Mrs. Surratt at the time of the latter's arrest, she said. She had known Mr. Booth. She had known Mr. Atzerodt only as "Port Tobacco." She definitely had not seen him at Mrs. Surratt's the night before the assassination; she had not seen him since early that spring, in fact. She had seen Payne but she had thought his name was Mr. Wood. She had not seen John Surratt for about two weeks before the assassination. After brief questioning, Pierrepont released her.

Benjamin W. Vanderpool, New York lawyer and Union veteran, presented himself with every evidence of enjoyment. As member of the Lone Star Club which Booth sometimes frequented in New York, he had met the actor there. Booth, he recalled, smiling agreeably, had always addressed him as "Major Vanderpool." In Washington on April 14 he had spoken three times to Booth.

At the instruction of Marshal Gooding, John rose to his feet. Then, said Vanderpool, "This is the man I saw on April 14, 1865, with Booth in a music hall." The prisoner, Surratt, with Booth and two or three other men had sat at a round table in a hall located near Eleventh Street. There had been glasses on the table, of course, and on a stage at the back of the room a woman had been doing ballet figures. Booth and Surratt had been not more than ten feet away, said Vanderpool, and he had seen them plainly.

"At that time did you speak to Booth and Surratt?"

"No, sir."

"Did you know the prisoner at that time?"

"No, sir."

Mr. Bradley's opening question on cross-examination was not particularly gracious. "You went into this place where, I believe you said, some fifty or sixty persons were sitting at round tables and at the lower end a woman was dancing on a stage?"

"Yes, sir. I recollect that."

"It was a woman, you said?"

"Yes, sir. A woman or something."

"Was it dressed like a woman?" Listeners snickered.

"It was dressed like a woman."

"Was this hall by any chance the Metropolitan Hall?"

"The Metropolitan or the Washington; I couldn't positively swear to the name."

"Whom did you tell about this?"

"I don't recollect I told anyone."

"You knew, after the murder, there was a hot pursuit but you didn't tell anyone you had seen Booth?"

"Well, other officers said they wouldn't want to be in my shoes because I had seen him, so I picked up my traps and started back to the Army. I'd been on three-day leave."

"When was the first time you told it?"

"Now. Here in this room; just today."

"Then how did it become known that you knew anything about it?"

"I read in the papers, and came on, myself. I reported to Mr. Carrington."

"You came on here without a summons?"

"Yes, sir. Without a summons."

"Had you seen the prisoner before that day in the café?"

"No, sir. I had not."

"Then how could you tell the district attorney it was Surratt?"

"I came on to see if one of these men was Surratt. When I saw him here in court, I knew he was."

"Now, just what is your capacity for remembering faces?"

"I have seldom seen anyone who remembers faces as well as I do. I have seen people and recognized them after fifteen years."

"Do you remember the face of the woman you saw dancing?" slyly inquired Dick.

"I didn't pay much attention to her face. I looked more at her legs."

"Would you recognize them?" Dick began blandly, but an outburst of laughter stopped him short.

The judge rapped sharply. The prosecution released the witness.

Saturday's brief session brought John Pyles to the stand. He had been a resident of Prince George's County for forty years, he said. For ten years he had been justice of the peace. At present he was commissioner of the tax. He had known John Surratt since he was a small boy.

"Tell the court of your conversation with him about his going to Canada."

"Well, it was about three months before the assassination, as well as I can recall. I was working at the Lower Place, and Johnny Surratt came down to have some papers signed."

"What kind of papers?"

"I really can't tell anything about the import of the papers. I just signed them to make them legal."

"State what he said about the object of the papers."

"He seemed to be urgent about it, having me sign them, and having no pen and ink there, we went over to my brother-in-law's house, 'bout a half mile off. Going along, I asked him about his business and so on; the draft was at hand at that time, and I asked him about it. He said either he wanted to get some money for his mother, or fix some papers for her, or something like that. He told me he wanted to go away; I asked him where, or something like that. I didn't want him to go away, he'd been in the neighborhood so long.

"He said he was going away to avoid the draft. I think he told me he was going to Canada. It was rumored about that time that a good many went there to avoid the draft. He said something about wanting to make his mother safe, or leaving her some money, or something of that sort."

Broadly as he dared, Justice Pyles sketched the past. John listened to the familiar voice apologetically testifying against him; no one could doubt the regret behind the man's slow words.

"State what he said about coming back."

"I think he said," the speaker hesitated, "that if he didn't return he wanted to make his mother safe. I don't remember just exactly."

The defense offered no cross-examination.

Joseph Bradley was in an excellent mood. Gentle old John Pyles, whose gaze crossed the room to where John and Isaac sat together, might not be a wholly satisfactory prosecution witness, but the defense could scarcely ask better support than that so honestly given by a Prince George's County neighbor.

Judge Fisher then adjourned the session until Monday.

21

Overnight the cool, dogwood spring had burst into hot, blackberry summer. Four-petaled wild roses, which a few days before had lined Prince George's County roads, had given way to ivory Queen Anne's lace and gaudy trumpet vine. In rail fence corners, orange tiger lilies turned toward the sun their black spotted faces, splotched with dust from hoofs and wheels. In unkempt yards along the way, garden flowers dropped their leaves and yellow Harrison rosebushes showed only the multimillion briars that edged their scraggly stems. No one tended gardens now, for women, along with their men, were court-bound to hear about their tragic neighbors, the Surratts.

On this day, June 24, another encounter between court and defense prefaced the session.

"I have again been called upon by the defense," declared the judge peevishly, "to order the recall of prosecution witnesses after cross-examination has been concluded and the witnesses dismissed, so that the defense may re-examine. But suppose we take the witness from Maine, who has just gone home. Suppose he said something there that is in conflict with what he has said here, he is sent for and denies it. John Jones, George Smith, and

Tom Brown must be sent for to prove it. They return home and the defense finds something in their testimony that appears to be falsified. They must be recalled, re-examined, two more witnesses are called in, and so the matter goes forward, involving a multiplication of witnesses in mathematical progression."

He paused for breath, and the room watched the displeased face of Joseph Bradley.

"Where would the case end?" demanded the judge. "The only termination would be the death of the prisoner or of the jurors. It would be difficult to decide which of two events would happen first, the end of this trial or the return of the children of Abraham to their holy city, the ancient Jerusalem."

His voice ceased, and his deeply pouched eyes turned to the defense lawyers. "If counsel for the defense still believes he is right, he may note an exception."

Quickly Dick Merrick made the exception. Bradley appeared unable to trust himself to speak.

John M. Lloyd was called next, a stolid, unhappy man with a fat, pale face, whose testimony had been awaited by Washingtonians and Prince Georgians alike. He had rented Mrs. Surratt's farm, he stated, and he had lived there in April, 1865.

"Were you a witness in the Conspirators' Trials?" asked Pierrepont.

"Unfortunately, yes," Lloyd answered in a scarcely audible tone.

At Pierrepont's direction, John Surratt rose. With impassive face he looked across at the witness.

"That's him. That's him, John Surratt. I had a short acquaintance with him." He continued with the admission that he had known Mrs. Surratt, Herrold, and Atzerodt. About six weeks before the assassination, Surratt had called him into the tavern's front parlor, where guns, a monkey wrench, a bundle of rope big around as his waist, lay on the sofa. John Surratt had wanted him to keep these things for him. He had objected, but finally had been induced to do so.

"You have stated that you knew Mrs. Surratt. I will ask you if you saw her shortly before the assassination, and if so, where?"

Morosely the man replied, "I do not wish to go into the examination of Mrs. Surratt." He looked at Edwin Carrington boldly. "She is not on trial in this court."

"The court will tell you if it is a proper question."

"I cannot, Mr. Carrington. Indeed, I cannot talk about Mrs. Surratt," he repeated miserably.

"You will have to answer," ruled His Honor.

Mournfully he replied. "I saw her in Uniontown Tuesday before the assassination. She was with Mr. Weichman." Under questioning, he admitted sadly that she had been sitting in "one of those high, narrow buggies."

"What was your conversation?"

"She called my attention to something I didn't understand." His voice carried little past the bar. He hesitated. "I don't want to say one solitary word more about Mrs. Surratt than I am compelled to."

"State what she said and did," ordered Dick Merrick over Mr. Carrington's protest.

"I cannot tell it, except in my own way; it is out of the question. I cannot." His voice quavered on the edge of a sob.

"Tell it your own way," Merrick ignored Carrington, "but tell what she said, not your impressions."

Lloyd stumbled over his words. "As well as I can recollect, she said, 'Have the shooting irons ready,' or something like that. I forget just what she said. I told her I heard the soldiers were going after Johnny to arrest him for going to Richmond."

He wiped his white face with his hand and kept his eyes turned away from the motionless prisoner at the defense table. "She laughed," he said in a quavering voice, "she laughed very hearty at the idea of anyone going to Richmond and back in six days. She said he must be a very smart man if he could do that." The words fell on hot, still air.

"Did you see her again before the assassination?"

"She was at the tavern Friday evening, I think."

"Were you there that day?"

"I was in Marlboro, 'tending the trial of a man that stabbed me."

Under questioning, he admitted he had been drinking until

George A. Atzerodt

Sometimes called Port Tobacco. During the war he provided boats for Confederate runners along the underground mail route. He agreed to provide boats for the capture plot but refused to take part in any assassination plan. When told of the plan he fled to the house of a relative and got a little drunker than usual. He was caught and hanged.

BELOW: As Wallace saw him.

LEWIS (LOUIS) THORNTON
POWELL

Alias Lewis Paine, Lewis Payne,
Reverend Wood.

The son of a Florida Baptist
preacher, Powell enlisted in the
Confederate Army and was
wounded. He deserted and was
picked up on the street by Booth.
During his imprisonment alien-
ists pronounced him mentally
deranged. He was hanged.

ABOVE: As General Wallace saw
him. Note the General's initials
on the sketch.

pretty late. It was five, six o'clock, mebbe, when he got home; he thought the sun was about a half hour high. As near as he could remember, Mrs. Surratt had been in the back yard when he drove in, and she'd handed him a package. She'd told him to have the guns and some whiskey ready that night. He spoke the words like a lesson learned by rote.

He couldn't remember if he'd answered her, for he had gone into the house and at once been sick from the liquor he had taken. As he had been raising up off the lounge in the back parlor, she had come in and said her buggy spring was broken and he must do something about it. After the spring had been fixed, she and Weichman drove off. Sweat stood out on his forehead as he finished the words.

The questioning went on. The package Mrs. Surratt had brought that day, he said, contained field glasses. Later that night when Booth and Herrold had stopped at the tavern and had said, "For God's sake, hurry and get those things," he had turned over to them guns, whiskey, and the glasses.

Reluctantly Lloyd admitted that Herrold had asked about doctors and that, as nearly as he could remember, Booth's companion had said, "We have assassinated the president!"

Lloyd, uneasy enough during the examination, faltered at the first cross fire, which began after the afternoon recess. Never, so long as he lived, did Lloyd forget that cross-examination.

He had been promised no reward for his testimony at the military trial, he said. He had been assured only that he would be protected, his property would be taken care of, and he would be returned safely home. In Carroll Prison, the military officer, Colonel Foster, had said he required a fuller statement.

"Did he say anything to you about a reward, or threat, for making it fuller?" asked Bradley.

"He asked if I knew what I was guilty of. I said I did not. He said, 'You are guilty of being an accessory to a crime, the punishment for which is death.' "

"Did you ever say to George Dent or anyone else," young Joe asked, "that they threatened to hang you unless you testified? That you testified to save your life?"

"No," he answered feebly, "I don't remember that."

The prosecution objected to the tenor of the questioning and Bradley explained: "We do not wish to trespass on any ruling of the court, but we do wish to ask whether or not he did not state within the past three months that he had been threatened with hanging unless he signed a statement written out for him, and that he said he swore to that statement to save his life."

"Overruled."

"Note an exception." Then, to the witness. "Did you know Mrs. Surratt's business in the country on April 14?"

Well, he had heard that she wanted to talk to John Nothey about some money. Mrs. Surratt[1] had been alone when he spoke to her that day, but his sister-in-law, Mrs. Offutt, had come out right after. He couldn't remember anything else about that day, not even who took his horse and buggy when he drove in.

Mr. Bradley at that moment began the pressure that onlookers had been anticipating with pleasure.

"When you went to speak to Mrs. Surratt, did you stagger?"

"That I do not recollect."

"Did you fall down?"

"Really, I can't remember."

"Had you been drinking all the day?"

"Not until after court in Marlboro. I knew what effect liquor has on me."

"What effect does it have?"

"It makes me forget a great many things."

"Were you very drunk that day?"

"Well, I was so drunk that when I laid down I felt sick."

"How long after Mrs. Surratt left did you lie down?"

"I lay down before she left."

"Did you take something after she left?"

"No doubt. I may have. I was drinking very freely."

"When you get drunk do you just lie down and get sober or do you keep up spreeing?"

"Sometimes I keep it up for several days," he said unhappily.

---

[1] At Mrs. Surratt's trial, Mrs. Offutt testified that Mrs. Surratt had given her the package and that Lloyd had not seen it until later. The prosecution was successful in preventing her testimony in this trial.

"Had you not got into the habit of taking a good deal of liquor?"

"Yes."

"Did you begin to drink again the next morning?"

"As soon as I got up."

"Do you remember what happened the night before?"

"I could not charge my mind with what had happened the night before, until the soldiers came. They told me what had been done."

His fat shoulders slumped over his sagging body; his lips quivered in his pasty, sick face.

Bradley motioned to Dick, who resumed the questioning while the older man dried his bald head with his handkerchief and relaxed in his chair beside Johnny.

"Didn't you testify before the Military Commission that one of the men asked you if you wanted news?" Dick demanded.

"Yes, and I told them they might use their own pleasure about telling me."

"And then one of them said, 'We have killed the president'?"

"Yes."

"They told you they had killed the president, and you didn't think much about it until the next morning when the soldiers told you?"

"I thought the man was drunk."

"Didn't you tell the detective Clarvoe that Herrold had been there?"

"I don't recollect."

"Why?"

"I had been drinking. I was frightened after the soldiers told me what had been done. I didn't know what to do."

"Try to remember what Clarvoe said to you."

"He said, as well as I recollect, there was money enough in the thing to make us both rich if I would give him the information I had."

Bradley jumped back to his feet. "Can you recall distinctly things that happen when you are drunk?"

"There are a great many things I could not pretend to remember when I am drunk. You could tell me something, and five minutes after it I would not remember it."

"The package that you say Mrs. Surratt handed you, where did you lay that package first?"

"I laid it on the sofa in the back parlor."

"Now, that package on the sofa in the back parlor, wasn't that the same package Mrs. Offutt handed you?"

"I don't know."

"Don't you remember that Mrs. Offutt handed it to you?"

"I don't recollect."

Bradley stepped back and eyed the shaken man. "We're finished with him," he said contemptuously. "So far as we're concerned, he may go."

Lloyd staggered from the stand, looking uncertainly around him, and at the courtroom door broke into a run. Down the street a saloon offered solace.

Behind him, Johnny sat motionless, contemplating the wreck of John Lloyd, tavernkeeper. His fingers beat a soundless tattoo on his chair arm until, conscious of newsmen's eyes, he stilled the motion.

The reporters wrote in their accounts that day "the prisoner grows thin and nervous. Formerly while the lawyers argued and the judge deliberated, he found time to talk with friends, sometimes to laugh. He doesn't even smile now. He sits with twitching lips, and he eyes the witnesses, scarcely turning once to look at the crowd and speaking to no one but his brother or his counsel."

John W. Garrett of Caroline County, Virginia, was called to the stand.

"State what you knew of John Wilkes Booth," ordered Carrington. "State when and where you first saw him."

"I saw him at my father's house, about two days, I think, before he was killed there."

"State Booth's physical condition."

"He was very lame. He said his leg was broken."

Ordered to describe Booth's capture, he went into easy description. "It was in a large tobacco barn about 150 yards from the house. It had spaces between the boards to air the tobacco.

We used to have a great deal of tobacco—before the war, that is—but in 1865 the barn had hay, fodder, and some farming implements in it." Carefully he avoided mention of the stored furniture and the beds that had rested weary, homeward-bound Southern soldiers.

"State what happened when the officers came to the house."

"The first I knew, three of them were talking to my father. Colonel Conger asked who I was. He said, 'You go in that barn and demand surrender of the men's arms or I'll burn it down.' I went in there. Booth picked up a pistol and said to get out at once or he'd shoot. I went back to Conger and said I'd risk my life no further."

The uneasy rustling caused by folded papers and palmleaf fans struggling against the stifling air quieted as the tension of that scene was recreated by the man who had lived it. Even the street noises receded. The torpid air hung heavy and still.

"The flames were growing higher . . . Booth looked around as if he tried to estimate how long before the fire reached him. He called: 'I will come out . . . I am but one and you are fifty . . . but give me a hundred paces and I will defend myself against you all.'

"I heard a rifle shot." John slumped in his chair, eyes closed. Release from tension sighed through the room as the witness told how Booth had been carried to the house porch to die. There, soldiers had turned his body from side to side while they stripped his pockets. The Yankee sergeant, rifle still warm in his hand, had muttered: "I allus prays for Rebels afore I shoots 'em." Relentlessly the details went on: how weeping Mrs. Garrett had held a cup of water to Wilkes's lips, how Lucinda Holloway had cut a lock of his hair, how Booth's hand had moved as he moaned "Useless," and then had crumpled on his stilled heart.

In the hot courtroom the day passed in anger and discomfort. Listeners snickered at the animosity of the defense, the fury of the prosecution. The prisoner sat with unseeing eyes, his lips drawn into a thin line.

Lt. Colonel Everton J. Conger took the stand. He had led the capture party, he said. He received from Pierrepont a small red-bound book and identified it as the diary he had taken from

Booth's pocket. As Pierrepont read aloud from a copy of its contents, Dick Merrick checked the wording of the little book. John listened to Wilkes's dying message about his Enterprise:

"Until today nothing was ever thought of sacrificing to our country's wrongs . . . for six months we had worked to capture, but our Cause being lost, something great and decisive must be done. I can never repent although we hated to kill . . . our country owed all her troubles to him. . . . Tonight I will attempt to escape . . . who can read his fate? God's will be done. I have too great a soul to die like a criminal . . . oh, may He, may He, spare me that and let me die bravely."

Even Pierrepont's dry voice could not rob that plea of its pathos.

22

Recall of witness John W. Pettit came as a surprise.

"Examine this whistle," said Carrington, "and see if you have ever seen it before."

"No. I never saw it before today, but it's a dog whistle."

"Did you ever hear it?"

"I don't know if I heard this one or not, but on the night of the assassination I heard a whistle."

"Did you hear anyone blow on it?" Chuckles swept the room and Carrington glared at the front rows. "Did it resemble the one you heard at the theater?" His voice boomed above the continuous mirth.

"Your Honor," Dick Merrick choked with deliberate laughter as he interrupted the witness. "Your Honor, is not this degenerating into a farce?"

The room rocked with the license thus given its amusement.

"I submit," roared Pierrepont, muttonchops acquiver, "I submit, sir, this is competent evidence."

The spectacle of the pompous Yankee political lawyer and their own self-important district attorney arguing about a dog whistle while old Joseph Bradley laughed at them, tickled the Washingtonians. Encouraged by the defense they laughed aloud, and the Prince George's neighbors echoed their amusement.

Judge Fisher rapped sharply.

"It is not our purpose to practice a farce or anything we deem improper," Carrington asserted. "The witness testified that he heard a whistle near the theater the night of the murder. This whistle was found in the possession of a person whom we charge to have been implicated in the conspiracy.[1] The witness can state to the court whether or not the sound which he heard on that occasion resembled the one which he heard from this whistle today."

"Suppose we found an Alpine horn," adroitly suggested Pierrepont, "the principle would be the same."

"Or a drum," offered Dick, drying tears of laughter from his eyes.

"Have you a very accurate musical ear?" asked Bradley, and again the room rocked with exaggerated glee.

"I have a taste for sweet sounds." The witness smiled too.

"I do not see," observed the court sourly, "that any reliance can be placed on testimony of this character."

"I hope Your Honor will not treat this case with the levity defense counsel seems disposed to."

"I have no disposition to treat this matter with levity at all," answered the court tartly. "We will dispose of the question by getting the witness to make a sound with this whistle and then state whether the sound he makes resembles the sound he heard the night of the assassination and took to be a signal whistle."

Gingerly the witness took the whistle and blew a short blast. Merriment nearly drowned out his reply. "It sounded like that."

"I don't see anything ridiculous," the court declared and rapped again.

The spectators quieted, but for that day the tension was broken and one by one people drifted away convinced the fun was over.

"Any more witnesses to go on the stand?" inquired the court.

---

[1] Actually, the whistle had been found in the Surratt household but in Lou Weichman's trunk.

"About a half dozen out there in the penitentiary," replied Bradley, nodding toward the witness room door. "They've been waiting out there all day."

"Not in the penitentiary now, but they will be." Dick Merrick, still pleased with the deflated whistle business, laughed quietly.

Following the noon recess, Lieutenant L. B. Baker, federal detective, confirmed the episodes of Booth's pursuit and capture. Heatedly he denied telling anyone that Booth, before he died, had said the assassination plan was his alone and that no one else had been involved in it.

During the next two hours two former officers contradicted each other heartily. Captains Harry W. Smith and Richard Morgan both had headed searching parties at the Surratt home. Each one claimed command. Smith testified that while he was there Lewis Payne had shown up and been arrested, and that the Surratt ladies had been taken into custody.

Mrs. Surratt had been extremely agitated, he swore. When Payne had appeared in muddy, shapeless clothing, the sleeve of an undershirt pulled over his head and a pickax on his shoulder, she had thrown up her hands and said, "Before God, I've never seen him before." But Morgan, next on the stand, swore Mrs. Surratt had said no such thing. Captain Smith hadn't done much questioning because he, Morgan, had been in charge and had personally questioned Mrs. Surratt. He had heard no such words from her; she had not seemed agitated. She had seemed composed and had talked in low, controlled tones.

He had found a trunk and had thrown into it everything he thought might be evidence. He remembered a bullet mold, a portfolio, and a whistle.

"Can you identify this?" Carrington held up the tin whistle with which Sonny Holohan had driven the Surratt household to occasional distraction.

"I think it's the whistle I picked up at Mrs. Surratt's house," he said, and the spectators laughed again.

Decorum returned when General Ulysses S. Grant took the stand and testified that in 1863 Jacob Thompson had entered Vicksburg on a flag-of-truce boat. The people listened respectfully. Then Pierrepont declared that Thompson's responsibility for inciting and financing the assassination through the prisoner, John H. Surratt, would be clearly shown.

Following him, James W. Pumphrey testified that on April 14 Booth had rented a horse from his stable at 244 C Street. Bay, she was about fourteen hands high, he said, and added mournfully, "I put an English saddle and snaffle-bit on her. I've never seen saddle, bridle, nor Booth since."

"Did you ever see Mr. Surratt at your stable?" asked Bradley in cross-examination, "at your old stand at Sixth and H Street?"

"He came very often with his father to that corner."

"How large was he then?"

"He was very small."

"When did you go to your present location?"

"In 1858. Mr. Surratt was a very small boy then."

"A very small boy in 1858?" asked the court, suddenly interested.

"Yes, sir," said Bradley. "He is only twenty-three now."

"I should have thought him much older," grunted the judge.

If the courtroom atmosphere was gloomy that day, it was equally unhappy in the small adjoining chamber where witnesses waited their turn to be grilled. Newspaper accounts of the trial were available to them and among the least cheerful of their readers was Lou Weichman.

The two years following Mrs. Surratt's execution had been full of tribulation for him. At first he had attempted to explain this situation to his former friends. He had been under great stress, he said; he had been questioned by the Secretary of War himself. It had been a terrible inquisition; he had been threatened with hanging. "I didn't want to hang," he had explained miserably.

Old friends from St. Matthews and the War Department had snubbed him as an informer. He had been hissed at on the street by strangers. He had been called to account by priests of his church.

Worst of all, he had been repudiated by Bishop John McGill. On May 22, 1865, immediately following his appearance on the stand at the Conspirators' Trial, the Bishop had written Father Doubrille, superintendent of St. Charles Seminary. Weichman's conduct, he had written, had not been consonant with that expected of a minister of God; he would regret having any seminary in his diocese admit this young man to further divinity study.[2]

Desperate at this rejection, rebuffed by his former friends, Lou had returned to his only supporters, the Radicals. In August following Mrs. Surratt's execution he had written out a statement more incriminating than anything he had sworn to during her trial. Radical influences had obtained for him an appointment in the Philadelphia Customs House, and he had hastened home. But the story of his perjuries had come out.

Few Washington people, whatever their political or religious persuasion, entertained much respect for Lou. Many said that responsibility for Mrs. Surratt's death lay less with the military commission than with John M. Lloyd and Lou, who had saved their own necks by false witness against her. Now Lou had returned to testify against his longtime friend John Surratt, the dead woman's son. If the spectators anticipated his appearance on the stand with enjoyment, Lou did not.

Lou had expected Honora Fitzpatrick to avoid him. He had expected no friendliness from John M. Lloyd, for he remembered Lloyd's attack on him in the carriage conveying them from the Arsenal Prison back to Old Capitol. Still, he had not expected the cold contempt even that sodden derelict showed him in the witness waiting room. There remained only Dr. McMillan who had informed for money; Lou had done so in fear for his life, but he sought the company of the physician to fend off loneliness.

23

By June 26 spectators crowded every corner of the dirty old courtroom, jamming aisles and clogging doorways. Even window ledges were full, for attendance had more than doubled since the trial's opening. This, of course, was because of the reporters.

[2] From photostat records in the author's possession.

The *Washington Chronicle* as a Radical mouthpiece slanted its news toward the politicos in power. Going as far as it dared, the *National Intelligencer* contradicted it at every opportunity. Caught between them, Washington finally came in force to see and hear for itself, obtaining passes through personal or political friends, from ticket sharpers, or simply by crowding in past the guards.

The summer air was suffocatingly close and the heat sharpened tempers already edged by days of legal battling.

"If it pleases Your Honor," Carrington opened the day. Yesterday's paper, he complained, contained a report of an incident that occurred before the afternoon recess in the previous session. He opened the sheet, begged the court's indulgence, and read: " 'The court asked if there were any more witnesses to be put on the stand. Mr. Bradley replied, 'There are a half dozen out there in the penitentiary and have been there all morning.' Said Mr. Merrick, 'No, not in the penitentiary now but they will be.' "

He had heard Mr. Bradley's remark, Carrington admitted sorrowfully, but he had considered it playful and not worth replying to. He had not heard Mr. Merrick's comment but he felt strongly that such remarks should not be tolerated during examination.

He hadn't heard the remark, the court said—if it had been made —and Dick Merrick jumped to his feet.

"Certainly I made the remark. I made it in the same playful way Mr. Bradley made his. However," here he bowed to the district attorney, "I will take it in serious aspect and hope in the course of human events to make the remark good."

"It is not proper for counsel to reflect on the character of witnesses by side bar remarks. Witnesses' characters will be open for discussion at the proper time and place."

The judge spoke not to Merrick but to Joseph Bradley, as if the two men stood alone in the room. Angry color ran into the lawyer's face. His keen old eyes narrowed unpleasantly and the day was off to a bad start.

Into this charged atmosphere walked witness Lou Weichman. John Surratt, perhaps remembering that April night when he had entrusted to this friend a final message to his mother, looked up as Lou entered briskly. Lou paused for the oath to be administered, and then, hand still raised, turned toward the witness stand. His gaze traveled the room and, as if pulled by a magnet, stopped where John sat, his deep-set eyes burning into his former friend. Hastily Lou turned away.

Some of the boyish impulsiveness that had endeared Lou to his friends had faded but he stood straight and slim, his wide shoulders displaying the handiwork of his father's shop. His burnished chestnut hair lay in the same soft curves above his forehead, but his tiny mustache hovered over lips no longer smiling and youthful. Slanting lines etched their corners, emphasizing the faint unhappiness of his expression.

Face to face with acquaintances of other days, conscious of their curiosity if nothing more, he moved uneasily. Helplessly his eyes were drawn again to the defense table, where once more Johnny's look impaled him.

"State your full name." Pierrepont spoke sharply.

Nervously Lou ran his tongue across his lips. "My name is Louis J. Weichman. Before the trial of the assassins I spelled my name W-e-i-c-h-m-a-n. I distinctly gave it that way to the reporters but they spelled it W-e-i-c-h-m-a-n-n so I have spelled it that way since."

"It's not the slightest consequence how you spell your name. If you know the prisoner, state when you first saw him."

"I first met John H. Surratt at St. Mary's College in Howard County, Maryland, in September 1859." As he went on relating background facts already familiar to half the people in the room, his air of apprehensiveness subsided. He had visited the Surratts two, perhaps three times at Surrattsville. In November 1864 he had moved into the family's home in Washington.

He recalled meeting Dr. Samuel A. Mudd at the New National Hotel where Wilkes Booth had a room. He had seen Booth at the Surratt home; he had met Atzerodt there and found him a very witty fellow indeed. Very funny. Yes, he had seen Payne in the Surratt house that same month; once he had taken supper upstairs on a tray to the man.

Mrs. Surratt had not seemed to know Payne; Payne had called himself "Wood" on that visit. Once, in March, he had seen Herrold come to the door with Atzerodt. They had been on horseback, but they left at once. Certainly he had gone to the theater with Booth and Surratt. Once he had received a wire from Booth at his office. Mrs. Holohan brought it over. It had asked him to telegraph Booth the address John used in New York. Later he had asked John Surratt why Booth wanted it and John had said, "Don't be so damned inquisitive."

John sat at the defense table, his eyes never leaving Lou's face. With equal determination, Lou kept his face turned away.

"Now," said Pierrepont, "I come to the morning of the assassination. What happened that day?"

"I went to my office. About ten-thirty an order came from the Secretary of War that clerks might have leave to attend Good Friday services. I went to St. Mathews and then home to Mrs. Surratt's. About two-thirty she rapped on my door and said she had a letter from Mr. Calvert about her property and asked me to drive her to the country. She gave me a ten-dollar bill to go out and get her a carriage. I went out. Booth went in. We shook hands, and he went into the parlor.

"I got a buggy," he said and went on easily. "Mrs. Surratt came downstairs and was just getting into the buggy when she said, 'I forgot those things of Booth's.' She went back into the house and came out again with a brown paper package, about five or six inches long, tied with a string. She said it was glass and brittle.

"About three miles from Washington, on the way to Surrattsville, pickets were lolling along the road. Mrs. Surratt halted and asked how long they would remain. They said they would be withdrawn about 8 P.M. She said she was glad of it, and we drove on."

The continuous swish of fans, the discomfort of perspiring flesh filled the room. Pierrepont flicked his face with his handkerchief. The relief with which the court called the evening recess was felt by everyone present.

Next morning Pierrepont continued his questions.

"Proceed from your point of progress yesterday."

Lou began with animation. "Well, Mrs. Surratt's manner all the way down to the country was lively and cheerful. We arrived about four-thirty, I think. I gave her the package and she went into the house. A few minutes later she asked me to write a letter to Mr. Nothey."

"What was in the letter?"

"It said, as I remember, that unless he came forward and paid her the money he owed her, she would enter suit against him. I computed the interest on it, $479 for thirteen years, sealed and addressed the letter."

"Were you there when Mr. Lloyd returned?"

"Mr. Lloyd came in about six-thirty, just as Mrs. Surratt got into the buggy to return to town. He said the front spring was broken and she told him to get something to fix it with."

"When did you start home?"

"About six-thirty. Mrs. Surratt wanted to get back by nine o'clock. I said something about Booth being in the city and not acting, and she said, 'Booth is done acting.' She asked if I didn't know he was crazy on one subject, and I said I didn't."

"Did she state the subject?"

"No, she didn't."

"When you reached home what happened?"

"I returned the buggy and went down to supper. Mrs. Surratt showed me a letter she had just had from her son. While I was eating supper with Mrs. Surratt, Miss Anna Surratt, Honora Fitzpatrick, and Miss Olivia Jenkins, someone came to the door. It sounded like a man in boots, but he did not stay but a moment. After supper Mrs. Surratt's manner seemed restless. She walked up and down with prayer beads in her hands. Once she asked me to pray for her intentions, and I answered that I never prayed for intentions unless I knew what the intentions were. We were laughing and jesting a great deal, and she said, 'You are making too much noise; it's time for you to be off to bed,' and in a playful manner she chased all of us out of the parlor."

"Did anything pertaining to your health occur that night, requiring you to get up?"

"Early morning I had been out to the yard and had just gotten back to sleep when the bell rang violently. I put on my pants over my nightshirt and went to answer the bell. It was the police to search the house."

At this point Lou embarked on a new version of that evening, sharply different from his testimony at the military trial. Anna had gone into hysterics when told of the crime, he now said, and had cried out to her mother, "All this will bring suspicion on our house! Just think of that man being here within an hour of the murder." Her mother had comforted her and had declared "Say what you will, I think Booth was only an instrument in the hands of the Almighty to punish a proud and licentious people."

"Did you see John that night?"

"No, not that night. The next morning I said to Mrs. Surratt and Mr. Holohan that I had my suspicions and that I was going to the government and name all I had seen in Booth's company—to bring the parties to justice."

"I went to Superintendent Richardson's headquarters. We went, Mr. Holohan with me, down to the end of Maryland that day."

"And then?"

"We went to Baltimore next day, looking for Atzerodt, returned Monday April 17, and that afternoon we started to Canada in pursuit of John H. Surratt.

"Who went?"

"Mr. Bigley, Holohan, and myself, Clarvoe, Mr. Neece, or Reece." Briefly he outlined the hours of arrival in Burlington, Vermont; in Montreal, and back to Washington on April 29.

Noon recess intervened. The spectators returned eager to hear Lou taken apart by old Mr. Bradley. They always loved to watch Bradley's cross-examinations.

The lawyer walked deliberately over to the witness stand, his keen blue eyes on Lou's uneasy face and began his questions. Lou had been educated at St. Charles Seminary? He had taught at Pikesville? He had met Benjamin Ste. Marie there? He had taught at St. Mathews Institute? Had he left there of his own motion?[1]

"Yes," Lou replied, "I was paid thirty-five dollars a month, and as I always look out for self-interest I accepted one for eighty-five."

Then he had left voluntarily?

Yes. His pupils had been compelled to sweep the floor and he had remonstrated. Here, he assured Mr. Bradley in reply to the question, he had considered himself the principal teacher because

[1] Several small falsehoods mark this section of testimony. Records show difficulties with St. Mathew's personnel in 1863.

he had taught upstairs and Mr. Murphy had taught downstairs, and had the little boys with the bare feet.

"Where did you live at that time?"

"At twenty-two Pennsylvania Avenue, at a house kept by a colored man. A Mr. Purnell."

"How long did you stay there?"

"Until I went to Mrs. Surratt's."

"At St. Charles were you studying for the priesthood?"

"I was."

"While you lived at Mrs. Surratt's you had an opportunity to observe her life and conduct?"

"Well—yes."

"Now state whether or not it was exemplary as a Christian woman's."

"Object!" called Pierrepont.

"Sustained," ruled the judge.

"All right, then, state what her deportment was toward you."

"It was kindly."

Had he not the freedom of a son, asked Bradley. When he was sick had he not been nursed? Had he not seen many respectable persons visiting her house?

Well, Father Wiget, Mr. Jenkins of Prince George's, Mrs. Kirby, Mrs. Dean, two Sisters of Charity. Slowly he named them.

The afternoon wore on and contending over every word, Bradley and Lou continued their duel.

Utter panic swept Lou when Bradley, with ominous quiet, asked if during the Conspirators' Trials, while he was under arrest and confined to the Old Capitol, he had ridden back and forth with John M. Lloyd to the Arsenal where Mrs. Surratt was being tried for her life?

Lou ran his tongue over dry lips and admitted he had. Did he remember Lloyd's charging him with trying to incriminate him?

Lou did not remember, he said. But many listeners recalled how Lloyd had attacked Lou for his testimony about a whispered conversation between Lloyd and Mrs. Surratt, and that Captain William P. Wood had separated them.

Back Bradley went to dates. Did Lou remember when his friend, John Surratt, had first gone to New York? Did he remember that John had said he went to bring a lady back with him? Did he remember that on John's return the lady had been with him?

None of this could Lou recall, and Bradley smiled significantly.

"Where was it that he told you he had seen Booth and that Booth had an elegant house?"

"In his own home."

"When?"

"I don't know the day, the hour, and minute of everything!"

"You have testified with such particularity to so many dates that I want to see how much you remember of others. Now, when he told you about Booth's house, did he tell you he brought a lady back with him?"

"I don't remember."

"Do you remember his bringing a lady?"

"I remember that."

"How long did she stay?"

"I don't remember."

"Now," said Bradley stepping a little closer to the witness as the tension in the courtroom mounted, "I want to know if in the communication with the government at the time of the military trials you were told by any official that if you did not testify to more than you first stated, they would hang you too?"

"No, sir. I will say that before the trial in 1865 I detailed my evidence to Mr. Stanton, and Mr. Pittman took it down in shorthand."

"That was an improper question," interrupted Pierrepont, "and I hope no more such will be asked."

"They may inquire of a witness," ruled the court, "whether or not he made some officer of the government a statement different from the one he made here. I do not apprehend they may go into every conversation he has had with anybody during his lifetime."

"I don't remember that—" Lou answered in reply to Bradley's rephrased question: "I wasn't afraid," then spoke out boldly, "I had no fear of hanging."

Had he not made a written statement, corrected it from the Conspirators' Trial testimony, and given it to the Grand Jury for this case? Adroitly Lou avoided a direct answer. On and on went

194

the questions. Again and again the witness sidestepped or answered smartly.

Finally Bradley snapped at him. "Will you be good enough to answer my questions and not show your spirit to Surratt as you are constantly doing?"

"I am not aware he had been showing—" began Carrington, but Bradley cut him off.

"Well, he has, and this is the fourth time this morning."

The judge's voice was heavy with weariness. "Answer the questions put to you and stop there."

"I observe the court is extremely unwell," offered Carrington. "I suggest we recess until Monday."

"I see His Honor is unable to proceed," agreed Bradley. "I agree to recess."

Feebly Judge Fisher adjourned the session and sought his chamber.

24

On Monday, July 1, War Department officials asked Albert G. Riddle whether or not he regarded the case against Surratt as watertight.

"It is conceivable that witnesses coud be mistaken," he wrote in reply. But he nevertheless believed the government had a good case "even supposing that two or three witnesses are mistaken and three have committed perjury."

Meanwhile Bradley went on with Lou.

"Did this man Howell you say John Surratt introduced you to, did he teach you a cipher used by the Signal Corps of the South?"

"No, sir. He taught me a cipher but I was not aware it was used by the South." [1]

[1] An ivory cylinder, the key for decoding the Confederate cipher had been found in Lou's room by Washington police.

"Did you use it?"

"I coded some poetry with it."

"Yes. Well, did you know a gentleman in this city by the name of Rocoffort, and did you ever tell him you were employed to furnish information for the South?"

"I never had any conversation with him except at his feet in the tribunal of penance."

"You mean, that is, in confession? Your memory is distinct?"

"Yes."

"Now, I think you stated you were not under arrest the morning after the assassination?"

During the long wrangle that followed Bradley read from Lou's testimony at the Conspirators' Trial that he had been arrested on Saturday morning, April 15, and so he could not go back to the Surratt house; also, that when he went to get some clothing a detective was with him, and he was held under arrest until the trial. Further, he had gone to Canada to help find John Surratt, and on his return he had been ordered to report to Mr. Stanton.[2]

"Now I ask you," said Bradley, "whether at any time you said that in this interview you told the Secretary of War where John Surratt was on the night of the assassination?"

"I didn't know where he was."

"I asked if you had told anyone you had informed the secretary where John was."

"No, sir."

"I ask you now if you did not tell Mr. Ford that you so told him."

"I told Mr. Ford I had an interview with Mr. Stanton. I believe I did tell him what happened at the interview."

"Did you not tell Mr. Ford that John Surratt left here a considerable time before the assassination and that from a letter you had seen he must have been in Canada at the time?"

[2] No official record has been found of this interview. It seems possible this record made by Ben Pittman may have been among the papers which William P. Wood said Stanton had given him for safekeeping, and in the event of Stanton's death were to be destroyed. Also missing are the reports of the operation of the Arsenal Prison in which the conspirators were held and hooded. According to the report of the adjutant of the prison, he personally delivered these reports to Stanton's office and received a receipt for them.

"I may have said that, but I did not say that I knew where he was when the blow was struck."

"Didn't you also tell Mr. Ford about the cipher that had been given you and explain how it was?"

"I don't remember."

"I ask if you did not tell Mr. Gifford and Mr. Maddox that you were told by Mr. Bingham[3] that if you did not state more fully than you had done that you would be tried as one of the conspirators?"

"I don't remember anything of the kind."

"I want to know whether or not you have said since you were a witness that your character was at stake and you intended to do all you could to aid the prosecution?"

"I may have."

"Now, I ask you if you told Mr. Rocoffort that the Philadelphia appointment was given you to fulfill a promise of government office in return for your testimony?"

Quickly Pierrepont objected to the question, and as the court quickly sustained him, Bradley favored the room with a knowing smile.

"Now, about breakfast the morning after the assassination," he resumed. "You said then that you intended to go out and tell all you knew?"

"I said I intended to tell all I knew. I didn't know about the murder. Mrs. Holohan and Mrs. Surratt heard me say it."

"Mr. and Mrs. Holohan, Olivia Jenkins, and a little girl named Dean were all there?"

"I don't know about Dean. Anna Surratt was there, and I know very well what remark was made."

"Bolt it out."

"That the death of Abraham Lincoln was no worse than the death of any Negro in the army."

"Did you tell that at the Conspirators' Trial?"

"No. Mrs. Surratt didn't say it. Anna Surratt said it."

"And you never told it before? Why not?"

"I had too much sympathy for the poor girl."

"Then why tell it now?"

[3] Henry Bingham, assistant judge advocate.

"Because you bring it out." A thin film of perspiration showed on Lou's forehead.

"I brought out your voluntary statement?"

"I tell it because I have been hunted down and persecuted by these people." His voice fell on a soundless room.

"Isn't it your impression that if John Surratt is acquitted you will be hunted down a little harder?"

"I'm not afraid of being hunted." He spoke a little too loudly.

"All right. Now let's ask if you know Mr. Louis Carland? Mr. John Brophy?"

"I know them."

"Do you remember telling them that if Captain Gleason had not reported you, you would never have said a word about this affair?"

"I don't remember."

"Have you seen an affidavit made by Mr. Brophy before Mr. Callan?"

"I saw it two years ago."

At this point the court ordered a recess.

"Now," said Bradley after the session convened, "do you know George T. Jarboe?"

"I met Jarboe in the Old Capitol."

"I think you stated here that on the morning after the assassination you went to Major Richardson's office and made a disclosure of all you knew?"

"I didn't know anything about the assassination."

"While you were confined in the Old Capitol did you tell Mr. Jarboe that the next morning you were arrested and carried before Mr. Stanton?"

"That's news to me. I never said anything of the kind."

"Were you carried before Mr. Stanton?"

"I wasn't *carried*. I met Mr. Burnett on the street. He invited me to go to Mr. Stanton's office. That was the first and only time I ever had an interview with Mr. Stanton."

"Who is Mr. Burnett?" called out a juror from the box.

"He was the assistant judge advocate general at the Conspirators' Trial. He conducted examinations," replied Pierrepont.

Bradley resumed. "While you were employed in the office of the commissary general of prisons, did you ever furnish information to anyone outside the office on movements of prisoners?"

"Well, I said something one evening to Howell when he was reading the *Evening Star* about the number of prisoners."

"When you were talking with Howell, didn't you say your sympathies were all with the South?"

"Oh, I have talked *Secesh* very often in my life. Just for buncombe. Specially with such men as Howell."

"And you have associated with such men as Atzerodt, Booth, Payne, John Surratt? I think you said you hardly knew Payne?"

"I never had much to say to Mr. Payne. Anybody, before the assassination, would have been glad to associate with Mr. Booth."

"Why?"

"Because he was in such respectable society, he was such an elegant, polished gentleman."

"What do you mean by respectable society?"

"Well, members of Congress—" Faint laughter swept the room.

Noon recess came; Lou and Dr. McMillan sauntered through the grounds. They stopped at the pump for a drink, ate their sandwiches together.

"Before recess," said Mr. Bradley as they began the afternoon session, "I mentioned a conversation you had with Mr. Carland. Do you remember stating to him that you were troubled about the testimony you had given at the Conspirators' Trial, and that you were going to confession to relieve your conscience?"

"I don't remember."

"Mr. Bradley walked slowly toward Lou and looked him severely in the eye. "Do you remember his saying that the way to do it was to go to a magistrate and make an affidavit? And your replying that you would do that except that you would be indicted for perjury?"

"I don't remember."

"Do you remember telling him that your testimony was written out for you? That you were told what you must swear to?"

"Oh, pshaw, now."

"Do you remember telling him that you had to swear to that statement or be charged as one of the conspirators?"

"I don't remember anything of the kind." Lou's breath came

short. "These questions look so silly I almost hate to answer. I—I never heard of such things before." He moved uneasily in his chair, and brushed his handkerchief across his mouth.

"We'll see about that. Do you remember a man in your room at Carroll Prison? To whom you said these things and he wrote them down?"

"I positively swear—" Lou's voice was close to cracking, "I said nothing of the sort. I would put my word against the whole world in such a matter," but he trembled slightly in his chair.

"Did you not state to him that you would have given very different answers had they not been written down for you?"

"No. No, sir."

"Did you tell him you could have given an explanation of Mrs. Surratt's visit to Surrattsville that day which would have been greatly in her favor, if you had been allowed to give it?"

"No, sir. I didn't."

"Then, as I understand you, you don't remember any time at all in which you spoke to Mr. Carland about the testimony at the military trial?"

"I spoke of the testimony because it was uppermost in my mind."

"Do you, then, remember reciting portions of *Hamlet* to Mr. Carland, in regard to suicide or self-destruction?"

" 'To be or not to be,' do you mean?"

"I don't care exactly what the words were, I asked if you conversed with him on self-destruction?"

"I might have," defiantly, "*I* don't care whether I have or not."

"Do you remember taking a pistol and talking of self-destruction?"

"I don't remember."

"And you say positively that when you discussed your testimony with Mr. Carland you did not recite passages from *Hamlet* on self-destruction?"

"I said I don't remember. I have recited that passage some hundred times. I might have taken a pistol and looked down its barrel—"

Bradley waved his hand in contemptuous dismissal of the shaking young man.

Pierrepont moved toward his chief witness, and his voice

boomed. "State what there is about this confession[4] you've been asked about."

Lou's tormented eyes, round and large, turned pitifully to the counsel. "I never spoke to Mr. Carland about a confession."

Listeners exchanged glances and whispered words, then leaned back in their seats, but John sat rigid. Around him the crowd fanned with their folded papers and palm leaves, but he moved not a muscle. Defense lawyers rested. The court sought the tumbler of water on his desk. Lou stumbled back to the witness room and was succeeded by Dr. McMillan.

The doctor was a small, dapper man, impressively clothed in dark broadcloth and braided waistcoat. He advanced to the stand with conscious dignity and with an elegant gesture raised a white and womanish hand to take the oath. As he did so he pulled his chin up from the tight collar around his small, birdlike throat. He bowed to the bench and then mounted the stand, alert but withdrawn from what he obviously considered his sordid surroundings.

Pierrepont opened his questioning in a respectful manner.

"Please give us your professional connections in 1865."

Quickly McMillan complied. He established the trip that had

---

[4] The Rt. Reverend Msgr. Thomas M. Conroy, Ft. Wayne, Indiana, in an affidavit prepared for me, stated that as a young priest he followed Lou Weichman's brother, the Reverend John Weichman, into Anderson, Indiana, at a time when the presence of Lou in his brother's home caused some dissatisfaction in the parish.

During his life following the execution of Mrs. Surratt, Lou never again lived as a Catholic and at his death his brother heard his confession and then asked another priest to pronounce absolution. According to Catholic clergy with whom I have consulted, this was an irregular procedure and, in their opinion, would not be considered valid in the eyes of the church.

This contradicts the story related by Lloyd Lewis in his *Myths After Lincoln*, that as he lay dying Lou wrote a note for his two sisters that what he had said at the Conspirators Trial was true.

Unfortunately this note has never been seen by anyone but the grieving sisters, and may have gone the way of other documents. Among Lou's missing papers are chapters of a manuscript he was preparing for publication, in which he laid the blame for Lincoln's assassination at the door of the Catholic Church and its Jesuit Order. Proof of its existence is given by a young man who copied some of its pages for Lou and by letters of Major Loring Porter, the surgeon in charge at Arsenal Prison, with whom he consulted.

left Quebec on September 16 and ended in Liverpool on the ninth day. The prisoner, he said, had crossed with him.

His narrative continued easily. Before sailing, a priest, Father LaPierre, had notified him that a particular person would be on this trip. He had met the priest at Montreal aboard the small mail-boat; with him was a passenger who registered as Mr. McCarthy. Father LaPierre asked that the passenger be allowed to remain in the doctor's stateroom until after the ship had sailed. He had seen the prisoner, whom he recognized as the passenger called Mc-Carthy, talking with the Rebel general, R. S. Ripley of South Carolina, and William Cornell Jewett; also with a colored man who said he had been Jefferson Davis' servant. Beverly Tucker had gone from Montreal up to Quebec with the passenger, but he had not sailed for Europe. The ocean-going ship they boarded had been the *Peruvian*.

"If you had conversation with the prisoner, state what he said to you."

Without waiting for questions, McMillan offered his narra-tive account of the trip. He had talked often with the prisoner, and Surratt had talked freely to him. He had said that he carried dispatches between Richmond, Washington, and Montreal. On one occasion, the prisoner had related, he had met a woman in New York with whom he started for Richmond, along with sev-eral other persons. South of Fredericksburg they had been riding a platform car drawn or pushed by Negroes[5] when they saw five or six escaped Union soldiers coming toward them. "Let's shoot the damned Yankee soldiers," the woman had said. They had shot the soldiers and then gone right on, paying no more attention to them.

"Did he say what the woman's name was?"

It had sounded like "Mrs. Slater," but he could not be positive. However, that name had been very conspicuous in Montreal dur-ing the trial of the St. Albans raiders, as one of those who had gone up from Richmond to help the raiders.

---

[5] The Richmond, Fredericksburg and Potomac Railway, the only one operating in this area in 1865, has written me that it has no information on any equipment answering that description in use at that time.

The prisoner had said that he had received money from Secretary of State Benjamin in Richmond, in amounts up to $30,000 and $70,000 and that he had been in Richmond a few days before its fall.

"I remember his saying, too, that one day as several of them crossed the Potomac they were hailed by a gunboat and ordered to surrender or they would be fired upon. They said they would surrender, and the gunboat sent out a little boat. They waited until the little boat came 'longside, and then fired right into them and escaped to shore."

"They fired into the gunboat, or the gunboat fired into them?" inquired Dick Merrick.

Nearby, someone snickered softly and the judge looked up.

"I will tell the counsel," shouted the doctor, "and I will repeat it, and if he is not deaf he can hear, THEY FIRED INTO THE GUNBOAT!" He whirled furiously on Dick Merrick. "You have insulted witnesses on this stand! That's the act of a sneak, a coward—" His voice trailed off in screeches.

Catapulted to his feet by the sudden outburst, Bradley's eyes seared the witness. The judge, who had been turning over papers on his desk, looked up in momentary consternation, then noisily gaveled for quiet. Johnny, warily motionless, watched Isaac's black head and great bulk loom up beside him and then subside into his seat again.

Carrington's pontifical voice broke into the furor. "Quiet, gentlemen," but Pierrepont's loud protest drowned out his words. Mild little Nathaniel Wilson stood dumbly, half risen from his chair, staring at the turbulence inside the bar space. The court rapped down the agitation swelling through the room.

"Such language is not becoming." His words were directed to the witness but his look turned on Bradley. "Neither is it becoming for counsel to worry a witness into bad temper."

"The counsel said the other day," rose the doctor's indignant voice, "that all the witnesses in the waiting room ought to go to the penitentiary or something to that effect. I'll have him know that I'm just as good as he is!"

Carrington spoke to the witness who quieted his voice, although he continued to glare at the defense table. He shrugged his shoulders and dried his sweating hands on a kerchief pulled hastily from his long coattail pocket.

"Proceed," wearily directed the court, and sipped his glass of tepid water.

"On his last Sunday aboard," went on McMillan, "Surratt pointed to the coast of Ireland and said, 'There is a foreign land. I hope to be able to come home again in about two years. I hope to God,' holding a pistol in his hand, 'that I shall live to serve Andy Johnson the way Lincoln was served.' In talking of England he said he'd rather be hanged by an Englishman than a Yankee. He said he knew if he went home now he would swing."

Pierrepont released the witness and the session recessed in confusion.

On Thursday, July 2, no breath of air stirred in the streets nor in the courtroom where yesterday's fetid atmosphere was rebreathed by the curious listeners who crowded in.

"Oyez! Oyez!" shouted the crier, and the court opened. Judge Fisher slumped weakly in his chair but before the prosecution could begin proceedings, Mr. Bradley addressed the court.

"If Your Honor please, before we proceed with this trial I beg leave to call the attention of the court to an incident of yesterday. Your Honor was very much occupied at the time and I desire the record to be read."

With a quick motion, Court Reporter Sutton flipped back the pages of his notebook and read McMillan's words, ending with the charge that Dick Merrick was a sneak and a coward.

Deliberately the court replied, again addressing his cool words directly to Bradley as if the room were empty of all other persons. "I did not hear what was said at the time. I was busy preparing passes for a friend, but I was under the impression that the witness had been provoked to it by something said by the counsel. However, I cannot perceive in anything that has been read any justification for the remarks of the witness." Turning to the doctor, "You must not, hereafter, make use of any expressions to counsel that are at all insulting no matter how much you may feel yourself aggrieved. In this connection it may not be improper to observe that never in my judicial experience have I seen a case where there had been so much feeling of bitterness expressed. I confess I see no reason why it should be so. I will say further that never have I seen witnesses cross-examined with such asperity. I suggest we all endeavor to hold our tempers while conducting this case."

His gaze came back to the defense table where Bradley met it head on.

"I will call your attention to the early part of April," resumed Pierrepont's examination. "I will ask what the prisoner said about dispatches."

Surratt had informed him, the witness said, that he had delivered a letter from Richmond to Montreal early in the week of the assassination. While in Montreal, he had received word from Booth that their plans must be changed and he should return to Washington.

"Did he mention his escape?"

"He said he arrived in St. Albans a few mornings after the assassination. At breakfast he had seen his own name in the paper, and it unnerved him so he dropped the paper and that was the last of breakfast for that day."

"Did he tell you about a handkerchief?"

"He said he heard some parties saying he must be in St. Albans because a handkerchief with his name on it had been found. He clapped his hand to his pocket and found he really had lost his handkerchief. He thought it was time then to make himself scarce."

"What was his conduct with relation to being quiet?"

"His general conduct on board ship was gentle, but he would show signs of nervousness if anyone came up unexpectedly behind him."

Soft little chuckles came from the back of the room and the court pounded again.

The prisoner had landed in Ireland, but the witness had met him later in Liverpool and helped him to locate an address to which he had been directed. The prisoner told him of the plan to abduct the president but said it had been abandoned.

The room rustled as Dick Merrick rose for cross-examination. A deliberate manner became Dick and today he made the most of it.

"Can you state at what time they found they could not carry out the abduction plan?"

"I cannot."

"Did the prisoner at any time mention being in Washington or associated with the assassination?"

"He did not."

Easily Dick brought the witness to admit that he had been in Washington for six months and that his expenses were being paid by the State Department. Certainly he had expected the reward for Surratt's arrest even after he had been told it had been re-called. Then pressure began to build and increased ever so gently until McMillan trembled under Dick's unmoving gaze, and sweat broke out on his face.

"Have you ever stated to anyone that Surratt told you the whole abduction plan was Booth's?"

"I never did."

"Have you ever stated to anyone that John Surratt told you he was in Elmira at the time of the murder? That he learned of it the next morning?"

"I never did."

"Have you ever told anything different from what you have told on this stand?"

"Nothing contrary to it."

"At the time Surratt called on you in Liverpool, had you already made an affidavit to the consul?"

"I had."

"Did you keep him in ignorance of what you had done, planning to have him arrested and collect the reward?"

McMillan hesitated a moment before his answer. "I did." He was then released from the stand.

In this day's afternoon session spectator interest picked up. Now listeners would hear from a former local teacher, former Union soldier, former friend of the prisoner.

Henry B. Ste. Marie's examination proved short. Pierrepont drew from him that he had been a soldier in the Papal Guard, 8 Company, Zouaves. He first had seen John Surratt in Zouave uniform about April 15, 1866. Later the prisoner had told him about his experiences; that he had had a hard time making his escape;

that he had left Washington either the night of or the morning after the assassination. The witness was not quite sure which. Later he had seen Surratt at Malta after his arrest and then again on board the *Swatara*.

At the close of this brief testimony Joseph Bradley, without even looking up from the defense table, waved Ste. Marie away, and the deflated witness faded from sight.

Defense counsel anticipated the July 4 holiday with little pleasure for on that day they must work harder than before. They must digest new testimony, run down desperately needed witnesses, prepare the presentation of their own facts in such a way as to break through to the court and gain them equal consideration with the prosecution.

Any optimism they might have shown at the trial's opening had long since disappeared from view. The questionable character of prosecution witnesses and their improbable testimony were not the chief dangers. Unsound or manufactured testimony Bradley and his staff could meet. The real peril lay in the ill and surly judge who, impatient of delay, querulously supported the prosecution and overruled the defense on virtually every question.

Continuous sarcasm and insult were not customary in Washington courtrooms, nor were laughing nor hissing by spectators. Neither were court personnel accustomed to the ever darkening complexion of the public. The packed doorways were dotted with Negroes, free Negroes of respected standing in the city, and strange Free-Issues, husky young men whose bearing suggested recent military drill and who pushed their way insolently through the crowds. Pistols protruding from hip pockets seemed to say that no one dared silence the people for whom Abraham Lincoln had been murdered.

As the ailing judge grew more choleric, Joseph Bradley made less effort to conceal his impatience with thrill-seeking crowds, with the prosecution methods and manufactured testimony. But what really infuriated him was that he would lose this case because of his personal politics. Old Line Whig he had been, Democrat he had become, and although he had supported the Union during the war, the Lincoln administration never had won his love. Edwin M. Stanton, the Radicals, and all their works he violently hated and said so openly. He knew, as all Washington now knew, that these Radicals had used perjured testimony not so much to obtain the death of an innocent woman as to ensure their political control. He knew John S. Brophy and Louis Carland. He knew all about Lou Weichman's false testimony in court and his retractions in private. Captain William P. Wood's story had been the last straw.

Infuriated by the prosecution's bland denial of War Department control, he showed malicious delight in leading unsuspecting prosecution witnesses to admit they had been examined in Judge Advocate General Holt's office. Worse yet, the prosecution knew him well enough to be sure that he would appeal an adverse verdict—and he would fight them to the last drop of his legal blood. For all these things he would be held accountable. For this, his client's life might be forfeit.

On Wednesday the defense recalled Dr. McMillan for further questioning.

"Did you ever cross the Atlantic with Stephen F. Cameron?"

At Dick Merrick's question, the witness bristled. "I did."

"Did you ever state to him that John Surratt told you he was in Elmira at the time of the assassination and went from there to some town in New York with an Indian name that he could not remember?"

"I did not."

"Did you ever say to Cameron that John Surratt learned of the assassination in Elmira, and he immediately turned his face toward Canada?"

"I did not," but the witness began to look uneasy.

"Did you ever say to him that Surratt could not have been guilty of the assassination; therefore you regarded him as a political offender only; the victim of compromising circumstances, and so felt no scruples about extending him aid?"

"I did not."

"Did you ever state to Cameron or anyone else that Surratt said the first knowledge he had of his mother's peril was of her execution?"

"I don't think anything of the kind was said. I think something was said about her, but I could not say what it was."

"Don't you recall telling Cameron that Surratt told you he knew nothing of his mother's danger until the time of her execution?" Merrick's voice held incredulity.

"I don't think I did."

Merrick looked at him piercingly for a moment, and then excused him from further questioning.

At the defense table, Joseph Bradley was watching the prosecution counsel with some concern. If the prosecution ended its testimony the next day, as he had heard intimated, then something had gone wrong with the Honorable Mr. James H. Ashley's arrangements.

So far, there was no evidence connecting the prisoner with Booth's plan. Nor had he been linked with President Johnson as Washington gossip had predicted. Waves of gossip, rippling in overlapping circles, washed up rumors to the very door of the courtroom. Attorneys, witnesses, spectators, all had heard the talk. How, then, could the judge fail to know, and to wonder what had happened to the anticipated testimony?

Gnawed by anxiety, Joseph Bradley worriedly asked himself what Conover-inspired testimony might be sprung on them at the last moment. His apprehension and distrust intensified. He could not believe in the objectivity of the presiding judge.

From jail Conover watched and waited, too. His release had seemed so sure once the influential gentlemen whose interests were so compatible with his own joined forces with him. Mr. Ashley had written out for him the type of evidence needed by the Judiciary Committee and Conover had the letter in his possession. He had agreed to all it called for; he would provide plausible witnesses as soon as his pardon was delivered. But the Judiciary Committee as a whole was less cooperative than its individual member, Mr. Ashley. It refused to act before it had received evidence and had time to check on it.

No pardon, no evidence, said Conover. No evidence, no recommendation for pardon, said the Committee.

Once more the Reverend Mr. Matchett carried a *sub rosa* message to Judge Advocate Holt asking a speedy pardon for Conover. Holt hesitated. Washington opinion could no longer be depended on to follow where Stanton led. And Conover was a perjurer

MICHAEL O'LAUGHLIN

Boyhood friend of Booth, he joined the plot-to-capture group. Here he wears his dahlia colored jacket with green and dahlia striped vest and pants. He died during the yellow fever epidemic at Dry Tortugas.

ABOVE: As General Wallace saw him.

ARSENAL PRISON

The accused enter Arsenal Prison, midnight April 27, 1865. From a
sketch made by a Federal officer at the time. The original is in the
library of the Army War College, Ft. McNair, Washington. The
Washington Penitentiary had been used as an arsenal during the war
but when wholesale arrests after the assassination overtaxed the city's
wartime prisons, the arsenal became a prison for the so-called conspirators only.

whose testimony had helped to hang a Washington woman. The situation was delicate.

Quibbling over evidence promised but not delivered, sparring over a pardon promised but not obtained, got no one anywhere. Trotting back and forth between Conover and his betters, Matchett came up with his own little plan. There was Mr. Ashley's letter of instruction, he reminded his fellow-workers. Suppose, just suppose, that Conover didn't get his pardon and showed that letter and other Ashley-Conover-Matchett correspondence to Andrew Johnson?

All this, of course, Joseph Bradley could not know. Nor could he know that while he worried over testimony the prosecution might produce, the prosecution worried about witnesses it could not produce. And the prosecution had good cause to worry. Without further evidence the case against Surratt was not strong. Even Riddle admitted that.

Then sudden help appeared. From time to time various newspaper readers had come forward with pieces of information of one kind or another. This day one of those volunteers took the stand for the prosecution.

Charles H. M. Wood, Negro barber, operated a shop on E Street, near the old Grover Theater. He was, he testified, well acquainted with Washington's theatrical trade. He had known Mr. Booth very well, very well, indeed, for the actor had been an old customer. On the morning of April 14 he had shaved him and dressed his hair. With him had been a gentleman by the name of Mr. McLaughlin.[6] Mr. Surratt and another man had sat in the rear and waited. The other man had been short, thickset, and had a full, round head. He had been wearing what "we usually call Rebel clothes."

Mr. McLaughlin had been very funny that morning. Very funny. He had strutted around before the mirrors, wearing a braid and curls of false hair, sometimes hanging them down behind him, or trying them at the side of his head. He would make a very good-looking woman, he said, except for his mustache. All the people in the shop had laughed heartily at his antics.

[6] Later it was proved he meant Michael O'Laughlin.

Mr. Surratt, not so funny, had said, "Give me a nice shave and clean me up, for I am going away for a day or two." Wood had shaved Mr. Surratt, applied the usual hair preparations.

Mr. Bradley rose for cross-examination. "What time was this?"

"About nine, I think."

"Describe Mr. Surratt."

"Mr. Surratt, sir, he wore light clothes, I think. I put the hair gown over him so only the tips of his pantaloons showed, but I think they were light. I took more notice of Mr. McLaughlin."

"Had you known any of these men before?"

"Oh, yes, sir. I knew Mr. Booth very well. I had known him in Baltimore, and I used to cut his hair when he was a little boy."

"Have you seen any of them since that day?"

"Well, about last Monday or Tuesday as I was going to my dinner, I passed the courthouse. Mr. Surratt was coming out with his jailer. I stood aside and looked at him. I was perfectly astonished because I instantly recognized him as the gentleman I had waited on the morning of April 14."

Bradley excused him without comment.

"Charles Ramsdell," called the guard, and through the witness door came a soldier. His story was brief.

On the morning after the president's murder, he had been on his way back to his station, Fort Bunker, out the Bladensburg Road, after a night in town. He had seen a horse hitched to a fence; a brown horse with a white star on its forehead, and a few minutes later a man had ridden up on the same horse. The man had asked if there would be any difficulty in getting through the pickets. Ramsdell had said he thought there might be because of the assassination. The man had laughed sneeringly at the mention of the murder but had appeared uneasy. A mail orderly was approaching, and when the man saw him he took off at a fast pace.

Here Pierrepont asked the guard to have Johnny rise and turn his back. "Have you seen that back before?"

"I think I have seen that back before. I think I saw it on the back of a horse."

A snicker broke out in the room.

"Back?" asked Bradley. "Bah. No cross-examination."

The agreeable-looking little man who followed identified himself as Theodore B. Rhodes. His recital held his listeners spellbound. On the day of the assassination, he had gone to the theater just to see what it was like, and as he had stepped into a box to look down on the stage, someone had stepped out of it. In a moment the man had come back and in conversation explained that the president would attend the play that night and there'd be a big crowd. The door had to be fixed so no one could disturb the President's party. The man had gouged a little hole in the plaster wall and another in the door panel, to prop a stick that would hold the door shut. The more anybody pushed from the outside, he explained, the tighter the door would hold.

The man had asked Rhodes if he thought it would hold, and he had said he thought it would.

"I will ask the prisoner to stand," said Pierrepont, and once more John rose.

"State if this is the man," Pierrepont pointed an accusing finger, "if you saw him in the box."

"I should judge that is the man."

Joseph Bradley leaped into cross-examination. It had been between eleven and twelve? He had watched the man fix the stick? He had not been called on to testify at the trials of the conspirators? Did the witness mean he had not mentioned this to anyone until right now?

Well, Rhodes explained, he hadn't been sure until he'd gone up to the prison to look at him. Then he'd known the prisoner was the man because at the time he'd thought the man wouldn't make much of an actor. His face was pretty meager and his jaws didn't have much expression.

Bradley waved the old man away contemptuously. He turned to stare at the judge. How could a judge, any judge, permit such a travesty, but before he could begin his scathing onslaught, the court ordered a recess until July 5.

Judge Fisher descended from the bench and moved slowly into the hall. Behind him the crowds melted away, dribbling into outer rooms and halls.

At the defense table, John waited for Gooding to manacle his wrists. The Bradleys and Merrick talked in low tones as they gathered up their papers. Even the low tones could not conceal that old Mr. Bradley was seething mad. Judge Fisher made his way back to the bench, picked up the old cotton umbrella he had forgotten and headed again for the hall door just as Bradley moved out. The unexpected appearance of the judge right next to him in the straggling crowd, stopped him abruptly.

"That young man, Ste. Marie," remarked the judge. "It seems to me I've seen him. With the Delaware troops, I believe. Doesn't it seem to you he was with the Delaware—"

The name of even one more prosecution witness was more than Bradley could take. He whirled on the speaker. "I don't care where he served—or if he ever served—all I care about is your insulting me from the bench every time you get a chance."

"Insulting you?"

"Insulting me from the bench," shouted Bradley, his bald head purpling.

"I'm not aware—"

"Well, you do!—I'll—I'll—" Bradley swung his doubled right fist under the judicial nose.

Astounded, Fisher fell back, raising his left arm to shield his face. A woman screamed. The judge wheeled and ran heavily down the hall to escape Bradley. Out the courtroom door came a yammering, screeching crowd to follow the fleeing judge and his pursuer.

"I'll have satisfaction!" yelled the judge.

"You'll cite me for contempt!" insulted the lawyer.

"No refuge, my official position!" panted the pursued.

Back in the courtroom young Joe Bradley dropped his manila folders and flew. Dick, paralyzed for a moment, bolted after him through the milling crowds toward the old men, ludicrous in their puny attempts at violence.

"—match my age against your illness!" shouted Bradley, dodging the judge's feeble fist.

"Don't, Pa! Don't!" Joe Bradley caught his father's flailing arms. The judge reached his chamber door and hurried inside, where he fell into a chair.

Spectators followed. "Get him some water . . . Fan him . . .

Do something!" The words batted back and forth from wall to wall.

Joe Bradley towered over the half-fainting judge.

"What are you doing here?" Fisher scrambled to his feet, hands defending his head.

"I only want to see there is no more trouble."

"Sensible young man," moaned the judge. "Sensible."

The crisis past, Marshal Gooding and his men hastily elbowed their way back to the prisoner they had left unguarded.

They found him in his chair, right where they had left him, his baleful gray stare holding at bay the menacing circle of brawny young Negroes who surrounded him. Head erect, the squire's vein pulsing, Johnny looked disdainfully at the young black giant who pointed a pistol at his heart.

With loud shouts and authoritative gun-brandishing, Gooding drove the Negroes back, shooting irons hanging from disappointed fingers.

The prisoner held out steady hands to be manacled.

25

July 5 brought eager throngs to the courtroom in anticipation of the first meeting of Judge Fisher and old Mr. Bradley, after their encounter in the courthouse hall. To the crowd's disappointment the session opened without incident.

Saturday, July 6, Carrington announced that he proposed to close the case for the prosecution. The Court now leniently ruled that such witnesses as still remained in the city might be recalled for further questioning if the defense chose to do so.

Young Joe Bradley laid down his notes, rose to his feet, and opened the case for the defense.

"May it please Your Honor and gentlemen of the jury, we have arrived at the point when an opportunity is afforded the prisoner for saying something in the way of defense not only of his reputation but of his life and honor. Also shall arise incidentally in the discussion of this evidence something in the way of vindicating the pure fame of his departed mother.

"Perhaps no case has ever arisen in the annals of this country presenting more extraordinary features than this one which you have under your consideration. Surely, gentlemen, your verdict will go far in settling the question that has agitated this country for the two years past and assist people to arrive at some intelligent opinion as to who the guilty parties really are.

"We come to you, gentlemen, with a profound conviction of the innocence of the accused. This conviction has been arrived at after careful, painstaking investigation extending over many weeks and covering the country from Mexico to Canada. All that we ask of you is that you give the prisoner the full benefit of what we shall adduce in his favor. The maxim of the law is that a man shall be considered innocent until proved guilty."

In this case, Joe went on, there were certain prominent features to keep in mind. The prosecution claimed there had been a conspiracy to murder the president. If they could prove that John Surratt was a member of that conspiracy, then, according to law, he was just as guilty of murder as if he had fired the gun. There was no doubt that Booth had been one of the conspirators. Payne had been one, Herrold and Atzerodt might have been, but the defense hoped to prove that Mrs. Surratt's conviction had been a grave error. Her son, the prisoner, was innocent and they would prove it.

The evidence showed that Booth had planned the affair, that he, a warm and liberal friend as well as courteous gentlemen and great actor, had visited John Surratt in his home. They had attended the theater together. There was nothing in their association for which to reproach the prisoner except for subsequent events and the prosecution depended for the evidence of these on the testimony of Louis J. Weichman and a man named John M. Lloyd.

Lloyd had admitted that he had been so drunk that he did not know whether he had fallen down at Mrs. Surratt's feet or stood up like a man to converse with her. He says she left a package with him. Yet he didn't even remember whether he had been in the house or yard, or whether Mrs. Offutt had been there.

Joe paused for a moment to let his words sink in. The spectators awaited his next words. Sometimes the testimony during the long hot days they had been listening had confused them. Statement of both sides had puzzled them. Now they would learn exactly what old Mr. Bradley and his lawyers were talking about.

"We will show you," said Joe firmly and distinctly, "that Mrs. Offutt received Mrs. Surratt and was told the reason for her visit; that Mrs. Surratt handed her, as anyone else would have handed her, a package to be given Mr. Lloyd. Mrs. Offutt will tell you what happened at that interview. Mrs. Offutt's testimony absolves Mrs. Surratt of any complicity in the affair."

"Louis J. Weichman," intoned Joe, and his inflection left no doubt about his opinion of that young man. A Union War Department Clerk, onetime divinity student, resident of Mrs. Surratt's house, college friend and roommate of her son, he had been principal witness in that other trial. He had been terrified of the consequences to himself, and his dastardly heart had led him to sacrifice the innocent.

"We have witnesses who will tell you that statements of his were utterly false. We shall show you who took him out of the house to the police station. We shall show you he was not allowed his freedom until he had rendered his account to the Military Commission. We shall show you that he furnished the Confederate blockade runners information from the Union War Department records in his office."

These two men, Lloyd and Weichman, were principal witnesses. Now, said Joe, the prosecution must show John Surratt in Washington on the murder day, and to do that they had produced Sergeant Dye. But the defense would produce the man who had stood in front of the theater and called the time. Smilingly Joe turned to Carrington. "Will you have any trouble with your witness?"

As for David Reed, professional gambler, and John Lee, discredited detective, the defense would establish with no trouble at all that neither witness could be believed under oath.

Now about William E. Cleaver, fresh out of jail. Cleaver, said Joe, had been committed to jail convicted of murder by the most foul and cruel means upon the person of a young and innocent girl. Only since this trial began, and since he became a witness, had he been admitted to bail. Joe paused to let his statement sink into the jurors' comprehension, and added, "He has now been granted a new hearing."

When he recognized they remembered the Cleaver case, he went on. A friend and companion of the infamous Conover, Cleaver had been introduced to certain dignitaries who had visited the jail and taught him his lesson. "Now," said Joe smiling, "Cleaver swore he had seen the prisoner on the day of the assassination—if you believe him. Cleaver said he would never be brought to trial again; there was a strong arm protecting him.

"Benjamin F. Vanderpool. A member of the New York bar, he says. Well, God help New York if he's a member of its bar, for he is utterly infamous. We will show you. Do you wonder, gentlemen, that we have sometimes been betrayed into indignation?"

The Negro barber, Charles Wood, had been clearly mistaken in his testimony. Charles Ramsdell had talked to a man on horseback and the prisoner is required to rise and turn his back. Ramsdell says "I think I have seen that back before; on the back of a horse."

"Whom would you hang on that testimony?" and a flutter of movement went through the room. "Benjamin Rhodes, jack of all trades. We want him recalled. I think I have done with the witnesses who testified here.

"I now call your attention to the reason for our conviction of our client's innocence. In April 1865 he went to Richmond, returning to his mother's house on April 3, and going the next day to Montreal. This is conceded by both sides. On April 12 he settled his hotel bill in Montreal and went on a mission. We shall show you where he went and for what purpose. We shall show you where he was on April 13, 14, 15, and on April 16, take him back to Montreal. He went to Canada not because he was a fugitive but because you know as well as I that Justice dropped her scales when she entered that building, the Arsenal Prison." [1]

The defense would show, Joe continued confidently, that Dr. McMillan had made statements the reverse of those he had sworn here. The defense had dismissed Ste. Marie without cross-examination as a man utterly devoid of character and unworthy of belief.

Also, they would show that the handkerchief said to have been dropped by Surratt on his flight actually had been dropped by a detective in pursuit of Surratt, and that the prosecution knew it had been dropped that way.

The room was still as Joe made his closing statement.

"In conclusion, independent of the declarations of Booth in his diary, as well as the testimony of other conspirators relieving Mrs. Surratt of any complicity, we will produce for you testimony showing the articles of agreement between the conspirators. Mrs. Surratt's name is not there. John Surratt's name is not there. We shall show you that, gentlemen, and then we may safely ask whether or not you believe the prisoner guilty of this crime."

The court recessed the session in thoughtful silence, and the prosecuting attorneys moved away, their faces devoid of readable expression. Listeners dispersed in chattering groups. The sound of their converse followed their departure on foot, in carriages, and aboard the horse car waiting at the corner.

On Monday, July 8, James H. Ashley wrote to Sanford Conover. The congressman was aghast at Matchett's implication that his own paid informer might now turn informer to the President. His letter recalled the many missives that had passed between Conover and himself and the complete confidence that existed between them. Nothing, he intimated, could destroy that mutual confidence. "I will see your wife at once," he promised delicately as he ended his letter. Shortly after this note his black coattails hastened in and out of departmental offices around Washington.

In court that morning, Joseph Bradley arose to re-examine

[1] The government arsenal building in which the Military Commission sat to try the alleged assassins.

Benjamin Rhodes. The witness, said Bradley, had not perfectly explained how he had entered the theater; would he please tell it again?

Obligingly Rhodes related that he had entered a small right-hand door at the foot of the stairs, had gone up a small stairway to a door that opened into the section where the audience sits. The outside door had been open but the inside door had been shut.

"When you went into the theater you saw a man opening the door, I believe you said. Is that correct?"

"I heard the door open and shut, and I went right up to the box. A man was retreating back."

"As you stood there, could you see on the stage?"

"Oh, yes," he answered. The curtain had been down but he could plainly see the parts of the stage in front of the curtain. He had stood in the box and talked to the man who brought the rocking chair for the President.

It required only a few questions to dispose of Rhodes. James J. Gifford, who had built Fords' Theater and now worked there as a stagehand, and John Y., James R., and Henry Clay Ford, who owned the theater and were well known to every Washington man there, presented a diagram of the building. It showed that Rhodes could not have entered the box area in the way he had described, and the stage was not visible from where he said he had entered. Besides that, the curtain had been up for rehearsals, not down as he had testified.

Henry C. Ford had prepared the presidential box, he testified, and he had placed the presidential chair in it. No stranger had been in or near the box. Using the floor plan, Dick Merrick showed that the vestibule clock was not visible from where Dye and Cooper had testified they had stood and watched a man check the time and call it out.

Worse yet, Gifford testified he had stood in front of the theater that night with Louis J. Carland. He had known Booth all his life, and he had not seen him that night. While he and Carland stood there, C. B. Hess, an actor, had come out and asked the time. Gifford explained the mysterious whistle. At Ford's Theater the signal for scene changing was a whistle. Smilingly Joseph Bradley turned to Pierrepont. "If you have the whistle you blew, will you let us have it?" Nathaniel Wilson leaned from his table to place the tin whistle in Bradley's outstretched hand. "I don't know whether or not I can blow it," said Bradley in high good humor, and he tootled a faint note. "Was the sound anything like that?" he turned to Gifford amid the spectators' giggles.

"It was a shrill whistle," offered Gifford. "In some theaters they use gongs, but here it was a whistle." He accepted the whistle gingerly, turned it in his hand and blew a mighty blast. "Sometimes we blew a long shrill whistle like that." He lifted it again and the judge palmed his ears.

Pierrepont's cross-examination, which followed immediately, did not shake Gifford. He had been in front of the theater with Louis Carland, who had told Mr. Hess it was ten past ten. John Wilkes Booth had been nowhere around.

C. B. Hess appeared next and pleased his audience as much as he had in any performance he had played on the Ford stage. A special song had been written for him to sing for the President; after the play's first act he had stepped out front for a breath of air while he waited his call to return to the stage.

Wearing a light spring overcoat, raglan type, and darkish pants, he had conversed with Mr. Gifford and Mr. Carland. Asked to recount the conversation, he re-enacted all the parts. Turning to one side, he called out in sonorous tones, "Mr. Carland, what time is it?" Then, becoming Carland, he took a few steps the other way, peered at an imaginary clock, and replied, "It is ten past ten." Then, himself again, he repeated his own words at the time. "Then I will be wanted in a few minutes." Within several minutes he had heard the pistol discharge and after that there had been uproar all over the house.

This testimony brought Pierrepont quickly to his feet.

No, answered Hess, he didn't really think he looked like John Surratt. He thought he looked just about as he had in 1865; certainly his hair and mustache were just as black; he had been no paler in 1865. He had never seen the prisoner before. No one had stood on the theater platform while he was there other than his companions and Mr. Lincoln's carriage man.

Glumly Pierrepont released him.

Carland, who followed, interested the spectators greatly. He had known Booth well. He had been at Ford's Theater on April 14. Rehearsal had begun at ten or eleven and lasted until two o'clock. It had been prolonged because of a song for the president that had been decided upon only that day. He repeated the ten-past-ten conversation; he had never seen the prisoner before; no one who looked like him had stood on the platform that night; no one had been there save himself, Gifford, and Hess.

Hours of cross-examination followed. Over and over Carland repeated his answers and at the end his testimony stood unchanged. The day had proved profitable for Johnny and his lawyers.

Tuesday, July 9, brought J. N. Eastman of the Naval Observatory. In a dreary quarrel with the prosecution, he testified that the murder night had been so dark that no witness could see anything in front of a three-story house on the south side of a street. William Dixon, Washington Fire Chief, stated that an alarm had sounded that night and he had jumped right on his horse and hurried to the fire. On the way he had nearly been run over by the fire apparatus—it had been so dark the driver couldn't see his chief's horse. A squadron of cavalry had passed him but in the darkness he couldn't tell the color of the horses.

A Surratt neighbor, A. Kiesecker, followed. The steps of his house were within fifteen feet of the Surratt house. On the murder night, he had sat out smoking until after eleven when his wife called him in. He had heard no conversation from the Surratt house, and if any had taken place he would certainly have heard it.

Was he looking up H Street? Pierrepont asked, and the witness replied soberly, no, he couldn't sit backward on the step. Amid mild snickers, he left the stand.

"John Lee, for further cross-examination," requested Bradley but was brusquely refused by Judge Fisher.

"If I grant this," he said sourly, "other witnesses might be recalled and this case would never end. A man might live to be a hundred or a thousand and this case would still be going on."

Mr. Bradley then presented a series of character witnesses, ten men who swore they would not believe Detective Lee on his oath. Among them, Brigadier General O'Bierne swore that as district provost marshal he had discharged Lee from the detective force because of his malodorous reputation.

Succeding witnesses attacked the character of William E. Cleaver, detailing his trial for fornication, abortion, and manslaughter, also his wartime record of passing worthless horses for purchase by the federal army.

A crowning blow came when Talmadge A. Lambert reached the stand. He located his home on the corner of H Street, English ground level basement, narrow front steps edged with an iron railing. The house faced north; it was identical in appearance with the Surratt house. However, it stood one block farther up the street.

Mrs. Fredricka Lambert, Talmadge's mother, spoke next. On the night of the murder, she said timidly, she had heard excited voices in the street. She had leaned out a window to ask two soldiers what the trouble was. They had replied, "John Wilkes Booth has shot the president."

The barrage of defense rebuttal had left the court and jury thoughtful again but no one looked more pensive than Albert Gallatin Riddle. Here, beyond hope of resuscitation, died the last of the Cooper-Dye evidence.

Valiantly Pierrepont strove to break down the lady's story, but just as valiantly she upheld it. Up and down her house the lawyer chased her in his questionings, in and out of her shawl, in and out of her bedroom, through her window, into the street, into gaslight, moonlight, drizzle, and rain. Had the soldiers worn light uniforms? Dark? Blue? Were they infantry? Cavalry?

The timid lady didn't know. One thing only she knew: she had heard shouting, she had opened her window to inquire what it was about, and the soldiers had answered "John Wilkes Booth has shot the president." Then, when she had read in the paper that soldiers had reported talking to Mrs. Surratt at her window that night, she had wondered how many other women on H Street had called out to them in her own words.

Mr. Bradley stepped forward. "You said that after this occurred to you, you came forward to tell me about it? Did you come to my office?"

"Yes, I did. You weren't at home."

"How long have you known me, Mrs. Lambert?"

"Why—why—as long as I have known myself," she answered and dissolved into tears.

26

For no witness had the crowd waited more eagerly than John T. Holohan.

Following the trial of Mrs. Surratt, and even during it, he had told all and sundry how, on the morning after the assassination, he had forced terrified Lou Weichman to the District police. Washington knew unofficially just what John Holohan would try to say; but every one who could squeeze into the courtroom was there to hear him say it.

He described his relationship with the Surratt family, noted that Lou and Atzerodt had been so friendly that the latter had often worn Lou's clothing, related his exchange of greenbacks for Johnny's gold on the night of April 3, and said he had not seen Mr. Surratt again until this day in the courtroom.

He described the torchlight parade the night of the murder. Next morning he had heard of the assassination, and detectives McDevitt and Clarvoe had shown him a piece of the president's blood-stained cravat. Three days later he had accompanied the detectives and Lou on their trip to Canada in search of Mr. Surratt.

"While you were at home," asked Bradley, "did you get any articles?"

"Yes, sir. The washing had come home and was spread out on the bed. I changed my shirt and took a couple of handkerchiefs from the bed."

"State whether or not one of these hankerchiefs was marked and if so, how."

"It was marked 'John H. Surratt.' "

On their way to Canada on April 19, he said, they had stopped at Burlington, Vermont, and he had gone out and bought shirts, handkerchiefs, socks, and comb. While waiting for the train he had rested on a settee in the depot. He had had the handkerchief in his overcoat pocket with his tobacco. It had been there Thursday morning, April 20, but later in the day he had found it gone.

After the noon recess, Pierrepont's cross-examination questions cracked across the room like artillery fire. Holohan, his crisp black curls plastered down on his head with perspiration, threw sizzling answers back.

Where had the party stopped? Where had it not stopped? He had gone alone to get a drink? Left his belongings with the rest of the party? On his return both handkerchiefs and tobacco were gone?

Whether the handkerchief had a "No." marked on it, Holohan could not say. There had been a figure on it but whether it had been preceded by "No." he couldn't remember. The prosecution reasked, repeated, rerepeated, and reworded the question until Holohan broke out in a fury, roaring, "I told you there was a N-U-M-B-E-R, a NUMBER!" Pierrepont withdrew a little from that black Irish wrath. Wrangling followed. More questions delivered as insinuations brought such blazing replies that Pierrepont retorted with sneers. Then, as the lawyer began hurling his questions with such speed that Holohan could not make his replied heard, Bradley interrupted.

"Your Honor will pardon me if I remind you that the other day you reproved defense counsel for their manner toward witnesses. I think the counsel on the other side has pressed this witness in a manner quite as severe as anything that has occurred during this trial. Even more so."

"I can't see anything improper," His Honor replied indifferently. "There seems to be an unwillingness on the part of the witness to answer. He makes explanations first. He must answer first and explain afterward."

The battle resumed. Holohan insisted that he had taken the handkerchief from the Surratt home, and that Clarvoe, knowing it had John Surratt's name on it, had said to him, "Hold onto it. We'll use it," or words to that effect.

"Look at it," said Pierrepont, handing him the prosecution's exhibit. "See if you think this is the same handkerchief."

"That is the handkerchief."

"Did you tell anyone you had lost it?"

"Not until someone told me it had been found. Then I told them I had lost it."

"Can you identify this as the one you lost?"

"I cannot be positive this is the identical one, but I think it is."

As he was excused, Eliza Holohan came in from the witness room. Her light summer dress, tiny straw bonnet, white gloves, and lace handkerchief brought a spot of freshness into the room. Dick Merrick rose to hand her lightly to the stand. She turned, conscious of her grace, and her eye caught Johnny's. She flashed a slight smile before she bent to touch the Bible the clerk offered her.

Following Bradley's lead, she described her life in the Surratt home.

"Did you mingle socially with the family of Mrs. Surratt, or did you keep yourself secluded?"

"I mingled with them freely. I met them at all times and any time." In a few sentences she related how Lou had been there when she and her husband had gone to board with Mrs. Surratt. She had seen Mr. Payne but she had never exchanged a word with him. She had seen Port Tobacco with Mr. Weichman more than with anyone else; she had seen him wearing Mr. Weichman's tall beaver and military cape.

On the night of the assassination, after her return from the country, Mrs. Surratt had reminded Mrs. Holohan of their plan to attend Good Friday services that night. They had started out, but after walking to Dr. Evans' house, two doors up the street, she had suggested that because of the dark, wet weather they return home. Mrs. Surratt had agreed. They had done so and Eliza had gone up to her room. She had not seen Mrs. Surratt until the next morning.

"While you lived in Mrs. Surratt's house, did you have an opportunity to learn and know her character?"

Objections to Bradley's question came quickly, and the court ruled as before that nothing might be said on that subject. The defense called attention to early prosecution testimony about Mrs. Surratt that had been admitted, but the judge did not change his ruling.

"Mrs. Surratt is not on trial here," Pierrepont remarked acrimoniously.

"I rather think she has been on trial here every day," retorted Bradley.

Pierrepont cross-examined Eliza carefully. Almost with deference he brought out the unsuccessful effort she and Mrs. Surratt had made to attend the Good Friday evening service, and her seeing Mrs. Surratt and her son and a lady leave in a carriage with two horses sometime before the fall of Richmond.

When she lived with Mrs. Surratt, she said, she had sent her washing out with Mrs. Surratt's. The Monday after the assassination she had sent it out as usual, but she had not seen it again until some three or four weeks later when she was allowed to go to the Surratt house for it. Asked when and where the laundered clothing had been distributed about the house, she answered in a tone of genteel reproof that she knew nothing about it; someone else sorted the laundry and put it away.

A few minutes after her release, a stout, very dark Negro woman waddled through the witness room door. Her eyes searched the room until she found Johnny. Having by this wordless greeting announced her allegiance, she climbed determinedly into the witness chair and waited.

Bradley spoke. "Tell these gentlemen what your name is and what it used to be."

"My name Eliza Hawkins. I used t' be called Rachel Seamus but they call me 'Liza for short, so I never go by Rachel any more at all."

Her deep pleasant voice filled the room with accents familiar to Washingtonians as their own.

"Do you know a colored woman named Susan Jackson who used to live at Mrs. Surratt's and had some other name?"

"Yes, sir. She was Susan Mahoney then. When she lived at Mrs. Surratt's she wasn't married."

"Do you remember when the president was murdered?"

"Yes, sir. That was Good Friday night."

She had lived in the country then. Down at the tavern with Mr. John Lloyd, and she had come uptown to see her children, who lived with her master, Mr. Wildman. She'd come uptown to make her Easter and to see her children, just like she did every holiday, and she had gone at once to see Mrs. Surratt. That had been Tuesday, but Mrs. Surratt had been arrested and so she'd seen only Susan."

"State what Susan said to you about Mr. John Surratt."

"Well, I was sitting in a chair by the window and Susan, she was sitting in a basket. It had some ironed clothes in it." Her tone was critical of Susan's behavior. "She was talking about the bad luck she'd had with the last homes she'd got. She was afraid she wouldn't get her money. Mrs. Surratt was arrested, so Susan thought maybe she wouldn't get it, she said. 'How long you been here, Ann?' I said, and she said, 'Two weeks and I'm afraid I won't never get it.' I said, 'She goin' pay you if it take the last cent she have got.'

"She say, 'The night the pres'dent was killed they was here lookin' for her son, John. He was here the first week I come here and I went in t' take some tea for Mrs. Surratt and she say to me, wasn't he very much like her daughter, Miss Anna, and I tell her, 'Yes'm, he was.' "

Rachel stopped for breath, then started afresh to fill the room with her reminiscences.

" 'Haven't you seen him since?' I says, and she says 'No, I never put my eyes on him since, and that was two weeks ago.' So that is before my Gawd an' I wouldn't say a thing I didn't believe in this court."

Edwards Pierrepont was not at his best when he undertook to cross-examine Rachel for her race was largely unknown to him.

She had come up from Mr. Lloyd's house after dinner, Rachel answered his first question, and then replied haughtily to his next query. "Of course, I know Mrs. Surratt. I live with Mrs. Surratt six years."

"Were you ever a slave at any time?"

"Yes, sir. I always a slave."

"Were you a slave of Mrs. Surratt's?"

"I was hired to Mrs. Surratt. My master, Mr. Wildman, he hired me to her and I live with her six years."

"Where did you see Susan?"

"At Mrs. Surratt's house when I go there Tuesday morning. I stayed there all day long. My little chile was at Mrs. Surratt's, and when I found soldiers there I wouldn't leave the chile there, but I couldn't take her away, so I stayed all day till eight o'clock. Then me and Susan and the colored man—I s'pose he the one she marry —we all go down to the provost marshal's that night.

"The colored man couldn't get away. Miss Anna Ward she come there and she couldn't get away. Soldiers was there all day, yes, sir."

Two of them had carried her down to the provost marshal general's office. She, and Susan, and the colored man.

"So Susan told you Mrs. Surratt said John looked like Anna?"

"Very much like Miss Anna," she reproved him.

"Did you know Anna?" Pierrepont asked unwisely and drew a torrent of reply.

"Certainly I know Miss Anna Surratt. When I live in th' house with them for six years, I think I ought to know Miss Anna Surratt."

Hastily he interrupted. "Were you very much attached to them?"

"Certainly I was very much 'tached to them. I'd be with them this very day, if I could. This very day." She dabbed her eyes.

"Are you very much attached to them now?"

"Yes, sir. I'm very much 'tached to them. They treated me well, and I certainly got the right t' be 'tached to them."

"Your feelings," interjected Bradley quickly, "are not strong enough to make you tell a lie for them, are they?"

"No, indeed. I wouldn't tell no lie. Before Gawd, I wouldn't tell no lie."

Pierrepont resumed. "When did you first tell anyone about Susan?"

"I went home and I told my young mistress 'bout it, soon's I got there."

"Who was she?"

"She marry Mista Henry Queen."

"Whom did you tell since this trial began?"

"I heard it read about in the papers. I told different people. 'Certainly,' I said, 'Susan couldn't go and swear to no tale like that. She know full well what she tell me. She couldn't go on the stand and swear to such a story,' I said."

"Whom did you say this to?" persisted Pierrepont.

"I said it to everybody would read the papers to me. The first one was a man lives with Mr. Barry. His name is Richardson, and he was reading the paper to me and I said it to him."

This cross-examination was not developing much of value so Pierrepont changed the line of questioning for the moment.

Yes, Rachel responded, she was married. Her husband's name was Tom Seamus.

"When did he die?"

"He aint dead yit." The spectators smiled at Pierrepont's surprise.

"You said *was* named, and I supposed he was dead."

"No, sir. When the colored people went away he went, too. But he was with a man he hadn't no call to leave because he did better then than he do now and that I know. But he went away."

"And he hasn't come back?"

"No, sir, he hasn't never come back. I said he could go and welcome. He was lazy, but I had my childrens to work for and I just as lief stay where I was an' keep my little 'round me as t' come here and suffer." By this time Rachel, or Eliza as she now was called, was becoming a little vehement. Quickly her questioner changed the subject.

She had seen Susan last fall, down at Mr. Robey's where she had gone to do up some clothes for his daughter who was getting married. Susan and her husband had been on their way to her mother's house at T.B. and they wanted to stop and spend the night. Their horse had give out, Susan said, but Mrs. Robey was away and Rachel couldn't allow anybody to stay in a white lady's house that she was taking care of. In her house they could stay; in a white lady's house where she worked they could not stay without permission. Not even her own mother would she let stay.

"It was a tavern, wasn't it?" asked Pierrepont, "the Robeys often took in strangers to stay the night, didn't they?"

"Certainly they took in strangers," impatiently, "didn't they take in strangers their tavern wouldn't do them no service, but they didn't take in colored people. They didn't have any place for them to stay."

Rachel's standards having been expounded to Northern counsel much to the amusement of the Washingtonians, she was released. In the afternoon heat the court recessed.

Detectives Clarvoe, McDevitt, and Skippon on the stand departed from their listeners' expectations.

Clarvoe, according to his story, had searched the Surratt house the night after the assassination. Lou Weichman had opened the door and said John Surratt had been away for several days. In the kitchen a black woman had shrilled insistently that she had not seen John Surratt for about two weeks. Yes, he knew John Holohan had carried along a handkerchief with John Surratt's name on it. Holohan had told him about losing it in the depot.

"Mr. Clarvoe," said Bradley, "state whether or not Susan Ann Jackson is the woman who told you at the Surratt house that John had not been home for two weeks."

"I think she is the woman. I'm not positive, but it was a woman square shouldered and of her stature."

McDevitt, too, had seen a colored woman at the Surratt house and he had heard her say John Surratt had been away two weeks. It had been dark in the basement and he could not distinguish her features so he could not say positively it had been Susan.

Skippon added a little more. Only two Negro women had been in the house that night of the arrest; one dark and stout, and the other a young, slightly built mulatto girl. The witness, Susan Ann, was dark and stout.

At this point, Honora Fitzpatrick having been called once for the prosecution, now appeared for the defense.

Yes, she remembered the night of the assassination; yes, she remembered Mr. Surratt had not been at home for about two weeks or more before that time. She remembered the last night he was home. She had assisted with supper. Susan Ann had brought in tea and Mrs. Surratt had commented on her son's and daughter's likeness. Mr. Surratt had not been home the night of the assassination.

Now that contradictions were pouring in, Pierrepont stepped up his cross-examination. Honora, frightened and at times disconcerted by his sharpness, still bore up bravely. She had been with Mrs. Surratt and Anna the night of their arrest . . . at all times . . . she had not heard Anna say that Booth had been there an hour before. Despite questions asked, repeated, rephrased and reiterated, she held to her story without change.

Slashing attacks on a quartet of Elmira, New York, merchants who appeared next held the listeners' close attention. Presented by Bradley, they detailed their stories under his questioning.

Charles B. Stewart testified that he was a merchant tailor of Elmira, and that on April 13 or 14, 1865, a gentleman wearing a style jacket he had never seen before came into his store. He had talked to the gentleman; he recollected his appearance—his face and his manner of speaking. In response to Bradley's questioning, he identified Johnny as the man. He had interviewed Mr. Surratt in the jail that morning and this had convinced him that Mr. Surratt was the gentleman he had seen in Elmira.

Pierrepont in cross-examination could draw out nothing further except that the witness knew it had been either April 13 or 14 because his partner had been in New York buying merchandise and had returned on April 15.

John Cass followed him. He identified himself as the present city assessor of Elmira, but in April 1865 he had had a clothing store at the corner of Water and Baldwin streets.

"Do you remember anything about the morning of April 15?" asked Bradley.

The witness remembered that at seven-thirty that morning he had seen a newspaper telling that the president had been shot. He had inquired at the Western Union office across the street from his store and had been told the story was true. At nine o'clock word of the president's death came in, and while he was instructing his clerks to close the store, a gentleman wearing Canadian dress came in. He wished white shirts which Mr. Cass did not have.

"I told him of the president's death and he made a remark which I took to be disrespectful but before he concluded I was satisfied that no disrespect was intended. My idea was that he was a Canadian and so had no sympathy with our people," explained the witness.

He described John's clothing, the darkish pants, blue mixed jacket pleated, with a belt around the waist. On request he identified the prisoner.

"That was on April 15?" inquired a juror.

"Yes, sir. While I was closing my store after hearing the news."

Cross-examination brought out nothing worthwhile for the prosecution.

Frank E. Atkinson, sworn, stated that he lived in Elmira and that he had the honor to be an alderman of that city. In April 1865 he had been bookkeeper for Stewart and Ufford. He remembered the gentleman who came into the store because of his jacket —it was dark blue or something—but it had a row of buttons up the front, which was pleated. The skirt was gathered into a belt.

He could place the date by his books because a member of the firm had gone to New York for merchandise and had withdrawn $105.00 on April 12 for the trip and on the fifteenth he had settled up. He had spent only $92.62. He recalled the gentleman's dress, but chiefly he recalled his manner and speech. He had no doubt at all that the prisoner was the man.

Joseph Carroll, cutter for Stewart and Ufford, did not get off so easily. By this time, Riddle's continuing appraisal of testimony may have alarmed prosecution counsel for Cleaver, McMillan, Ste. Marie, Lou Weichman all had admitted self-interest. Rhodes, Woods, Cooper, and Dye had been discredited. An intelligent Washington jury might contrast them unfavorably with the Elmira gentlemen, so cross-examination pressured.

At once counsel and witness ran into an altercation with Pierrepont trying to get the witness to admit he had told a local man the prisoner had been in his store on April 12, not April 13. The witness insisted his books showed it to be on April 13 and 14. He stuck stubbornly to this statement and equally stubbornly Pierrepont repeated and rephrased his questions.

Had he told an Elmira man named Knapp the man had been

there on April 12? He didn't think so. Had he told Major Fields, a hotel keeper in the town, it was April 12? He thought he had not. He could tell only by looking at his records. Did he tell Mr. Knapp April 13? Possibly, but not without looking at his records. The first time the man had come in had been on April 13.

Here Mr. Bradley stepped in. "Did the parties, Knapp, Field, and a man named Covell understand you had been summoned for the defense?

"Yes, sir."

"And knowing that they still came to talk to you about it?"

"Of course. Otherwise they wouldn't have asked questions. It's a small town, everybody knows everybody else's business."

"In the war did you take either side?"

"I wished the success of the Union, of course. I had a son in the Union Army."

Frank Atkinson, bookkeeper, took the stand only long enough to confirm the Elmira merchants' statements about seeing John in their stores.

The July 12 session ended in almost a stalemate.

Saturday morning, July 13, Joseph Carroll was recalled, and Pierrepont went into cross-examination again, hammer and tongs.

Mr. Knapp and Mr. Covell of Elmira were present in the courtroom, and Carroll was asked to recognize them. He did so.

"Now," said Pierrepont, "may I ask if you told Mr. Knapp you saw the prisoner on the twelfth of April?"

"I think I told him the thirteenth and fourteenth."

"Did you tell him the twelfth and thirteenth?"

"I think I did not."

After a long, contentious duel of words, Dick Merrick intervened. "I submit to Your Honor whether or not he has answered."

"Let him answer each day severally."

"That's what I'm doing," retorted Pierrepont, and went on, "Did you tell him it was the twelfth?"

"I do not think I did."

"Did you tell him it was the thirteenth?"

"I think I did."

"Did you tell him it was the fourteenth?"

"I think I did."

"Did you tell Mr. Covell about it?"

"I think I did."

"Did you tell him it was the twelfth?"

"I think I did not."

Did he tell him it was the thirteenth? The witness thought so. The fourteenth? He thought so. No, he had not told anyone the man came in twice on the same day. Questions and answers rattled, pounded, crowded onto each other.

"I must interpose an objection here," called out Bradley.

"Did you see Knapp with—" went on Pierrepont.

"I wish to have a rule established." Bradley spoke loudly. "If we interpose an objection I hope Your Honor will stop the counsel and not allow him to run on with his cross fire while I am attempting to address the court."

"State your objection—"

"I did."

"I did not hear it."

"It was impossible to hear it. I might as well make an objection in the midst of artillery fire. I only want some rule established when I interpose an objection."

"When an objection is made the counsel will stop putting any questions."

"I always do when I hear it."

"Then you must be very deaf—" grimly.

Twenty-nine times Carroll was asked the dates on which the prisoner was in his store, and twenty-nine times gave the same answers.

In sheer fatigue the prosecution changed the subject, leaving listeners to wonder why one day made so much difference.

Olivia Jenkins, called next, remained on the stand only long enough to say she had visited her aunt's home that Easter holiday. She had been with the Surratt ladies at the time of her arrest. She had heard nothing of Mr. Booth's having been there an hour before the assassination. Anna Surratt had answered the door once but it was only Mr. Scott with some papers for her, Olivia. She had been at breakfast the next morning. Lou had been there but she had not heard him say anything about giving information to the police.

Surprised, Pierrepont repeated his queries. She had been arrested with Mrs. Surratt? She had not been examined? Did she mean she had been released without questioning?

Edwards Pierrepont could not know of the long friendship between Zad Jenkins and Captain Billy Wood nor how simple it had been for the prison superintendent to slip little 'Livia Jenkins out of the Old Capitol. In all those hundreds of cackling, complaining, hysterical women and outraged men, one terrified little country girl had not been missed.

Mention of Michael O'Laughlin quickened listeners' interest. Bernard Early, a former lieutenant in the U.S. Army, and Edward A. Murphy testified they had known him for years, and on the night of the murder all three had stayed at the Metropolitan Hotel. A fourth man, Mr. Henderson, had been with them. All four had been shaved that morning in the hotel's shaving saloon; they had eaten breakfast together, spent the morning together. Booth had not been with them nor had John Surratt. They had been nowhere near the barber shop of the Negro, Wood.

On that morning O'Laughlin had worn a black, slouched hat, dahlia coat, and plaid pantaloons and vest. Definitely he had not worn a black frock coat, light trousers. He had not pinned false braids around his head and pranced to make Wood's customers laugh. He had not been the handsome man in the Wood shaving saloon.

Next, William Failing, Canandaigua's Webster House clerk, mounted the stand with a book under his arm. The hotel register, he explained, and pointed out the name, John Harrison, April 15, 1865. Legal cannonading rocked the room. To Pierrepont's objection that the book might have been altered since that time, the hotel owner, Frank Chamberlain, and the Bradleys, father and son, sworn as witnesses, accounted for the book's custody from that date down to the moment. No opportunity had been present, they swore, for any alteration or entry in the register.

Under loud insistence from Pierrepont that the book could not be admitted as evidence and Bradley's equally loud insistence that it should be admitted, the weary judge recessed the court until Monday.

"The Webster House register cannot be allowed to go to the jury." The first act of Monday's session, July 15, flooded Bradley's face with anger.

The proprietor of the hotel had sworn that after the book's pages were full it had lain on a shelf under his counter. There it had been accessible to anyone who wished to write in it, ruled the court. Even though the defense claimed to have proved the handwriting, that did not mean that the prisoner had been present on April 15; the book could have been sent to Canada, Rome, or Egypt for him to enter his name. He could have come down from Canada to do it

"Do I understand that if I prove the prisoner was under observation all the time he was in Canada it will not avail me?" Bradley demanded.

"That is the ruling. You must prove that some individual traveling as John Harrison was present and signed the register on that date."

William Failing, recalled, showed up with a second book which he explained as the night register. In it were entered the name and room number of departing persons, and from it were made up the bills for departing persons. Pages from April 12 through 20 in 1865 were missing. He could not explain why except that he had taken it home with him and his children might have played with it.

Well, ruled the judge, if this book could show that an actual person had stayed at the Webster House that April 15, had been assigned a room and paid for it, then the record might stand, but a name on a register would not. No evidence had been produced to show that John Surratt had not come down from Canada at a later date and signed the register. It remained inadmissible.

On that same hot morning when tempers were no cooler than the temperature, Edwin G. Lee took the stand, identified himself as a Virginian, a former brigadier general in the Confederate Army, who had been stationed in Canada during the last months of the war.

"State if you saw the prisoner, John H. Surratt, in Canada and when you saw him."

"I did. I saw him on the sixth day of April, 1865. He brought—"

Pierrepont's objections crackled. The witness might give no evidence of why the prisoner had been in Canada, what he brought there, whom he had seen. Judge Fisher upheld him.

"Your object is to prove an alibi," he informed the witness. "You are confined to this fact. You may not show he bore dispatches, to whom he bore them, nor anything of that sort."

"But there is another part to this case," argued Bradley. "Your Honor, the prosecution has charged that the prisoner received money from Mr. Thompson and is thereby connected with this transaction. I will show by this dispatch that Surratt did not receive one dollar—that he was on a special Secret Service mission to Elmira, on the thirteenth, the fourteenth, and the fifteenth; that he was on a duty that made any engagement in this other matter utterly impossible."

"If you want to show he had nothing to do with Thompson, then the witness must speak only as to his own knowledge."

"The dispatch is for that purpose. It is to show what the money was for—was not connected with the prisoner."

"You cannot show what it was," boomed Pierrepont.

"What? I cannot show what it was drawn for? When without a particle of evidence to connect it with the prisoner it is held here as a weight against him? If this prisoner had nothing to do with it, we cannot show an order from Mr. Thompson to pay the money over to another person? Cannot show the object of the payment? That it was entirely disconnected from the prisoner? We cannot show that?"

"Of course you can't."

"I do not see that you can," feebly agreed the judge.

"Then I will reduce it to writing and make it part of the record. I have a right to do that, I think."

"Very well," sighed the judge. "Very well."

After a brief recess, Bradley read his proposition aloud.

"I promise to show that on April 6 the defendant was bearer of a dispatch from Mr. Benjamin to the witness, Edwin G. Lee, which related in part to funds in the hands of Jacob Thompson

. . . and to show that no part of the funds were to be . . . or
. . . were paid to the prisoner but were to be transferred either
to Mr. Lee or put under the protection of a foreign government.
Second . . . that the prisoner was specially employed by the
witness, Edwin G. Lee, to ascertain the position and condition of
Confederate prisoners . . . to make sketches of the Elmira prison
camp. Third, that the prisoner having left Washington on March
25, 1865, reached Richmond on the twenty-ninth and on the
thirty-first was charged by Mr. Benjamin with the dispatch . . .
arrived in Montreal on April 6, remained there until April 12,
when he went to Elmira. . . . All of which evidence is offered
as tending to show the whereabouts of the prisoner from March
25 to April 17, 1865, and to show that he did not receive from
Jacob Thompson the money which it is pretended by the prosecution that he did receive. . . ."

"The proper plan," responded the judge, "would be to put
your witness on the stand, ask your questions, and I will rule
whether they may be answered."

"General Lee recalled," began Bradley.

"State whether or not the prisoner brought you a dispatch."

"Object—" called out Pierrepont before the witness might reply.

"Ruled out," responded the court

"Note an exception." Young Joe nodded.

"On his arrival did he deliver to you any papers?"

"Object!"

"Same ruling," responded the court.

"Note an exception, of course," said Merrick.

"Oh, of course," agreed Pierrepont caustically. "In every case."

"Do you know whether at that time Mr. Thompson had any
Confederate funds in Montreal?"

"Objection."

"Sustained."

"Exception."

"Do you know what disposition Mr. Thompson made—"

"Objection."

"Sustained."

"Exception."

"Do you know whether or not the prisoner received—"

"Objection."

"Sustained."

"Exception."

On they haggled for the rest of the session. Only one item remained uncontested. It was General Lee's memory that the prisoner had worn a heavy traveling shawl that covered his body down to the skirt of his coat. "He had a light mustache—like that of a man who never had shaved—a boy's mustache, and a very light goatee."

The afternoon appearance of Angus Bachus and his wife surprised no one for their probable testimony had been well discussed over town. They kept the only concert saloon in the area named by Vanderpool when he swore he had seen Johnny and Booth on April 14. There was no entertainment there on Good Friday, they swore, never any entertainment on Friday afternoon. There never had been round tables, either.

This quiet testimony left both jury and listeners thoughtful.

In evidence the following day Harry Hall Brogden was allowed to say nothing of what he had come to tell. He could not describe his own employment with Judah Benjamin, speak of his acquaintance with John Surratt, a Confederate courier, nor tell anything of his knowledge of dispatches entrusted to Surratt. He could tell nothing of the gold he had seen turned over to the prisoner nor the purpose for which it had been paid.

His statements were not in answer to anything the prosecution had presented, said Pierrepont, and the court supported him.

J. B. Tinsley, Jr., clerk in the Spotswood Hotel, Richmond, fared no better. The witness, explained Bradley, opened the defense's plan to show where the prisoner had been from March 24 through the 17th of September when he sailed for Europe.

"I object."

"Ruled out," confirmed the judge.

Furiously Bradley demanded an explanation.

"It is not in response to anything we have put in evidence," replied Pierrepont with obvious satisfaction.

"Is it possible, is it *possible*," Bradley's voice broke under his effort at self control. "Is it *possible* we will be allowed to give no evidence except in reply to what you have given?" To no purpose, he fumed, demanded, and then, exhausted, sat weakly down. The judge remained adamant.

The session moved slowly on. Mr. Lincoln's carriage man swore no one had sat on the theater's carriage platform the night of April 14. No soldiers had been there. D. C. Robinson explained that changes in ownership made it impossible to locate the April 1865 register for the Brainard House in Elmira.

"Stephen F. Cameron." Dick Merrick took over for exhausted Mr. Bradley, and with his first few sentences brought the room to life. The witness identified himself and stated that he had crossed on the *Nova Scotian* from Quebec to Liverpool via Londonderry. He had known Dr. McMillan well. Dr. McMillan had said he had made the previous crossing on the *Peruvian* with the prisoner, John Surratt, and they had discussed him.

"Did Mr. McMillan, in conversation, state to you that John Surratt had told him he was in Elmira the night of April 14?"

"He stated so distinctly."

"Did he state to you that John Surratt had said to him that on April 15 he learned of the president's assassination?"

"He so stated."

"Did he tell you that Surratt said after learning of the assassination he immediately left Elmira and turned his face toward Canada?"

"Yes. He assigned that as the reason."

"Did McMillan ever state to you that Surratt could not have been guilty? That he regarded him as a political offender and so had no scruples about aiding him?"

"He did."

"Did he ever tell you that Surratt had said to him the whole plan for Lincoln's abduction was laid by Booth? That it was an individual enterprise, that Booth procured the funds, bought the horses, and spent some $4,000 to $6,000 on it?"

"He did, and he mentioned those sums specifically He said that he had always considered it an individual enterprise from Mr. Surratt's account."

"Did he ever tell you that Surratt said his first knowledge of his mother's peril was her execution?"

"He did. He defended Surratt when I assailed him on that point."

"McMillan defended him? And told you Surratt said his first knowledge of her danger was her execution?"

"Yes."

Pierrepont took over for cross-examination, which included a long-drawn-out recital of Cameron's early life. He had not been a successful businessman. He had been reared a Catholic but his father had finally forbidden him to attend that church. He had then turned to the Episcopal faith and had attended General Theological Seminary in New York. He had been admitted to Deacon's orders on Trinity Sunday, 1861. That same month he had gone south as a chaplain with the Confederate Army. In May 1865 he had returned to the Catholic faith.

The room listened to his pleasant voice, watched his thin face as he answered with an occasional flash of gentle wit the questions poured into him by prosecution counsel.

He had been a chaplain with the First Maryland Regiment, C.S.A. He had never stolen any silk dresses for his wife but he had bought some for her. He had visited Maryland several times but he definitely would not name the families who had offered him hospitality during the war. He had gone to Canada on a mission for Mr. Benjamin; no, not as a chaplain. He had gone by way of Kentucky.

"Now tell these gentlemen how you got out of Kentucky."

"Well, sir, I propose to write a book on the Secret Service of the Confederacy in which, perhaps, my own adventures will be stated. I will send you a proof copy in advance."

"I'd rather you'd tell the jury about your secret service."

"Anything I know about Mr. Surratt or the assassination, I am willing to tell."

Under pressure he admitted he had ridden out of Kentucky with guides; he had worn Confederate uniform as far as Lexington. There he had donned civilian clothes and had taken the train. In January 1865, passing through Washington en route to Richmond, he had worn civilian clothes.

"Spectacles?"

"Yes, sir. Spectacles."

EDWIN M. STANTON

Andrew Johnson,
17th President of the United States

"To affect your eyesight?"

"Ah—no. To affect the eyesight of others." Laughter warned Pierrepont of listeners' sympathies.

"Did they have that effect?"

"If not, I should not be here today." Again laughter rose.

"Did you see Booth here?"

"I never saw Booth in my life, to my knowledge. I never saw Payne. I never spoke to Surratt in Canada. Never until I saw him in Liverpool."

"Did you ever see Surratt in Canada?"

"I caught a glimpse of him. Father LaPierre asked me if I wanted to see him and I said no."

In an argument that left spectators breathless, he admitted he had been in Canada on detached service. He had engaged in an effort to save lives.

The deftness with which he sidestepped answers provoked Pierrepont into shouting in annoyance, "I want you to tell this jury whether or not you call that chaplain service."

In a flash the witness wheeled toward the jury. "I will explain. I left Canada to save the lives of five of the St. Albans raiders. I risked my own to do it."

Contentiously the cross-examination went on. He had gone to Richmond to obtain proof of the men's military status as Confederate officers. He had returned to Canada with that proof. It established they were on duty there; they were doing in New England what New England men and the Union army were doing in Georgia. He had gone on this mission because they were his brother soldiers. He had started back south and then had heard that President Davis—Mr. Davis—had been captured.

Since the war he had lived with a priest in Canada. In England. In France. He had not seen John Surratt in France, only in Liverpool. They had shared no money. Yes, he had seen Dr. McMillan.

"What did you tell McMillan about Surratt?"

"I told him I had heard the reward for Surratt was about to be lifted. I knew he was after that, so I went to him and told him it was lifted. So he might not hunt Surratt down. I knew he was hunting, for he broke open letters in the post office to find the address where Surratt would be staying."

"Did you tell him Surratt was the greatest scoundrel you ever had seen?"

"No. On shipboard I said I would not aid Surratt because he had not gone to his mother at the time of her trial. McMillan defended him and said—" but here Pierrepont stopped him.

"Oh, let him go on," laughed Dick Merrick. "Let him tell it."

Hastily Pierrepont resumed his questions, but shortly after that, Dick Merrick halted Cameron as he was about to leave the stand.

"You were going to say you had made some harsh statements about John Surratt for not coming to his mother. Tell the jury what you were about to say when you were stopped."

"I told Dr. McMillan that I believed John Surratt innocent but because he had not taken the advice I sent him through Father LaPierre, to go to Washington and tell all he knew, I felt more like giving him up than protecting him. Dr. McMillan said, 'You do him an injustice because he was kept in so secluded a place that he knew nothing of it. He was sedulously kept in ignorance by the gentlemen who surrounded him. They kept saying, 'Everything is going well. Your mother is innocent. They cannot murder her. She will be saved if you keep quiet.' "

After a little unimportant quibbling, the court recessed for lunch.

"I suppose they think other people left a blank line right in the middle of the Webster Hotel book just for me to register," said Johnny as he walked with Isaac back to the jail. The brothers lingered along the way to delay entry into the dark cell ahead.

"I 'spose so," agreed Isaac thoughtfully. "But there's a lot to this I don't understand. Why'd Pierrepont get so upset about your handkerchief?"

"That's easy," broke in the guard. "They've got to prove he was there when their witnesses say he was. They swore to it, you know."

Johnny looked up in surprise at the friendly tone, and Marshal Gooding grinned.

"They say they got it on the eighteenth and Holohan swears he didn't lose it till the twentieth, and that's two days after they swore you were there. They got to show how you could run down here, shoot the President, and run back up there by the eighteenth. Holohan says he didn't lose it 'till the twentieth and that's two days after they swore you were there. That's bad, but when a government witness confirms Holohan y' can see how that looks to the jury. They got to do something about that." He emphasized his words with a spittle aimed at a grasshopper near his foot.

"It doesn't really prove anything—" Isaac said despondently.

"Proves a whole lot," Gooding spoke sagely. "Proves they need evidence mighty bad."

Johnny remained silent. He was learning fast that when the prosecution needed evidence it had ways of obtaining it.

If Louis J. Carland's first appearance had disappointed his listeners by his failure to mention Lou Weichman, his recall now compensated for it.

In the summer of 1865, he said, after the close of the military trial, he had gone for a walk with Lou Weichman. On that stroll, Weichman had asked the witness to walk with him to St. Aloysius Church. There he would go to confession for his soul was so burdened by the testimony he had given against Mrs. Surratt that he had no peace.

"Did you say to him," asked Merrick, "that was not the right way? That he should go to a magistrate and make a statement under oath?"

"I did, and he said he would do so except he was afraid of being indicted for perjury. I asked him for particulars, and he said if he had been let alone and allowed to give his testimony as he wanted to, it would have been quite a different matter for Mrs. Surratt."

"Did he say who troubled him?"

"He said the parties who had charge of the Military Commission troubled him."

"Did he say he had been obliged to swear to a statement that had been written for him?"

"Yes, sir. He said it had been written out for him and that he was told he would be tried as a conspirator if he did not swear to it."

Listeners were in a turmoil as James J. Gifford replaced Carland. The witness admitted swiftly that he had been in Old Capitol's Carroll annex with Weichman.

"Did he ever say to you or in your presence that a government officer told him that unless he testified to more than he had already said they would hang him, too?"

"I heard the officer tell him so, myself."

"Who else was present?"

"James Maddox."

Altercation broke out again based on prosecution protests. Was this evidence substantive? Collateral? Had the defense not waived any objection by being late with it? Was not the testimony inadmissible?

Into the midst of this hostility stepped John Matthews. Once more an actor held the crowd as from a stage. He had played at Fords' Theatre during April 1865 and on the afternoon of April 14 he had seen John Wilkes Booth whom he had known for years. They had met on the corner of Pennsylvania Avenue and 13th Street. Booth, on horseback, was headed toward the Willard Hotel. He had stopped. Leaning over his horse's shoulder he had talked with the witness.

Booth had seemed nervous, agitated. He held his horse's reins in his left hand while he grasped Mathews' fingers with his right —so tightly that the imprint of his fingers had been left on Mathews' skin. Booth had given a sealed, stamped envelope to the witness, but here pandemonium broke out.

"Inadmissible," shouted prosecution counsel. It could not be given to the jury. It had not been admitted as evidence.

"It is not yet evidence," agreed Bradley, "and I propose to argue its admission before it is given to the jury."

To Pierrepont's quick objection Dick Merrick replied. "We should adopt the rule of ordinary practice, but so far as I am concerned I am willing that everything on God's green earth connected with this case should go to the jury. But if Your Honor rules against it—"

"What is this paper?"

"The original articles of the assassination conspiracy," replied Bradley, "and signed by the conspirators."

Total silence fell on the courtroom.

"I feel it my duty to suggest," hastily improvised Carrington, "since we have made very little progress today—"

"I think we've made very great progress," retorted Bradley, belligerently.

27

Joseph Bradley opened Wednesday's session with John Matthews' letter. Booth, Atzerodt, Herrold, and Payne, he explained, had entered into a contract on April 14 to assassinate the President. They had signed their names to the contract, four of them, no others. Booth had left the contract in a sealed envelope which he had asked John Mathews to mail to *The National Intelligencer* the next day but on hearing of the assassination, Mathews had opened the letter, read it, and in panic had destroyed it. He had already related its contents to the Judiciary Committee and if allowed, would give it to the court.

"Here is a contract signed by the parties," said Bradley. "This is evidence of the highest importance not only to this poor prisoner here but to those in their graves, murdered unless they were participants in this conspiracy. It is of the highest interest to the public for this question has agitated the nation. The halls of Congress have rung with it and will ring again. . . . This was not a thing to which the prisoner was party or with which he could have been associated. He was not here. As was proved by a government witness, he was in Elmira. I ask the court to admit this letter as evidence."

He sank into his chair and Carrington arose.

"I dismiss the question, sir. All who were condemned by the Military Commission deserved and met a felon's doom. We expect to satisfy all men whose opinions are worth consideration that this prisoner was the armorbearer of Booth, that his heart conceived, his mind matured, and his voice issued the order that terminated the earthly existence of Abraham Lincoln."

"I cannot see," said the judge in a surly tone, "that this paper is legal evidence to establish any fact except two; one is that fools as well as knaves signed that contract and the other is, if there were more parties engaged in a conspiracy to murder the president they had more sense than those who signed it. It is therefore ruled out."

"We desire an exception noted," said Bradley haughtily.

Recall of previous witnesses filled the day. Listeners confused by the furious exchanges between counsel ignored the battle of technicalities going on over their heads. They were eager to know only one thing—would the prisoner hang as had his mother? In that eagerness the session adjourned.

The following days were little different. Father Louis Rocoffort swore he had talked to Lou outside the confessional but was allowed to say no more. Father Walter, over a barrage of objections, was able to say only that on her way to the gallows Mrs. Surratt had reiterated her innocence. Payne had told the priest in the presence of General Hartranft that Mrs. Surratt had known nothing of the murder plan, nothing of the abduction enterprise.

"We object," the prosecution intervened again, "Mrs. Surratt is not on trial here."

"I think she has been on trial every day," retorted Bradley once more.

"Irrelevant," ruled the judge.

"Exception," replied the defense.

"John J. Reeves," called Joe Bradley and shortly the little Montreal tailor stepped through the witness door.

His business and personal affairs all went into the record. He knew Henri Benjamin Ste. Marie, he said. He knew the poor reputation for truth enjoyed by Ste. Marie. All that cross-examination gained was a relation of John's visits to his house, of the tailoring he had done, and of John's lost cane. After intense grilling he was released, shaken and annoyed, but with his story unaffected.

For Johnny time and fact had grown vague. Hours passed,

sessions dragged, nights lingered long and heat-laden in his tiny cell. Days were scarcely better when court proceedings waited on endless contention. Pierrepont having produced a witness to swear that John was in Washington on April 14, Bradley at once produced one to swear he wouldn't believe the witness on his oath. Pierrepont then countered with six, all reputable citizens they said of themselves, who wouldn't believe Bradley's man on his oath. The din of battle growing louder, Bradley brought up a new set of ten, none of whom would believe the prosecution's six on their oath.

They were, swore Bradley's ten, gamblers, embezzlers, or abortionists. They came, they went, six, ten, thirty, fifty, seventy, up to eighty-eight, none of whom believed any opposing man on his oath. The jury must have lost all count of what they believed or didn't, or why.

Only one thing of importance stood out: Major Almiron Richards, Chief of Police for Washington in 1865, admitted that Lou had been arrested as a conspirator. This noticeably impressed the listeners. In retaliation, Pierrepont rocked the room with his questioning of the defense witness, Dr. Bissell.

The prisoner, swore Dr. Bissell, had stumbled over his crutches in the Brainard House on the evening of April 13, 1865. He remembered the day because he had been in Elmira in connection with an insurance suit over his injuries. He had snubbed the prisoner's attempts at conversation because he had thought him to be an insurance company snooper. Dr. Bissell, Pierrepont brought out, was an inventor but so far only one of his inventions had been marketed, a chamber pot.

John, sitting white and drawn, his eyes fixed on witnesses who came and went in contentious clamor, pondered the lengths to which men will go to accomplish their ends. From the highest position in the country to the lowest the pattern seemed the same. Andrew Johnson had refused even to listen to a doomed woman. Why? Why had the war secretary, why had the army's judge advocate general determined she should die? How could she, an unimportant country woman, endanger them?

The prisoner's questions whirled not only in his brain but in every corner of the courtroom, in every city in the nation. If justice could not be expected from the judge advocate's Military Commission, from the army's legal head, from its commander in chief, where could it be found?

How quickly Carrington had backed down when Bradley had charged military interference in a civilian trial! No wonder then that gamblers, embezzlers, rapists, abortionists, professional dirty-workers did not hesitate to perjure themselves for profit or preference.

As for John, pondering the matter, he debated whether a few years ago anyone could have convinced him that Lou would lie against anyone, and then recalled that a few years ago he had not seen Lou nor anyone tested as everyone connected with him now was being tested. It was, he saw, more understandable for a man to perjure himself for life than for money or preference, and Lou's life had hung by a thread.

Even Wilkes had been proved a better man than Lou for, facing death by fire and bullet, he had shouted through the flames "Here is a boy who has done no wrong . . . harmed no one . . ." and had thrust David Herrold out the barn door. Crippled, hunted by dogs through swamp and thicket to his death, Wilkes still could shoulder his own sins.

He, John Surratt, was now a prisoner because he had boasted himself as cunning, adroit, able to accomplish miracles. Instead he had been a feather-witted loon, able to judge no one rightly. General Lee, John Porterfield, Father Boucher, Canon LaPierre, despite all they had done for him had deceived him in the doing. They had saved his life so far, but in doing so they had also protected themselves.

McMillan had advised, consoled, admired, but today under Mr. Bradley's scorn he had confessed that even as he befriended, he was turning over information for reward. Ste. Marie too had come running with his tongue hanging out to claim a share.

Only a fool believed another man.

As he sat brooding, chin in hand, the July heat increased and tempers of counsel grew shorter. The judge eyed with less tolerance the women who simpered in nervous tension; he watched with mounting irritation the exasperated defense lawyers, observed Joseph Bradley wear himself thin in body and jagged in speech. As the judge's rulings piled up against him, Bradley's frustration grew until he showed scant respect for the words handed down from the bench.

"Perhaps," scornfully, "Your Honor is very sharp, but I have my own intelligence which I think is certainly equal to yours. . . . I have no intention of being browbeaten by the court . . . Your Honor is to have the glory of finding out what no man living under common law ever knew before . . . a law made for a case after the offense is committed . . ."

In ominous silence the court heard the insulting protests. Charges of misconduct, perjury, criminality flew thick and fast between opposing counsel.

"I honestly believe, as I am responsible to Almighty God, that witness is lying with the full knowledge of the United States government—" thundered Dick Merrick.

"Prove it," taunted Pierrepont, secure in the knowledge that confirming documents lay safely locked away in War Department custody.

It was surprising, then, how friendly counsel became during recesses. Inside the courtroom, while ladies opened paper packages and lunched on dry sandwiches, opposing counsel ate, drank, and joked together. Mr. Carrington stretched across Joseph Bradley's desk for a moment of relaxation, while Joe Bradley shared a jug of ice water with His Honor, whose servant had not yet appeared with his lunch basket. Joseph talked pleasantly with one of the six who had sworn against his ten; Dick Merrick and Edwards Pierrepont strolled in the yard for a breath of air, each respectful of the other. Crowds that stayed through the noon hour rather than miss a word of battle made way for counsel or clustered around them at the pump beside the horse watering trough.

"Astonishing," whispered Isaac, as he walked with John, "makes you wonder about their fighting in court."

On Thursday, July 18, frightened Joseph DuTilley took the stand.

Through an interpreter, he informed the court that he was well acquainted with Dr. McMillan, whose reputation for truth was *"méchant mauvais,"* or "wicked bad," as the translator put it. His wife, said DuTilley, was sister to Father Boucher, the priest, and sometimes he drove the carriages for his reverend brother-in-law. McMillan had practiced chicanery on the priest, and he, DuTilley, had seen Father Boucher throw McMillan bodily out of his house. DuTilley left the stand with no questions asked about John Surratt.

Difficulties increased for the defense. John R. Ford and James L. Maddox were not allowed to testify that Lou had told them he had informed the Secretary of War that John Surratt was in Elmira on April 14; that he had read John's letter mailed in Montreal before he left for Elmira. Father Rocoffort was not allowed to testify to Lou's statements outside the confessional. Dr. Gillette, who had heard Payne's dying word of Mrs. Surratt's innocence, was blocked in his testimony.

Summing up this, Joseph Bradley addressed the court.

"We have witnesses in town but their testimony is not admissible under the court's ruling. I think there are some twelve or thirteen whose testimony is now thrown out and we did not choose to trouble the court with bringing in witnesses only to let them be dismissed. We retained them in town until the last, hoping their testimony might be admitted."

"Then," said Judge Fisher, ignoring this statement, "shall we recess with the understanding that you finish your case tomorrow?"

"So far as we can promise we will certainly close tomorrow. We have telegrams that our remaining witnesses are on the way."

Father Boucher's arrival was dealyed so it was not until Monday, the thirty-sixth day of the trial, that he appeared. In the meantime Isaac had occupied the stand for a moment and brought forth some neck-cranings from onlookers who wanted to see the tall, dark young man, former Confederate soldier, and the only Surratt, other than the prisoner, to appear at the trial. His brother John, said Isaac, was twenty-three years old for he was born April 13, 1844. He was then released from the stand.

Father Boucher in accented English explained he knew the prisoner well. Mr. Surratt had visited him in St. Liboire in April, 1865. He had known him all that summer and had seen him in Montreal.

"Do you know," asked Bradley, "whether or not during that time the prisoner received any information about his mother?"

The battle joined. Nothing, said Pierrepont, could be said about the prisoner's mother.

Slowly Joseph Bradley delivered his chilly reply. Jurors, roused from their discomfort, listened to the cold incredulity of his words. As he spoke apprehension grew inside the bar space.

"It has been the burden of the opening of this cause, and has twice been subsequently stated, that the prisoner fled, deserting his mother and thus showing himself a coward. I mean to show he did not know of his mother's condition. I mean to show facts were concealed from him. I propose to show when he was informed."

"It cannot be admitted." Pierrepont shook his head ponderously. The prisoner's mother had not been mentioned by the prosecution in its opening of the case, therefore the defense might not bring in this statement. That she had been assailed by the prosecution since that time was not important. She had not been mentioned in the presentation.

"It has been stated that the prisoner deserted her," Dick Merrick hastily prevented the menace of Bradley's possible reply. "We propose to show that when he learned of her condition he was restrained, prevented—"

"The matter has been decided—" ruled Judge Fisher.

"Note an exception." Bradley's tone carried its own warning.

"Now, Mr. Boucher, what was the condition of the prisoner's health?"

"Do not answer. We have given no evidence about his health."

"Is it possible—" demanded Bradley shaking with anger, "is it possible, we are to be confined to answering statements produced by the prosecution? May we not produce any new facts to repel the facts they produce?" He turned to the court.

"Your Honor. It is alleged that the prisoner had an opportunity to leave Canada, go to Canandaigua and enter his name in the hotel register. Now if we show that he was actually under the eyes of persons all that time, that his health was such that he could not come and go, we offer evidence tending to prove that he did not do so."

"You may give in evidence the prisoner's health," agreed the judge. "I hardly think it admissible, but I will give you benefit of the doubt."

"He was in very poor health," stated Father Boucher. "He had fever and ague. At my house he had the disease once or twice a week and in Montreal every other day, or every second day, as you say in English."

He had often doubted the prisoner could survive, so pale, so weak, so reduced by illness, continued the priest. Yes, he knew the witness McMillan. Their acquaintance was of long standing, and McMillan's reputation for truth and honesty was very bad. They had, truly, a certain contestation over a matter of five dollars, for which the priest now held the doctor's receipt, and so the matter was ended. Of other matters he felt reluctant to speak. Still, if necessary, it was about a principle, about abortion. The priest had objected in a case where McMillan had been called as medical and he as spiritual attendant. After that, loud complaints had come to him and he had advised the doctor not to practice abortion again among his people.

Pierrepont, covering every hour of every day, led the questions toward the fact that the prisoner had been hidden by clergy, assisted by priests, who were therefore legally accessories after the fact. Implications of personal misconduct came next. The witness had visited an American seaside hotel? He had worn civilian, not clerical dress? Two priests with him had worn cassocks, why not he? When guests at the hotel had assumed him to be a lawyer, why had he not shouted that he, too, was a priest?

At the resort, Father Boucher explained, he had not worn clerical dress because of the publicity he had received over the Surratt affair; he had not wished to discuss it with anyone. Finally, at the end of the ordeal, he was permitted to say he believed John Surratt innocent but not to give a reason for this belief.

Another effort failed to get the Canandaigua hotel register admitted. The defense, ruled the judge, had not proved that the prisoner had not come down from Canada and signed it in order to manufacture evidence for himself.

Following this decision the defense announced close of its evidence, and the judge ordered the first rebuttal witness for the prosecution.

All through those July days the fury of testimony unfolding attracted more listeners than the heat repelled. Each session was now so crowded that only a small space before the bench remained open. Spectators jammed windows, women stood in line long before opening hour, or slipped inside the building to usurp choice seats ahead of pass holders who arrived at 10 A.M. They hemmed the prisoner in, eager to catch every change of expression, every move of his long-fingered hands. In his hearing they chattered of his white cotton clothing, handsome black cravat, his long fair hair, and his thin, aristocratic nose.

Congressmen deserted their committees to attend. Every stranger in town made the trial his first stop, said the newsmen. Even Admiral Goldsborough who had interviewed Johnny on the *Swatara* came, and then wrote to Secretary of Navy Gideon Welles: "He is a handsome, cultivated, well-behaved young man, perfectly self-possessed. He conducts himself with great propriety."

To the trial staffs the hours seemed unending. As time dragged on they awaited, each day, the break of noonday recess. Then for a few moments tension would give way and in the privacy of offices and judge's chamber collars would be loosened, faces splashed, lunches eaten.

Waiting along the sidewalks, carriages and buggies lined up like a stalled parade. Heading the line stood the judge's shining carriage, its driver guarding, on the seat beside him the wicker napkin-covered basket sent by His Honor's dutiful lady.

Behind it, lesser vehicles waited for their masters. Joseph Bradley's body servant arrived in a light gig with basket and tray for father and son. On a day that Colgate Hall perched on the carriage block with sandwiches and fruit for Dick Merrick, Lou and Dr. McMillan strolled into view and instantly Colgate, thumbs to ears, waggled his fingers at them and shouted, "Murderer, perjurer," to the great astonishment of bystanders. The insulted gentlemen took out after him and, dignity disregarded, McMillan caught up and seized him by the arm.

Lithe Colgate squirmed away, sped down the block, but at the corner paushed long enough to thumb his nose and repeat his taunts in a manner most unbecoming to a budding law clerk. The day's papers made the most of it according to their political bias.

Fascinated watchers returned with lunch half swallowed to enter the courtroom on the tail of the judge's robe. Across the yard, inside the dark jail walls, Anna waited for Johnny and Isaac. Like his judge, Johnny had little appetite and Anna, tempting him with summer fruits and dainties, despaired of getting enough food down him to keep his lanky body alive. He could not swallow, said Johnny, and Anna, remembering the Old Capitol, shudderingly agreed.

Johnny, without much interest, rose when Marshal Gooding appeared and offered his hands for the wrist irons.

"Skin getting raw?" asked the officer and Johnny shook his head.

A few minutes through the curious crowds and up the steps brought them to the courtroom where audience and trial members waited. Each afternoon passed in a heavy, hot miasma. Contention freighted the air. Every minor point produced by either side turned into a major conflict over its admission. It was not, thought Johnny, so much a trial where a man's life was at stake as like the old store porch debates where every statement was torn to pieces simply to allow the victor to receive the admiration of his listeners.

Like the old squire's and Uncle Zad's political encounters, the debaters here were received as equal in importance with the issue.

28

At the trial's beginning five weeks before, the prosecution had presented witnesses who swore to Johnny's presence in Washington at the time of the murder. McMillan and Ste. Marie had strengthened this testimony by swearing Johnny had admitted to them his difficulty in getting out of town the morning after. To follow up this, the prosecution now set out to establish how he had traveled to and from Washington at that time.

Proof of his presence in Washington was vital to his conviction for otherwise he could not be proved a principal in the murder. By a series of witnesses the prosecution on this day endeavored to show how he had traveled from Elmira on April 13 and his arrival in the District of Columbia in time to murder the president the next day.

They presented train schedules to show the connections from Elmira via Williamsport, Pennsylvania, across the Sunbury River, through Harrisonburg, into Washington by which, they said, he could have reached Washington in time to be shaved by the barber, Wood.

But Johnny remembered the weather in Elmira on April 13, and the defense shot a stunning bolt. There hadn't been a single southbound train out of Elmira that day; all the bridges had been washed out by a flood; train travel had been at a standstill. Later on, passengers had been ferried across the Sunbury River but their travel had been delayed by at least nine hours. With great satisfaction Bradley presented railroad officials with company records which established that fact.

The prosecution was in desperate straits for unless travel south could be proved their case was lost. They produced George W. Strayer, an engineer, who swore that on that day an engine and one caboose had carried a road superintendent out to inspect damages; out of the road's twenty bridges, four were gone and the remainder damaged beyond use. He had driven the engine and had not seen any passengers, but he admitted under prosecution examination that checking on passengers was not his job.

Z. B. Glines and Gunboat Drohan swore when introduced by the prosecution that they had operated the Sunbury ferry on April 13. Drohan in a thick Irish brogue remembered no Elmira train coming in, but he recalled a man on the Williamsport side who wanted badly to get across the river.

"Ef ye'll pay me," he had said, "I'll take yez across."

"Was there anything about this man that arrested your attention?" asked Pierrepont.

"Yes, sir. They was."

"How was he dressed?"

"He had a peculiar coat onto him," the witness replied, then looked around at the roll of laughter through the room.

"I don't see anything so extraordinarily funny," observed Pierrepont, after Judge Fisher rapped for order.

"I don't see that there is," replied Bradley contemptuously, "suppose you go on with your witness."

The proceedings resumed in quiet.

The man had said he wanted to cross the river? Pierrepont wanted to know. What did the fare cost? Fifty cents? Ah, whenever the passenger had no ticket Drohan stopped mid-stream and collected his ferry charge? Just to be sure he'd get it? Laughter rippled but quickly died out.

"The man said he'd no change at all, at all. He gave me a dollar bill and said to keep the change," went on Drohan.

"Have you seen this man since?"

"I have, to th' best o' me knowledge."

"Where? I must request the prisoner to stand up."

Johnny moved. Dick Merrick caught him by the shoulder, shoved him back into his seat.

"No—no—" shouted Bradley. Drohan's gnarled finger, aimed three yards away from the prisoner, pointed to no one at all.

"Is that the man?" Pierrepont ignored the wavering finger.

"To me best belief," the witness replied against half-suppressed chuckles.

"You may take the witness, gentlemen," offered Pierrepont.

"We don't want him," laughed Bradley, "You keep him. Well —just one question." He turned to Drohan. "Who brought you here?"

"Him." This time Drohan's finger pointed steadily at Richard Montgomery in the rear of the room.

"That's enough," insulted Bradley. "That'll do."

The room turned to look and then stared thoughtfully at the man known to be a producer of false witness at the Conspirators Trials. Not a member of Conover's group, he had worked alone but had also been exposed.

On July 23 while Conover still waited his pardon, Riddle wrote letters suggesting clemency for one Charles Dunham. An elaborate pretense of ignorance that Conover and Dunham were the same person controlled the wording of the letters he addressed to

Secretary Stanton and Judge Advocate General Joseph Holt. The government, wrote Riddle, was indebted to Dunham for valuable facts and evidence, therefore Dunham was entitled to pardon.

Meanwhile, in the courtroom, avalanches of character assassination smothered all previous testimony. Prosecution charges swirled against Stephen F. Cameron and Father Boucher. Defense witnesses tore savagely into the reputations of McMillan, Ste. Marie, Lou Weichman. With equal vigor new witnesses attacked everyone who appeared for either side. The room resounded with their angry cries. Reverberations echoed through the city. Judge Holt paced his office while Secretary Stanton brooded over the newspapers or listened to an unnerved subordinate's report of the day's progress.

Joseph Bradley, watching the prosecution's daily triumphs, seethed with anger. During the military trial certain illegalities, bias, and intemperate procedures had been minimized by the city's legal corps on the grounds that rage held the nation. In the haste and chaos of that hearing, baseless and perjured testimony had contributed to the death of accused persons but, said the lawyers, the military men who formed the commission had not recognized this at the time. Every lawyer, agreed the District bar members, at some time or other had been duped by witnesses who perjured themselves for money or for other reasons as varied and complex as the witnesses themselves.

As he remembered, Joseph Bradley's choler grew. The prosecution here must recognize the contradictions in McMillan's testimony, must know that Weichman had bought immunity by turning informer and had then so embellished his first statements that now they were almost unrecognizable.

Bradley would have sworn that the original of John's telegram to Booth, which would have proved his presence in Elmira on April 15, lay safely guarded in prosecution files. He was convinced that not until Ste. Marie had been promised a reward had he changed his story to include Surratt's statement that he had left Washington after, not before the murder. That Ste. Marie had left Montreal with police on his heels for embezzlement of school funds would not affect the prosecution's regard for his testimony, Bradley was sure. Along with counterfeiters, horse thieves, discharged and disgraced detectives, rapists, abortionists, professional and amateur perjurers, a petty embezzler made little difference.

Through the long hot days the same words were whispered through Washington. Once spread on the record, said the defense and its friends, the testimony in this trial differed very little from that offered in the military trials of 1865.

But these were not duped military men, argued laymen and experts alike. Prosecution lawyers represented the nation's top legal talent, men who knew how to present evidence, to evaluate it, how to prevent its admission. How to destroy it. Defense lawyers noted that Mr. Carrington began to look as if he passed sleepless nights, and that when the going became rough, he often took ill and remained quiet.

The heat bore down on counsel. They left the courtroom exhausted, Southerners' light summer clothing limp on their steaming bodies, gray from dusty chairs and tables. Even Pierrepont's expensive garments lost their smartness.

Only the prisoner remained unchanged. His light hair curled damply above his collar, his linen handkerchief lay untouched in his cuff. Pale, tight-lipped, almost motionless, he sat as if unaffected by the animosities sweeping the room.

"I may as well announce now that the passes that have been issued heretofore will be of no worth after today."

Judge Fisher made this announcement on the morning of July 27, Saturday, the forty-first day of the trial. "There will be a new set of passes, for we have been so overcrowded here sometimes as to make it impossible to breathe. I will also announce that during the argument of the case I do not wish to have any display of approbation or disfavor. The marshal will station his forces so that any party guilty of improper conduct will immediately be put out of the room. Are you ready, gentlemen, to proceed?"

After some preliminary squabbling between counsel, the judge ruled on the admissibility of certain evidence. He would admit, he said, evidence concerning Payne's attack on Secretary Seward and Atzerodt's conduct, because they tended to prove that the murder arose from a conspiracy to abduct. Evidence against Jacob Thompson would not be admitted since he had not been proved a member of the conspiracy. Surratt's shooting down Union soldiers as related by McMillan would stand, since it substantiated the conspiracy to assassinate not only the President but other heads of government; the conspiracy was a plot against the government, and shooting soldiers proved malice against the government and its soldiers.

Defense evidence concerning transportation of passengers would not be admitted. No comment would be allowed on the April 15 telegraphic service between Elmira and New York City because the original of the prisoner's wire had disappeared and the court would accept no copy.

At the end of the court's ruling, Edwin C. Carrington rose for the prosecution.

"May it please the court, and you, gentlemen of the jury, I have reason to regret the state of my health in view of the task before me. I shall, notwithstanding, endeavor to do my duty. Permit me, gentlemen, to return to you my sincere acknowledgment of this long, tedious, and painful investigation. Your dignified and solemn bearing is a rebuke to the spirit of levity which, I regret to say, has sometimes pervaded this audience. . . .

"I cannot regard this cruel and miserable assassin as a representative man of the South, as an embodiment of Southern honor and chivalry; and if an attempt should be made to present him as such, I call upon you to spurn it. I am aware that I address Southern men, but men loyal to the laws and constitution of your country. That there were some honorable Confederate officers and men I am free to admit, for I thank God I do not cherish in my heart any sectional sentiment."

For three hours Carrington's oratory filled the air, as his angular body paced the bar space.

"The scene before us is as solemn as the grave. You behold in the person of the prisoner at the bar a dying man, his life forfeited by a deed of horror unprecedented in ancient and modern history." Did they remember, he demanded, when the news of victory had come in? When word had come that peace, sweet peace, had returned? Did they recall that great and loyal soul whose work the victory had been? Did they recall his tall, familiar figure? His expressive language?

Hours passed, filled with eulogy of Lincoln and excoriation of John Surratt. No point of law was touched, for his oratory confined itself to emotional and sectional appeal. Lincoln after death he followed to the "Bosom of the Blessed Saviour," the conspirators he placed with vivid description in a different clime. Booth, he assured the jury, now agonized in hell forever, to atone his horrid crime in penal fire.

The prisoner, he said, equaled Booth in hatred, malice, and revenge, "with red and bloody demons lurking in his base, depraved, malignant heart."

Prince George's County neighbors sat spellbound. John, shocked from his unnatural quiet, listened intently. This could not be he, Johnny Surratt, whom old Mr. Carrington was describing in such words. ". . . false to her who bore him, the gallows on which she expired might have been his throne. There he might have palliated his horrid crime with show of parental affection . . . but false, false, he sought to save his wicked life in flight.

"I arraign him as the murderer, assassin of Abraham Lincoln. It matters not where he was; every man was at his place, performing his part; every conspirator was a member, and the act of one was the act of all." He paused for breath.

"Permit me now the order of my argument: if the jury believe the prisoner a member of the conspiracy to murder Abraham Lincoln, they must find him guilty no matter where he was when the shot was fired: if they believe that in the conspiracy to abduct the president, one of the conspirators killed the president without the knowledge or consent of the others, they must find the prisoner guilty; if they believe the prisoner encouraged, aided, abetted the conspiracy, they must find him guilty even though he was no witness to the killing; if they believe the prisoner a member of the conspiracy not present at the killing, it lies upon him to show himself unconnected with the conspiracy."

Following noon recess, Carrington returned for another three hours of oratory, its burden a continued personal attack on the prisoner. The court dozed, prosecution counsel sat listlessly attentive. One by one, listeners slipped out for a breath of air.

Only defense counsel sat alert, note pads in hand. The swiftly scratching pencils of reporters could be heard when the speaker stopped for breath. Late that afternoon as Carrington paused, slumped wearily against his chair, Dick Merrick spoke.

"As the learned district attorney appears fatigued, I think it proper to ask Your Honor to recess until Monday to enable him to conclude his argument."

Sadly, hotly, the disconsolate jurors entered waiting carriages to ride to their hotel and await the opening of the trial's sixth week.

Samuel Conover chose that week end to carry out his threat. On July 29 he wrote to President Johnson a missive that would have curdled the blood of the Ashley-Riddle-Stanton conspirators had they read it on that torrid day. Congressman Ashley, wrote Conover smoothly, had approached him through Mr. Matchett and had detailed to him the evidence needed by the Judiciary Committee in its effort to unseat the president.

This evidence must prove that Johnson had conspired with Booth; witnesses must be produced to swear they had delivered notes between the two, and who must further swear they knew the notes' contents because they had been invited into the conspiracy. Servants of the Kirkwood Hotel must be found who would swear to Booth's visits to Johnson while the vice-president had lived there. New York witnesses must testify that Booth had reported to them Johnson's approval of the assassination; that it had been set for Inauguration Day, and that Johnson's drunkenness that day had been an effort to nerve himself for the murder.

Conover's letter ended with the statement that he had promised to provide this testimony, and to obtain witnesses who would appear honest and intelligent. These witnesses had been found, he wrote; they had been rehearsed in their parts, some of them in the jail, others by Ashley and General Benjamin F. Butler in their offices. His own purpose, he assured the president, was to trap these traitors in their nefarious plans and to expose them to the chief executive that he might know by whom he was surrounded.

This letter made a noteworthy addition to others piling up in Andrew Johnson's desk.

While Johnson pondered his letter, the discordant voice of Edwin C. Carrington continued to saw the courtroom air. Once more he listed the conspirators by every opprobious name under Heaven, centering them all on the quiet prisoner across from him.

"Can you not see them, gentlemen, like a bunch of herrings —I beg pardon for using so commonplace an expression—Booth ordering the concealment of Payne, Surratt concealing him, his mother nursing him as you would a gamecock for the entertainment of the vulgar public?" But when he turned to the matter of Mrs. Surratt's death he made a mistake.

"If Your Honor please, the learned counsel who opened the defense spoke of the prisoner's mother as a murdered woman. Mr. Merrick has spoken of her as a butchered woman. At least by implication the counsel has charged the honorable members of the Military Commission with murder—"

"I am not aware—" cut in Bradley.

"I do most emphatically repudiate the imputation. They charge it upon us and I deny it—I undertake to prove the contrary—"

"Aha!" shouted Bradley, "The whole record is open? That's all I want!"

"The whole record is now open!" called out Dick while young Joe leaped to his feet. "We couldn't open it; they wouldn't let us. It was not their evidence and they stopped us . . . but now it is open! All open!"

At this gleeful chorus Carrington stopped in perplexity.

"I regret," he said reprovingly, "that it should have been necessary for an American woman to be executed. There is no man with a heart more capable of love for woman than myself, but when she unsexes herself, encourages, and is instrumental in committing murder, then she places herself beyond protection. I believe in the submission of woman, submission to her God, to the laws of her country, to her husband, but when she opens her house to murderers, conspirators, infuses the malice of her own treason and encourages them to murder, then I boldly say that public duty requires an example of her conduct."

Physically and mentally exhausted, court and counsel sought their homes that night.

29

Dick Merrick opened the defense argument Wednesday, July 31, the forty-fourth day of the trial.

"The feelings with which I approach the argument of this case," he said slowly, "are new to me." The courtroom hushed to quiet. "Its magnitude is beyond any I have known, and its surroundings are peculiar and painful beyond any experience.

"You have in charge the prisoner at the bar; his life is in your hands. The government has caused him to be arraigned before this tribunal, but there is in this prosecution something beyond the ordinary courses pursued in bringing a criminal to justice. I find arrayed against my client the best talent at the bar, a numerous combination of counsel in and out of court. I find certain officers of high government abandoning the duties committed to them, devoting themselves to the manipulation of witnesses to be sworn before this jury.

"This combination of legal gentlemen is aided by officials with motives such as we may see before the case is ended. I find them to be aided, also, by scores of spies and detectives scattered all over the country, supported from the treasury of the government, with hundreds of millions at its command. All this machinery is to pursue to the gibbet one penniless young man who rests upon professional charity for the vindication of his name and defense of his life.

"I regret it will become my painful duty to speak some truths I would rather leave unspoken and inquire into the motives of men. I believe, gentlemen, while we have been talking a great deal about conspiracies to abduct or kill on the part of Rebel sympathizers, there have been conspiracies to commit murder through forms of law and in utter disregard of the principles that govern just and honest men.

"In a case of this course, whatever can throw light upon the subject should be admitted to the jury. What has been the case in this trial? Whenever any technical rule of law could by constraint exclude testimony it has been invoked, bent from its uniform application and general uses to secure, if possible, the conviction of the prisoner against the manifest truths of the case. I shall find no fault with His Honor, but in justice to myself I must say that nothing has fallen from His Honor to change my settled conviction that all testimony should have been allowed to go to the jury.

"One hundred and fifty exceptions taken by defense counsel encumber this record. It is strange there should be so wide a difference between ourselves and the court. This can be accounted for only by the fact that attorneys for the government have strained every principle of law, invoked every discretionary power of the court against the prisoner.

"Every feeling that could rock the human heart has been invoked, every sentiment calculated to excite your prejudice has been urged on you with a violence, rigor, and virulence such as I have never seen equaled in a court of justice. Gentlemen, you are under oath to do justice according to the evidence.

"The charge is that the prisoner with Booth killed Abraham Lincoln; next that he conspired with Booth and others to kill Lincoln. Gentlemen, you are trying him for murder, but the prosecution, failing in that, now desires to try him for dispatch carrying, for being a Rebel sympathizer, for everything except murder.

"Mr. Wilson, opening to the jury, said it was simply an indictment for murder and they would prove him here in Washington helping with the murder. By their twisting and turnings they have put this case in such shape it is almost an insult for an intelligent jury to have to argue it. Not only have they shown John Surratt innocent of this murder, but by witnesses they themselves have brought here they have shown the physical impossibility of his being here. . . .

"Next the proposition is that the prisoner's personal presence in Washington was not necessary to prove his guilt. He could perform his part in Elmira and be equally guilty. Do you mean to say now that he was in Elmira performing his part? Turn back to the proceedings and blush with shame. When we offered to show you why he was in Elmira, you said there was no proof on your part of what he was doing there and so we could not show any. If you mean to contend now that he was there doing his part in the conspiracy, you have tricked us again.

"You remember, gentlemen of the jury, we had General Lee here to show what the prisoner was in Elmira for? What his business was? That it had no part in the conspiracy? But the court said, 'There is no charge that he was there helping the conspiracy.' They disclaimed the charge then; it is too late to claim it now. Too late for law, too late for honor.

"Let us deal fairly with this young man, and if the reputation of Joseph Holt should not have vindication of innocent blood shed by judicial murder, let us have justice still."

All day he talked, explained, clarified, quoted earlier testimony. All the next day he assailed Rhodes's testimony about making a visit to the theater, attacked the men who had sworn they had seen John on the murder day but when faced with the accused, backed away from identification. He called attention to Hess and Carland, who had called the time that night, and to Mrs. Lambert and her son. All of them were Washington people, he explained, all neighbors of the jurymen, all people to be believed.

The former detective Lee he followed through many years, many communities. "Troops of witnesses from every locality show he has established a reputation for lying almost beyond parallel. With all its countless detectives and spies, the prosecution could deliver only two men who would say they would believe him on his oath. Wood, the barber," Merrick said charitably, was mistaken, for the prosecution has shown by its own witnesses that the prisoner could not possibly have arrived in Washington in time for Wood to shave him.

"They fall back on William E. Cleaver. I confess I was very much surprised to see him on the stand when I recall the denunciations I heard the district attorney hurl at him a few weeks ago. Gentlemen, gentlemen, has the United States bowed itself to the low humiliation of using such an instrument as he? We have not been allowed to introduce any evidence against him nor the method by which he was prepared for his task, save as we have drawn it from himself. In jail with him was that most notorious felon, Sanford Conover, whose name has passed into infamy and upon whose body the doors of Albany Penitentiary grated just yesterday.

"Cleaver found in him a congenial companion, and they devised the story he has told in this case. Conover, having trained his pupil, calls on Ashley to see if the education is complete, and Ashley turns him over to the prosecuting attorneys, and they put him on the witness stand. Then, gentlemen of the jury, they ask you to believe him.

"David C. Reed told you he had known the prisoner from boyhood; that he was from thirty to thirty-five years old. Look at this boy broken by imprisonment, wasted, worn, suffering, but no sensible man would say he is thirty years of age. His brother says he is twenty-three. Reed now thinks he was mistaken."

Equaling Carrington in detail, he went on. "Unintelligent, mistaken Susan Ann, terrified Rachel, who loved the Surratt family but 'not enough to tell a lie,' showing the character of the faithful Negro woman with which all of you gentlemen are acquainted, who impressed you with her truth."

Weichman, Clarvoe, Vanderpool, he dismissed without oratory. Of the witnesses who had sworn they had seen Surratt in Washington on April 14, only one had ever seen him before, said Dick.

"There is another voice—from the grave, speaking in behalf of her child. Clarvoe says Mrs. Surratt said to him, 'I don't know where John is. He has not been here for two weeks; I got a letter from him today.' He turned to Carrington. "You broke the cerements of her tomb. You brought her here. Now close those cerements if you can. She is here, a mother pleading for her son, testifying in his behalf. You, gentlemen of the jury—" and he faced them again—"you have this their witness to prove that John Surratt was here, broken down. You have his mother casting her last protection about her child and saying he was not here.

"But," argued Dick, "even if he had been here, how did the prosecution get him here?" He traced the route from Elmira to Washington as the prosecution had presented it. "At Williamsport he was ferried across by Richard Montgomery."

"By Drohan," Bradley corrected.

"Oh, no, Montgomery," Merrick insisted; Montgomery had created Drohan the witness, paid him to come here. And Montgomery was the creature of Conover and had cooperated with him in perjury before the Military Commission. "Montgomery is that man's friend." Merrick pointed an accusing finger at Edwards Pierrepont.

"Drohan says, 'That is the man' and points three yards away from the prisoner. Too stupid to learn his lesson well is this witness. This man living in the backwoods identifies a 'peculiar coat.' If the prisoner traveled in that coat, gentlemen of the jury, why did he not have it on in Washington when, fresh from gravel trains, construction trains, without a change of clothing on the way, he appeared in Wood's shop? Reed thought he wore a nicely got up suit but nothing so fantastic as a Garibaldi jacket.

"Drohan was the only man who saw that jacket on the prisoner as he traveled. Montgomery has overleapt himself. He had better quit business until his senior partner gets out of the penitentiary. He does not do his work well, gentlemen." Dick turned scornfully to the prosecution table. "You should not have such a bungler in your service."

He moved swiftly back to the charges.

"There might have been a conspiracy to abduct the president," he admitted, "but what is the plain common sense of this? Here were a parcel of young men with their minds inflamed upon political questions, sympathizing earnestly with the South as a great many of our Maryland young men did, desirous of rendering such assistance as they could, probably helping persons across the river, carrying dispatches.

"It is not improbable there may have been some idea of abducting the president as a measure of war—a thing unjustifiable and for which they might have been taken and executed. It is not improbable for there were at that time, you will recollect, a great many prisoners in the North and many federal prisoners in the South. It has passed into history that the Confederate States at that time offered to surrender up to the federal government from ten to twenty thousand prisoners if the United States would send transportation to Savannah for them."

"And without any exchange," cut in Bradley.

"Yes. Without any exchange. They said, 'We are exhausted. Our resources are gone; our food is gone. We starve. Your prisoners starve. Come and get them, for we are unable to do that justice by them which the laws of war require.' Said the United States, 'You shall keep them.'

"For this starvation I hold the United States responsible. The South's men starved. Her own people had no food. Children fell from the mother's breast, and mothers withered and died for food. Soldiers fell by the roadside. The South asked the North to take their prisoners that the men might live. The United States refused. That has gone into history, gentlemen, uncontroverted. Undisputed.

"At the time of which I have been speaking, there may have been some purpose to hold Mr. Lincoln hostage. I hold Mr. Lincoln blameless for the errors of his administration, for he was dominated by those men who still dominate high places, from which they should be driven. There may have been this scheme, but that it was broken up is proved by Weichman's testimony."

There had been an enterprise to save the Confederate prisoners, he went on, for Booth's diary gave its beginning and end. "For six months we had worked to capture, but our cause being almost lost, something great and decisive must be done." This, said Merrick, the jury must believe, for it was the evidence of the only man who knew, John Wilkes Booth. He read it again, paragraph by paragraph, to the end:

" 'This night, before the deed, I wrote an article and left it for the editors of the *National Intelligencer* in which I fully set forth our reasons. . . .'

"Where is that article?" he demanded. "We were not allowed to present its contents. You promised," he reminded Pierrepont, "that all rumors concerning the execution of Mrs. Surratt would be set to rest. You said that after her conviction by the Military Commission it was widely circulated that men active at the seat of government prevented any effort being made to reach the president, but that the truth was, her conviction was brought before the president at a full cabinet meeting and that 'the full truth of record will be presented to this court.'

"Why did you not present it? You had the record of Mrs. Surratt's case right here in this room. Did you find with it something you did not like? Did you find a recommendation for mercy which the president never saw? You promised to show us, too, that nobody prevented access to the president for those seeking clemency.

"Why did you not do it? I should have been glad to hear that proof. Who of you in Washington that day will ever forget when the tolling of bells reminded you that the hour had come when those people would be hanged? You remember, gentlemen? Twenty-four hours for preparation? The announcement of death scarcely dying away before the tramp of the guard was heard, leading to the gallows? Priest, friend, philanthropist, and clergyman hurried to the president to implore for that poor woman only three days in which to prepare her soul to meet her Good. And yet no access.

"A heartbroken daughter stretched across the steps that lead to the Executive Chamber, praying to everyone who came, 'Let me have access, that I may ask but one day for my mother. Just one day.' But did she get there? No."

"And yet, says the counsel, there was no one to prevent access.

"Why did you not prove it? Oh, God, if it could be proved, I would rejoice for reflecting on that hour when my country was so degraded I could weep. I could weep tears of sorrow, of blood and of shame.

"Who stood between her and the seat of mercy? Does conscience lash the chief of the Bureau of Military Justice? Does memory haunt the Secretary of War? Or is it true that one who stood between her and executive clemency went to his sleep in the dark waters of the Hudson while another died the death by his own violent hand in Kansas?

"The learned gentleman came here to put these things to rest but he has not done so."

Over breathless silence the words lashed listeners' ears. The matter had become political, explained Dick, when charges were made in the House of Representatives against the Judge Advocate General, the Secretary of War, and John A. Bingham, Assistant Judge Advocate for the Commission. He recalled again instruction of witnesses by Judge Advocate Holt, and questioned once more why a high official of the War Department should instruct witnesses in a District court.

"All these things I have mentioned to you. Conover's story, Susan Ann Jackson's testimony, the story of Holohan's handkerchief—all these were known to the judge advocate who furnished the evidence in this case. You remember we brought here the man who lost that handkerchief? The prosecution knew all about the loss for it had been reported to the detectives and the government.

"Following this comes Mr. Carrington breaking the cerements of the tomb and demanding a verdict against Mrs. Surratt. In God's name, gentlemen, is it not enough to try the living? Will you play the ghoul and bring her here from the earth to hang a corpse? You brought her in. She is here. We have felt our blood run cold as the rustlings of garments from the grave rushed by us. Her spirit is around and about us in the courtroom and walks beside those who did her wrong. The judge advocate general will learn hereafter the eternal law that where guilt is, sorrow shall answer it.

"Gentlemen, if counsel propose to try her on this case, why not give us the benefit of her dying utterance? I put a witness on the stand and said, 'Did you administer the consolations of religion to Mrs. Surratt?' 'I did. I gave her communion and prepared her for death.' 'Did she tell you,' I asked, 'when she was going to the gallows that she was an innocent woman?'

"He nodded his head but could not answer, for the prosecution objected to that question and the court sustained the objection. If you try a woman who is dead, can you not have charity enough to allow her last words to speak for her? Were you afraid? Did you feel her words would sink deep into the heart of every man in this room and in the United States? Shame, shame. Prepared for the world to come, marching to the gallows with her God before her and the world left behind, and I ask you if at that time she cannot speak for herself.

" 'No,' you say."

Listeners sat rigid in their seats, save where tears rolled down a woman's cheek and she dabbed at them with a handkerchief. In the brief pause eyes turned on Merrick, then moved to where Johnny sat as if made of stone, eyes riveted on the hands tightly clenched in his lap.

"I cannot pursue this subject further. My feelings choke my utterance." He stopped, pulled himself together, and with an effort returned to his argument.

The district attorney had accused the prisoner of fleeing from his mother when she was in danger, but Surratt had known nothing of her danger until her death. Flee? What else could he do? That Military Commission was not organized to try; it was organized to convict. He fled from a blazing country, from lawlessness, oppression. Law was dead. Tyranny ran riot, and no man was safe. He would have had no trial. He would have hanged, unheard, like the rest.

"Gentlemen, I invoke for the prisoner not your mercy but your deliberate judgment. There has been blood enough in the expiation of that fearful crime, but if he is guilty, convict him. If he is innocent, acquit him.

"May the eternal God guide your judgment."

30

All Washington read the trial reports word for word, but perhaps no one read them more carefully than did the worried occupant of the White House.

Conover's letter to him confirmed the Ashley association, of which he was already aware. Whether he questioned his official family at that point is not known, but something happened to precipitate a flurry of disclaimers. On Friday August 2 Albert G. Riddle hastily wrote Secretary Seward that to the best of his knowledge, as manager of the Surratt case, Conover had supplied no names nor "can I recall any fact given in evidence which was derived from him." He went on to deny knowledge of the case history of Conover, of any association between him and Ashley, and of Ashley's letter to the judge advocate general asking help in obtaining Conover's pardon. Also, Riddle explained he had signed a certain Mrs. Dunham's request for her husband's pardon merely because a lady in distress had come to his hotel and had asked his help.

A few days later Judge Advocate General Holt entered his denial of any wrongdoing. His approval of Dunham's pardon had been on purely personal grounds; it had nothing to do with the Bureau of Military Justice or any other of his official connections. It had been merely "an indorsement of Riddle's request on the grounds of important services in the Surratt testimony."

The letters accumulated in Andrew Johnson's desk now mapped a trail from the District Jail through the House of Representatives, Albany Penitentiary, and straight to the top desk in the War Office at which sat Edwin M. Stanton. Improbable as it at first had seemed, it now lay clear that the attempt to destroy President Andrew Johnson politically was at the heart of the trial of John Surratt.

The trial had lasted forty-five full days when Joseph Bradley began his defense argument. Easily and quietly he spoke:

"I had hoped, gentlemen of the jury, that I should be spared any address on this occasion. The case has been so completely exhausted by Mr. Merrick that no further debate is necessary. It is an exceedingly simple case, plain in its facts. . . .

"The indictment names the prisoner as a principal in the murder of Mr. Lincoln. There is not a man among you who has been at this bar a year who does not know that to be a principal a man must either have been present to do the murder or be someplace else helping by arrangement. Yet the United States proved a month ago that Lincoln was murdered while John Surratt was four hundred miles away, ignorant of what was being done."

Bradley then reviewed the evidence that showed John leaving Montreal on April 12, in Elmira on the evening of the next day, there also on April 14, where he was seen by Carroll, Atkinson, Stewart, and Cass.

He paused, and when he continued his voice was crisp and incisive. "I have done with the defense of Surratt, but I ask your indulgence on one or two facts. It is clear to me that the government knew these facts before the indictment was found. If this evidence in their possession had been laid before the Grand Jury instead of that reptile, Weichman, and his statement, you would never have been troubled with the trial of this case.

"It is not my privilege to tell you now what William P. Wood told me on this subject, but after this case is over you may know what that statement was. But, independent of revelations made to me in the presence of three or four witnesses, the proof is clear that the government knew the abduction plan had been abandoned. When they recalled the reward for Surratt's capture they knew his innocence. Now we have taken the trouble to prove it.

"I agree he ought to have been put upon his trial. A great country should have helped to ascertain the truth, and when that truth was ascertained, it should have said 'Not guilty on the evidence,' and should have abandoned it. God help the country when, with the clearest proof of his innocence, a man should be prosecuted for his life to gratify not public justice but something else."

Bradley's eyes swept the intent faces of the twelve jurymen. He paused, then went deliberately on.

"There is a leaf in our public history which deserves to be read carefully. In October 1865, reward for the apprehension of this young man was withdrawn. In the political campaignings of that year, attention was drawn to the trial and execution of his mother. A voice made itself heard in the halls of Congress, calling her death a judicial murder, brought about through the suppression of evidence. The political effect of that voice was beginning to be heard.

"The government knew it could not convict Surratt but other men believe they may receive vindication of their conduct at the hands of this jury."

Bradley paused again, this time looking out over the crowds in the courtroom. They sat alert, listening expectantly, anticipating the political scandal they had been told underlay this trial. Satisfied with what he saw, Bradley resumed in his deliberate voice.

"For more than four weeks we have been trying Mrs. Surratt. More than four weeks ago the innocence of this young man was complete, but it did not answer the purpose of the prosecution. The Supreme Court has said that the Military Commission by which Mrs. Surratt was condemned and executed was illegal and without authority. Politicians and lawyers have denounced her execution as murder, based on insufficient proof. The prosecution said they would vindicate the men who conducted the Conspiracy Trials, but despairing of convicting her son, they began to bestow their time on the mother.

"Let us see who was Mary E. Surratt. I believe no tongue has spoken of her except in praise, unless it be Weichman and Lloyd. Not only happy in her temper and disposition but in her religious duties, she was evidently happy in her associations. No breath of suspicion ever crossed her path, no failure in any of the relations of life touched her, so far as we know. That she was lovable is shown by the testimony in this case; that she was loving is most true. She received under her roof a college mate of her son. She treated him as a son. In sickness she nursed him. In health she waited on him, poured out the freedom of her family on him as if he were a son."

Johnny sat rigid, his hands still clenched, as Bradley undertook a recital of homely little episodes of life in the family town house. Herrold, Wood, Atzerodt, Booth, all came to life. Breathlessly the listeners hung on his words, swiftly the newsmen scribbled. Lou, sitting at the table with the prosecution counsel, kept his eyes resolutely away from the defense and any chance encounter with Johnny's gaze.

"Weichman tells you he met Booth through the introduction of Dr. Mudd," said Bradley, and related the four different versions of time and place given by Lou for this event. "This man, treated as a son in the house, sleeping in the same bed with John Surratt, drinking the same whiskey with Herrold, wearing the same clothes with Atzerodt in the day and going out with him at night, could they have concealed from him what was going on among them? They could not, if they would; he is too prying, too inquisitive. He associated with all these men, conversed with Howell, a blockade runner, provided him with information from his work in the War Department, accepted a Confederate cipher from him. Did he not know what was going on?

"I tell you, gentlemen, that man knew everything as well as they did. He need not deny it, for it is written in broad letters on his face. You saw him, you all looked at him. You all felt that as your eyes fell on him he quivered, as if he tried to protect himself with a garment to prevent your penetrating into his innermost heart and seeing what lay there.

"There is not in the range of his testimony one single material fact, scarcely an immaterial one, that passed within the observance of another party where we have not flatly contradicted him."

Gravely the jury members eyed Lou who sat self-consciously under their gaze.

"Weichman stands convicted of having told one story to the Military Commission and another, infinitely more aggravated, to this tribunal. He says he does so because he recollects better now, two years later, than he did at that time, and because he had determined to give all his influence to the prosecution to be avenged on these people. This is the man you are asked to credit.

"I beg that when you have thought this matter over, you not leave the jury box but render a verdict at once, '*Not guilty*'; and if you can in your consciences, prepare a paper that, having heard the testimony, you are convinced of the innocence of the mother of the prisoner. I have done."

Joseph Bradley sank exhausted into his chair. The silence following his words broke into excited buzzing, and Judge Fisher rapped smartly for order.

"This court is adjourned until tomorrow."

31

Saturday morning, crowds converged on the courtroom and packed themselves rows deep in halls and yard. Edwards Pierrepont rose impressively after the opening routine, waited for the room to quiet, and began the argument for the prosecution.

"May it please Your Honor and gentlemen of the jury, 'Yea all that a man hath will he give for his life.' When the book of Job was written this was true. It is as true today. A man will give his property, his liberty, his good name. He will sacrifice his father; he will desert his mother. He will raise his hand before Almighty God and swear he is innocent.

"To me, gentlemen, this prisoner at the bar is a pure abstraction. I have no feeling toward him whatever. My business is to prove to you from the evidence that the prisoner is guilty. I have come for the purpose of proving that the prisoner was engaged in a conspiracy with Booth which resulted in the death of Abraham Lincoln.

"I have not come to prove Mrs. Surratt innocent or guilty. I do not understand why she was lugged into this case. I do not understand why counsel denounced the tribunal that tried her, why he thus indirectly censured President Andrew Johnson.

"The counsel certainly knew that the president ordered the tribunal, that he signed the warrant that ordered the execution; that the president, when that trial record was brought to him, brought it before his cabinet, and that every single member voted to confirm the sentences and the president with his own hand signed it. No other man ordered it. No other one touched it, and when it was suggested by some of the Military Commission that because of her age and sex it might be right to change Mrs. Surratt's sentence to life imprisonment, he signed the death warrant. There it is."

Dramatically he tossed onto the defense table a small packet of foolscap paper tied together with yellow linen tape.

"My friend can read it."

All eyes turned to the table where Bradley, Merrick, and young Joe stared at the packet, bearing the heading, *Formal Brief Review of the Trial of the Conspirators.* No one moved to touch it.

Reporters scratched furiously away at what would be the sensation of their Sunday issues. As they scratched, Pierrepont talked. All day he talked. He read from the Old Testament to prove that all government is of divine origin. "All government is of God," he loudly declaimed and then launched into an eloquent sermon on "the meek and lowly Jesus, Saviour of the world, who died for you, for me, for all."

Moving swiftly to Lincoln's letter to Mrs. Bixby, he read it with pathos that brought tears to the eyes of listening women.[1]

Avoiding all legal aspects of the case, he spent hours on John's evil nature as he saw it, his flight to Egypt as McMillan told it, his finding no "safety in gallant little England . . . no place for treason and murder . . . no corner in the Pope's land where he could hide. . . ." In Egypt, declared the counsel, even the Sphinx stared at him with stony eyes; here his knees smote together, and he surrendered himself to his pursuers.

The afternoon he gave over to the defense of his witnesses whom Bradley had assailed, until the room rang with contradictions of contracontradictions. Lou Weichman was pure gold, he said, but John M. Lloyd had so hated to testify that he had required "special treatment." Unless the prisoner was found guilty, he assured the jury, the city of Washington would no longer remain the nation's capital. The capital would be moved. People outside Washington wanted the capital moved. Other cities wanted it and would argue that the city was so full of Southern sympathizers that its jury would not convict John Surratt of the president's murder.

Sunday's newspapers carried a bombshell: *the majority of Mrs. Surratt's judges had not been convinced of her guilt.* Five of her nine judges had recommended mercy for her to the president. At last, the truth was out.

---

[1] Mr. Lincoln was misinformed. It has since been determined that Mrs. Bixby did not have five sons in service to be killed in action.

The source of the information was incontrovertible. The reporters had seen the official Report of the Trial of the Conspirators. More specifically, they had seen, attached to the end of the report, the half sheet of paper on which the request for mercy had been made to the president. It bore the signatures of the five judges.

The defense lawyers had not touched the report; it had not been admitted as evidence. At the end of the session Judge Advocate General Joseph Holt had come to the courtroom to retrieve the document, but the newsmen had already seen its explosive contents.

On Sunday August 4 Andrew Johnson read in the newspapers the speech that laid Mrs. Surratt's death at his feet. Early Monday morning a messenger sped away with an order for Secretary Stanton to come at once to the president, official trial report in hand. Three times the messenger carried the summons. At the third order, Stanton dispatched an office subordinate with the report but himself stayed safely away from the White House and Andrew Johnson.

William P. Wood, former superintendent of Old Capitol Prison, who for years had been lackey to Stanton, now appeared at the White House and entered into private conversation with the president. He told the president that after Mrs. Surratt's arrest he, Wood, had been sent to her brother, Zad Jenkins, with the promise that she would be released if she or her family gave any information about Booth's whereabouts. Relying on this promise, Zad had whispered that he had heard of two strange men down by Captain Cox's house. This tip had led to Booth's apprehension but Stanton had refused to honor his promise. Wood then tried to reach the president, but upon Stanton's written order had been refused entry to the White House.

That Monday, while the president pondered, Pierrepont talked on. Mrs. Slater's face and figure, her fashionable lace mask; General Lee's detached service in Canada; gentle old John Pyles, Stephen F. Cameron, all received his tongue's scathing attention.

He ignored all doubts about prosecution witnesses, discarded the impossibility of John's arriving in Washington in time to be shaved by Wood. Magnificently he ignored his own train schedule, which had proved that no traveler could have reached Washington before nearly 10:30 A.M. on the murder day.

"Now, get him to the barber shop in time to be shaved before 9 A.M.," gibed Bradley.

"Beautifully will I get him there," retorted Pierrepont, "to be shaved so clean he'll not want shaving like that again." However, there he promptly dropped the subject. "I have read so much I am hoarse in my throat," he complained, and Judge Fisher adjourned the session.

At the end of the Avenue in his office on the second floor of the White House, Andrew Johnson sat deep in thought. Wood's story had shocked him. Yet there before him lay the proof, the formal *Brief Review of the Case* which two years before had been delivered to him personally by Joseph Holt.[2] The long pages of report, convictions, statements of death warrants, all tied together with yellow linen tape. But there was something else; a half sheet of paper on which was written a recommendation for mercy for Mrs. Surratt. A black sheet of legal length paper separated it from the last page of the report. Judge Holt had held the report in his hands as he discussed its contents. The pages were fastened together at the top and each page as read

[2] David Miller DeWitt, in his *Judicial Murder of Mary E. Surratt* published Baltimore, 1895, writes on page 115: "The Judge Advocate General . . . brought with him . . . so much of the proceedings as was necessary to the accomplishment of his errand—viz: the record of the findings and sentences which the President was to endorse. This document consisted of a few sheets of legal-cap paper fastened together at the top, written on both sides in the fashion of legal papers, i.e., beginning at the top of the first page and, on reaching the bottom, turning up the papers and writing on the back from the bottom to the top.

"It was a document complete in itself, the written record ending on the first page of the last half sheet—this leaving blank the remainder of that page and the whole of the obverse side; ample room for the death warrant. To this record, but forming no part of it, the Petition, as we have said had been affixed, but in such a manner as to be easily separable without mutilation.

"He must have brought with him his official report of the trial—styled 'The formal brief review of the case' which was subsequently appended to the regular Report of the Judge Advocate General to the Secretary of War . . . it is dated July 5, 1865, and is signed J. Holt. It recites the verdicts and sentences; . . . certifies to the regularity and fairness of the proceedings; recommends the execution of the sentences; *but it makes no mention of the petition, or any suggestion of mercy.* . . ."

was turned back and folded under the unread portion. In that way the little half page had been hidden from sight.

But it was strange that the recommendation had not been mentioned by Judge Holt. It was stranger still that it had not been included in the official publication of the trial, approved and released by Stanton, nor in the judge advocate's annual report to the Secretary of War.

The time had come to add the last letter to the collection in his desk. Johnson pulled forward a sheet of paper, lifted his pen and wrote:

> *Mr. Edwin M. Stanton.*
>
> *August 5, 1867.*
> *Sir:*
> *Public considerations of a high character constrain me to say that your resignation as Secretary of War will be accepted.*
>
> *Andrew Johnson*
> *President of the*
> *United States.*

"If . . . he (Judge Holt) had turned the page up and continued his writing on the obverse side from the bottom down, as the foregoing had been written, then the petition of mercy . . . would have been, if still attached, directly under the eye of the President as he signed the death-warrant. But, as now appears from the record itself, the careful Judge Advocate did not turn the page up from the bottom. On the contrary, reverting to the layman's way of writing papers, he whisks the whole record over, and continues the writing of the death-warrant on the back of the last half sheet of the record from the top to the bottom— by this change of method, either throwing the petition under the leaves of the record, or, if disengaged, leaving it upside down."

This appraisal made thirty years after the execution of Mrs. Surratt has withstood all subsequent studies. No writer on this topic, including this writer, who has seen and studied this document, has found reason to dispute DeWitt's analysis.

32

By Tuesday, word of the president's action was over town, and Pierrepont opened the court session with a reference to the mercy recommendation.

"I brought the record here," he said. "The recommendation for mercy is part of the record I produced. Judge Advocate General Holt gave it to me and with his own voice told me he had laid it before the president when the president signed the execution order. That is all my knowledge, gentlemen; it has nothing to do with this case, but counsel called for it and it was produced."

The reporters who had exposed the existence of the recommendation were not satisfied. Was that all? They whispered to each other about the full cabinet meeting; about the cabinet's vote.[1]

But Pierrepont, after this terse comment, dismissed the subject. For the rest of the day he ground on. Wood the barber had probably been mistaken in the hour. Rhodes had probably gone into Ford's by some entrance other than the front door. Down the prosecution list he went, offering possibilities, not facts. It was almost evening when the end came into sight.

"Gentlemen, if any of you are doubtful, go on your bended knees and ask for the light which comes from Heaven. In 1843," he recalled, "I was in a case in which a man was tried for murder. His defense was insanity. Many doctors proved him sane, many others insane. The jury was out all night. They wanted to do right, and in the night we heard them on their knees asking the God of light and truth to enlighten them. They rose from their knees, entered the courtroom, and said, 'He is guilty.' "

The court adjourned.

Crowds returned bright and early Wednesday morning, Aug-

[1] No record has been found of such a cabinet meeting, nor has any cabinet member left any statement to confirm any meeting or vote.

ust 7, and even the yards were jammed. Today Judge Fisher would instruct the jury. Some onlookers said shrewdly you could almost guess the verdict from his instruction, but, countered others, if the jury followed old Bradley's exhortation and gave a verdict from the box, it would all be over today, and who would miss that?

There was plenty besides the trial to talk about. The president had called on Stanton to resign, not only over the Surratt affair but because of other disagreements, too. General Grant would probably be appointed to replace Stanton, except that the Radicals would never let Stanton be thrown out. Not old *King* Stanton.

Inside the courtroom a sudden hush signaled the opening of the session.

"Whoso sheddeth man's blood, by man shall his blood be shed." The judge's words sent shivers down sensitive spines. At the defense table, the prisoner's face assumed the imperturbable mask it had won for days. Old Mr. Bradley's thin mouth tightened and a flush began to creek up his sunken cheeks.

"When the dark clouds of war began to lift, when the sun of peace was about to gladden us again with its benignant wings, when the rebels who followed Lee had been overpowered and had surrendered to the great military hero of our age, when our city was radiant with the downfall of the most wicked and atrocious rebellion . . . the executive head of the nation was stricken down by the most wicked and foul conspiracy ever to darken the pages of history . . .

"You know, gentlemen, as well as you know you exist, that to strike down the president of the most powerful nation on earth is no less heinous than to compass the death of an emperor . . ."

In words almost as eloquent as Carrington's, Judge Fisher told the jury it had no part in sentimental excuses for murder: jurymen must judge blood guilt only and a man who helped conceive a murder was equally guilty with the man who perpetrated it. Man could not make a better law than God, nor could he better expound or administer it.

"There are two cases reported from the book of highest Christian authority, decided by a judge from whom there can be no appeal.

"The first case is that of Naboth and Ahab, First Kings, Chapter twenty-one, the conspiracy of King Ahab and Queen Jezebel for Naboth's vineyard. Two sons of Belial were perjured witnesses against Naboth, causing his death, but the Lord ordered Elisha to go down to Ahab and say, 'Thou hast killed . . . where dogs lick the blood of Naboth shall dogs lick blood, even thine.' And it came to pass.

"In the other case, Second Samuel, Chapter eleven, David conspired to bring about the death of Bathsheba's husband. Joab was not alone in the killing for the Lord sent the prophet to say to David, 'Thou hast killed.' The judgment was that he who does an act by another, does it himself."

Surprise rippled through the room. A reporter whistled softly under his breath. Defense counsel glanced at each other; heavy color mottled Isaac's dark cheek. Only John Surratt sat motionless.

The judge looked severely at the listeners and then continued.

"The defense has been an alibi, a line held in little favor in courts and one which the jury must hold in suspicion. The defense has stressed one hundred and fifty exceptions to the court's rulings. Never," he said with obvious irritation, "have I seen before exceptions neatly tabulated and used in argument."

On the other hand, he said, the prosecution had relied on evidence proving the malice of the prisoner to the government, and to Abraham Lincoln; his communication with the murderer, Booth; his presence in the city and the theater that night; his flight and abandonment of his mother; his concealment and disguise when he went abroad; his free and voluntary confession to McMillan.

Young Joe Bradley, listening, from time to time glanced apprehensively at his father's darkening countenance.

"You are to weigh these, to determine whether any or all are true, and make your verdict in accord with the facts. In this you will not fail to remember that flight, falsification of accounts, contradictory statements, all are circumstances strongly indicative of guilt. You will bear in mind that a confession freely given is one of the surest proofs of guilt, because it is the omniscient God speaking through the conscience of the culprit. You will not forget that circumstantial evidence carries the highest degree of moral certainty.

"As to the credibility of witnesses, you are then judge. You will take the case with the honest purpose to do justice to the United States on one hand, and on the other to the prisoner.

"If John Surratt is innocent, say so, thus assuring that a court is the asylum of innocence.

"If, on the contrary, you find him guilty, by your verdict guarantee protection to the intended victims of guilt and give a testimonial to the country that the District of Columbia guarantees protection to the public servants of the nation, safe and sacred from the presence of unpunished assassins within its border.

"Take the case, gentlemen."

In the bustle that followed the judge's closing words, the defense watched the jury intently but saw no hint of a verdict from the box.

While spectators whispered and speculated, bailiffs R. D. Hughes and W. L. Ross took the oath of custody and at 11:32 A.M. escorted the twelve weary jurymen to an upstairs room. In the courtroom listeners talked under their breath, the women fanning themselves in nervous tension. John sat as if numb. He answered with apparent indifference the remarks of Isaac and Joe Bradley. On the bench, Judge Fisher turned papers over, seemingly oblivious of the room's occupants. Only once did he look up when a newsman's whisper carried across the chairs.

"Kings and Samuel . . . excellent books but seldom substituted for the statutes of the United States."

"Careful," breathed young Joe.

"The jury foreman," said Dick Merrick to Isaac, "came from Massachusetts. He's the fifth juror who's either Northern or foreign born. Seven are Southerners, but all of them said they had opinions. Still, if they go by the evidence, not their opinions, we're all right."

At three thirty the judge arose from the bench and went out the door, leaving word he would return if needed. The crowds waited. At four, Marshal Gooding appeared.

"Can't agree," he said. "Notified the judge, and he said t' send him word when they got a verdict. Might as well leave too."

"Any hint?"

"Well, I sort of heard eight t' four for acquittal."

John rose from his chair, his muscles stiff from tension. Me-

chanically he offered his wrists for the manacles and walked
with his guards across the yard, back to jail. Anna, waiting in his
cell, turned her haggard, expectant face to the approaching counsel.

"No word yet," Dick Merrick said and stepped forward to
support her swaying body.

"You'd better go home, child." Joseph Bradley's compassion-
ate tone brought tears to her eyes.

After a word with John, Isaac drew her hand through his arm
and led her away.

"They're carrying bedding into the courthouse," reported a
guard about ten o'clock that night. "Looks like the jury's going
t' make a night of it." Old Robert Waters grinned at John. "No
need t' worry now. Too late to do any good now. Prob'ly turn
out all right anyhow."

Wednesday night dragged on. At daylight, candles flickering
in the courtroom showed reporters and a few stragglers from
the crowd napping in disorderly array, sprawled on benches or
uncomfortable chairs.

All day Thursday, August 8, the crowds came and went about
the courthouse and yard, carrying gossip but no news. Thursday
night was endless; hot, it was unbearably tense in jail, courthouse,
and town. Now, instead of praying, the jury sang. "Home, Sweet
Home," mourned the men who had not seen home since June 17.

Friday lingered, with John still in his cell, but at least protected from the insatiably curious gogglers who haunted the
jail's door. Isaac brought a lunch that neither brother could swallow, and he reported that at home Anna walked the floor cease-
lessly, although Dr. Duhamel had made a friendly call and had
given her a sedative.

Friday night came. Still no word. Instead of falling off, the
crowds increased and strong partisan feeling colored their conversation. Witnesses pro and con who had stayed to hear the verdict bickered and argued with each other. Lou Weichman kept
carefully away from Prince George's County neighbors and from
John T. Holohan.

Rumors circulated that if the verdict went against the prisoner, his friends would abduct him. It would be easy enough, said a *Chronicle* reporter, to pick him up almost anywhere along the four hundred feet of shaded path that lay between courthouse and jail. Curiously no one seemed to recall that those exact words had been said, a few years before, about Abraham Lincoln and his nightly strolls from the White House to the War Office.

Saturday morning, building and yard were packed solid. The jury simply couldn't stay out much longer, said the people who had been saying the same thing for three days and nights. Arguments flourished; men placed new bets, contentions approached a climax. No matter which way the verdict went Old Bradley would be worth watching, chuckled the onlookers whose necks were not in danger.

At noon no one went home to lunch, and when suddenly police took up their stations around the courtroom, excitement raced through the grounds. Crowds surged into the building, filling every seat, every window ledge, every aisle. The police could not keep them out. Mumbling crowds rushed in from the streets to stand under windows, around doors, anywhere in the yard, in serried ranks, men, women, children, black and white.

At one o'clock a little procession started from the jail. Crowds fell in to watch the handcuffed prisoner, flanked on either side by a U.S. marshal and preceded and followed by District police, cross the yard to the courthouse. In fresh cotton clothing with Anna's handkerchief neat in his cuff, John appeared rested and at ease. No one knew what it cost him to appear so, with the little knot of muscles that in the last weeks had tightened above his thin nose now deliberately relaxed. He even smiled as he greeted acquaintances along the way. In the courtroom, his counsel met him in apparent good spirits.

The court crier gave out with his "Oyez! Oyez! Oyez!" and the room quieted as Judge Fisher entered.

Down the hall, headed by Foreman Todd and flanked by the two bailiffs, came the jury. Their worn, exhausted faces told of endless discussions, sleepless nights, opinions unchanged and unchangeable.

"Gentlemen of the jury, have you agreed upon a verdict?"

"Your Honor, we have not been able—" Reporters' feet pounded out the doorway. The court gaveled angrily. The buzz of voices lessened. "Here is a letter from the jury." Judge Fisher intoned its contents. "We stand . . . precisely now as when we first balloted . . . ask Your Honor for dismissal."

Through the clamor the court pounded wrathfully. Bailiffs descended on protesting spectators. Joseph Bradley's voice filled the room, ". . . prisoner gives no consent to any discharge . . . dismiss against his will and protest."

Over his words rose the court's cold tone, ". . . third communication . . . precisely as your first ballot . . . discharged."

Under his loud gaveling the crowd quieted.

"I now have a duty to perform which I cannot forego," intoned the judge, ominously, this time. "On the second of July as the presiding justice descended from this bench, Joseph H. Bradley accosted him in an insulting manner and accused him of having issued a series of insults from the bench. The judge disclaimed any intent, but Mr. Bradley threatened him with personal chastisement. The offense is one that even Mr. Bradley's years cannot palliate. It is therefore ordered that his name be stricken from the rolls of attorneys practicing before this court."

"False!" screamed Bradley over sudden pandemonium.

"Crier, adjourn this court."

"Only the Supreme Court can expel me—"

"Make a speech! Take an appeal!" shouted Fisher.

John, blocked by the crowd, scarcely saw Judge Fisher moving through the door, scarcely saw the pursuing shadow that was Joseph Bradley, scarcely saw the lawyer's old cotton umbrella or heard its *thwack! thwack!* as it belabored the fleeing judicial back.

He stood unmoving in the shouting mob. Marshal Gooding touched his arm, and he offered his wrists for the irons. The crowd made way.

In the yard an unbelievable scene unfolded. Judge Fisher stumbled clumsily across the dry grass to scramble aboard a horsecar at the corner, while at his coattails Bradley, in uncontrollable rage, laid on with the furled umbrella. Behind them panted a screeching queue of onlookers.

Before John's eyes the crowd dissolved into the four corners of the earth from which it had come: General Lee's insulted virtue faded from sight; Father's Boucher's incredulity, Stephen Cameron's stern displeasure; Harry Brogden's astounded, contemptuous face. Gus Howell's open mouth and unhinged jaw passed swiftly from view along with Edwards Pierrepont, Edwin Carrington, and Nathaniel Wilson. McMillan, Ste. Marie, Lou Weichman, all slipped away from the uncertain-tempered crowd.

The jurymen, leaving for their homes, carried with them the same opinions with which they had entered the courtroom two months before. The listeners, streaming away, were none of them convinced against their first beliefs.

John Surratt, manacled, watched them go. He was not condemned. He was not free.

Afterword

"I doubt that anyone would be interested in anything Mr. Surratt has to say."

This statement was written by an editor of McClure's Magazine shortly after the turn of the twentieth century to William Harrison Surratt, Baltimore attorney and son of Little Johnny. It referred to an offer of a documented recital of his father's Confederate service and his acquaintance with John Wilkes Booth.

Following the assassination of Abraham Lincoln, the trial by military court of eight civilians, the execution of four, among them John Surratt's mother, an iron curtain of silence had been imposed by Secretary of War Edwin M. Stanton. This silence specifically covered all military and civilian personnel connected with the event, and attempted to include even the priests who had attended Mrs. Surratt to her death.

In the 1880s this silence was broken by a spate of magazine articles signed by participants and observers whose opinions still were geographically divided, north and south. Since publishing houses were chiefly located in northern cities, John Surratt's guilt was flatly stated much more frequently than any doubt was expressed.

Then, for the sake of his family, William Surratt persuaded his father that the time had at last arrived when he should tell his story. John agreed that his son might offer to McClure's, a magazine that had printed many related articles, a synopsis of the documents in his possession that would support the true Surratt story.

The McClure reply convinced John Surratt that the truth of

his misadventures never would be accepted by the United States public so on an afternoon a few months before his death on April 22, 1916 he ordered a bonfire kindled in the back yard of his Baltimore home. On that warm autumn afternoon, with the sun shining down on his head now silver, rather than silver gilt, he sat in his yard chair as his father had sat in his store-porch ladderback and reviewed the scene. Dan, also gray, set down the shabby little trunk containing the records they would burn. By this act John Surratt assured himself that no quirk of fate could let his letters, documents, and diaries fall into unfriendly hands to be misinterpreted to the further embarrassment of his children.

Into the fire went letters marked "Kindness of Bearer" dated during those months of exile when extreme caution had been imperative. With them went other missives carrying familiar names, Father LaPierre, Stephen F. Cameron, General R. S. Ripley, Harry H. Brogden, along with those from unknown but sympathetic pens. The scurrilous letters (there had been hundreds of those) had been destroyed long before.

Johnny's thin old hands lingered on the few lines that commissioned him in the Confederate Secret Service. His deep-set eyes that long before had lost their look of hooded wariness now looked for the last time on the scrawling signature, "Jefferson Davis, President, Confederate States of America," before he consigned it to the flames. Here went the diaries, the note from his mother's attorney, J. W. Clampitt, ". . . remain perfectly quiet . . . ," messages from Joseph Bradley, friendly greetings through the years from young Joe Bradley and Dick Merrick.

Here too were papers pertaining to events following his trial: E. C. Carrington's recommendation that the government drop the case and Riddell's endorsement of that move. Newspaper clippings told how the original indictment for conspiracy had been changed to "engaging in the Rebellion," and how release under thirty-thousand-dollar bail had brought to an end all action against him. Along with these was a clipping from the Halifax, Virginia, *Gazette*, November 14, 1889, in which Carrington wrote at length that the preponderance of evidence placed John Surratt in Elmira, New York, on April 14, 1865 and failed to connect him with the assassination. Less widely publicized had been

Carrington's later admission to Dr. Robert Hagner of Washington that he had entered the trial fully convinced of John Surratt's guilt but before it was half over was equally convinced of his innocence.

Carrington may have influenced the prosecution *nolle prosequi* but more persuasive, perhaps, was the arrival in Washington of the Webster House cashbook showing John's presence in Canandaigua over the week end of April 15. This book, which Judge Fisher had ruled to be the only evidence he would accept, reached Washington too late to be introduced by the defense but not too late, perhaps, to influence the prosecution against attempting another trial.

There were other things to remember that afternoon. Dearer than the records now nibbled by flame were memories of happy years with Mary Victorine, his wife. Descendant of proud old Maryland families, Scotts, Hunters, and Keys, kinswoman of Francis Scott Key, Mary by sweet insistence had won family consent to her marriage. In the years that followed she had watched her husband gain her family's friendship and then its affectionate confidence.

Captain John R. Sherwood, head of the Old Bay Line Steamship Company. Here again only the memories of aging men recalled the warning to Sherwood that U.S. Mail delivery contracts could scarcely remain in the hands of a firm that employed John Surratt. Sherwood had answered firmly. John had remained and so had the contract. He had always been grateful, Sherwood said later, that the Baltimore rebels who had manned the company had permitted him, a Union veteran, to become its superintendent and then its president. Rebels and Yank worked together many a year until Sherwood, John Surratt, and then Isaac too retired from the Old Bay Line employ.

Present only in memory was the insurance policy which had been denied him because in answer to a routine application question, "Cause of mother's death?" he had written in youthful passion, "Murdered by the U.S. Government."

Bitterness and resentment held him fast until mature years had taught him unswerving reticence. Painfully he had learned to disregard strangers, whispers, pointing fingers, and to ward off well-wishers who offered good will only to pry and whisper of him later. He learned to maintain a constant guard against the newsmen who haunted him or sent decoys to pick up any word that could be turned into print and credited to an anonymous source "close to Surratt." These experiences had caused his virtual retirement from everyone except his own family and long-proved friends.

So he sat that afternoon in the warm autumnal sun, holding in his hand the only explanation he ever had made of Booth's Enterprise. He leafed through it and then into the dying fire dropped the pages of his lecture at Rockville, Maryland.

Flames licked out to reach its pages one by one. Their worn edges curled, their faded words leaped up for one last moment of bright record, ". . . rash . . . foolish, perhaps, but honorable. I honestly believed . . ." and then became gray ashes with the rest.

Bibliography

RECORDS LEFT BY PARTICIPANTS

ARNOLD, SAMUEL B. "The Lincoln Plot," *Baltimore American* (August 1902).

BROPHY, JOHN P. "Address to Friendly Sons of St. Patrick," Jan. 6, 1908, *Washington Post* (January 8, 1908).

CLAMPITT, JOHN W. "The Trial of Mrs. Surratt," *North American Review* (September 1880).

FORD, JOHN W. "Behind the Curtain of a Conspiracy," *North American Review* (April 1889).

GARRETT, THE REVEREND WILLIAM H. True Story of the Capture of Booth, *Confederate Veterans Magazine*, April 1921. *Log of the Vallette* (Manuscript entry), Mrs. A. T. LaVallette

GLEASON, CAPTAIN D. H. L. "The Plot to Capture Lincoln," *Magazine of History* (February 1911).

HEADLEY, JOHN W. *"Confederate Operations in Canada and New York,"* Neale Publishing Company (New York 1906).

HOLD, JOSEPH, Judge Advocate General, U.S. Army. "Vindication," *Washington Chronicle* (1873).

RATH, CAPTAIN CHRISTIAN, U.S. Army. "Execution of the Lincoln Conspirators," *McClures Magazine* (October 1911).

SURRATT, JOHN HARRISON, JR. "Lecture," Rockville, Maryland (May 6, 1870).

WEICHMAN, LOUIS J. Interview in *Washington Daily Chronicle* (May 21, 1867).

WALTER, THE REVEREND JACOB A. "A True Statement of Facts Regarding the Surratt Case," *Catholic Review* (August 29, 1891).

WATTS, CAPTAIN R. A., U.S. Army. "Trial and Execution of the Lincoln Conspirators," *Michigan Historical Society Magazine* (No. 11, Vol. 6).

REPORTERS

PETERSON, T. B., and brother. "Trial of the Alleged Assassins and Conspirators," by the reporters for the *Philadelphia Inquirer*, Philadelphia (1865).

PITTMAN, BENN. "Special Report of the Assassination of Lincoln and Trial of the Conspirators," by the official reporter Cincinnati (1865).

POORE, BEN PERLEY. "The Conspirators' Trial," by one of the attending reporters, Boston (1865).

SUTTON, ROBERT. "The Trial of John H. Surratt," in *The Reporter*, by R. Sutton, chief of the official corps of reporters, U.S. Senate, Washington, D.C. (1867).

———. "The Trial of John H. Surratt," *Official Issue*, Government Printing Office, Washington, D.C. (1867).

OFFICIAL RECORDS

Official Records of the Union and Confederate Armies in the War of the Rebellion, 1880-1891, Washington, D.C.

Official Records of the Union and Confederate Navies in the War of the Rebellion, 1894-1927, Washington, D.C.

HOUSE OF REPRESENTATIVES *Executive Documents:*
    39th Congress: Second Session: Nos. 9 and 25
    40th Congress: Second Session: No. 36

———. *Reports:*
    39th Congress: First Session: No. 99
    39th Congress: Second Session: Nos. 31 and 33; No. 105, Committee of the Judiciary.
    40th Congress: First Session: No. 7, Committee of the Judiciary.

———. *Congressional Record:*
    40th Congress: Second Session: Vol. 29: Part V, Appendix

———. *Impeachment Investigation:* Committee of the Judiciary, Washington, D.C. 1868

PARDON ATTORNEY'S OFFICE: Records of Court and Executives Section, The National Archives, Washington, D.C.

PITTMAN, BENN: Manuscript report of Conspirators Trial, J.A.G.O., War Department, Washington, D.C.

PRINCE GEORGE'S COUNTY, MD.: Deed, Will, Court Order books, Law and Equity records, County Clerk's Office, Marlboro, Md.

SURRATT, JOHN H., *trial of:* Court and Executive Section, The National Archives, Washington, D.C.

SURRATT, JOHN H., JR. *notations concerning:* Manuscript book, unsigned, believed to be the notebook of Stephen F. Cameron, Confederate Museum, Richmond, Va.

U.S. NAVY DEPARTMENT: Log of the *Montauk*, Washington, D.C.

U.S. POST OFFICE DEPARTMENT: Appointments, Maryland, 19th Century, Washington, D.C.

WEICHMANN, LOUIS J. *death of:* Affidavit of the Rt. Reverend Msgr. Thomas M. Conroy, Ft. Wayne, Indiana. Author's possession.

Index of Names